W9-AVF-173

R006&0 40137

TJ
263
•H397   Heat exchanger
1988   technology

$86.50

DATE			

© THE BAKER & TAYLOR CO.

HEAT EXCHANGER TECHNOLOGY

HEAT EXCHANGER TECHNOLOGY

Edited by

D. CHISHOLM

Heat Transfer Research, Inc.,
Alhambra, California, USA

ELSEVIER APPLIED SCIENCE
LONDON and NEW YORK

ELSEVIER APPLIED SCIENCE PUBLISHERS LTD
Crown House, Linton Road, Barking, Essex IG11 8JU, England

Sole Distributor in the USA and Canada
ELSEVIER SCIENCE PUBLISHING CO., INC.
52 Vanderbilt Avenue, New York, NY 10017, USA

WITH 19 TABLES AND 87 ILLUSTRATIONS

© 1988 ELSEVIER APPLIED SCIENCE PUBLISHERS LTD

British Library Cataloguing in Publication Data

Heat exchanger technology.
1. Heat exchangers
I. Chisholm, D.
621.402′5

ISBN 1-85166-195-6

Library of Congress Cataloging in Publication Data

Heat exchanger technology/edited by D. Chisholm.
   p.   cm.
Bibliography: p.
Includes index.
   Contents: Introduction/D. Chisholm—Single-phase coefficients on the shell-side of baffled heat exchangers/J. D. Jenkins—Two-phase flow in shell-and-tube heat exchangers/D. Chisholm—Fluidized beds/J. R. Howard—Dryers and drying/H. Hardisty and J. Black—Heat transfer in agitated vessels/G. Breber—Falling film evaporation in vertical tubes/J. W. Palen—Non-Newtonian flow and heat transfer in tubes/D. Chisholm—Run-around coil systems/W. H. Emerson.
   ISBN 1-85166-195-6
   1. Heat exchangers. I. Chisholm, D. (Duncan)
TJ263.H397 1988
621.402′5—dc19

No responsibility is assumed by the Publisher for any injury and/or damage to persons or property as a matter of products liability, negligence or otherwise, or from any use or operation of any methods, products, instructions or ideas contained in the material herein.

Special regulations for readers in the USA

This publication has been registered with the Copyright Clearance Center Inc. (CCC), Salem, Massachusetts. Information can be obtained from the CCC about conditions under which photocopies of parts of this publication may be made in the USA. All other copyright questions, including photocopying outside the USA, should be referred to the publisher.

All rights reserved. No part of this publication may be reproduced, stored in a retrieval system, or transmitted in any form or by any means, electronic, mechanical, photocopying, recording, or otherwise, without the prior written permission of the publisher.

Printed in Great Britain at the University Press, Cambridge

BST OPN

886.50

PREFACE

This book is intended to be used by the professional engineer in keeping himself abreast with developments in industrial heat exchangers. It will also be of interest to postgraduate students studying topics related to heat transfer. A number of heat exchangers not covered in my earlier volume (*Developments in Heat Exchanger Technology*–1, Applied Science Publishers, 1980) are discussed here, and in addition this volume looks in more depth at a number of aspects discussed in the previous volume.

Since 1980 the heat exchanger industry has seen a contraction in business arising from low oil prices and the slowing down of the nuclear industry in a number of countries arising from safety considerations (as well as low oil prices). However, industrial heat transfer will always be with us; there are few industrial processes which do not involve heat transfer at some stage.

Once again I was fortunate that those internationally recognised authorities whom I approached to contribute to this book were willing and able to do so. I greatly appreciate their contributions. I am sure that the excellent presentation of their chapters by Elsevier Applied Science Publishers will give them considerable satisfaction.

D. CHISHOLM

CONTENTS

vii

LIST OF CONTRIBUTORS

J. BLACK

  School of Engineering, University of Bath, Claverton Down, Bath BA2
  7AY, UK

G. BREBER

  Heat Transfer Research, Inc., 1000 South Fremont Avenue, Alhambra,
  California 91802-3900, USA

D. CHISHOLM

  Heat Transfer Research, Inc., 1000 South Fremont Avenue, Alhambra,
  California 91802-3900, USA

W. H. EMERSON

  National Engineering Laboratory, East Kilbride, Glasgow G75 0QU,
  UK. Present address: Bureau International de Métrologie Légale
  11, rue Turgot, 75009 Paris, France

H. HARDISTY

  School of Engineering, University of Bath, Claverton Down, Bath BA2
  7AY, UK

J. R. HOWARD

  HH Associates, 84 Silhill Hall Road, Solihull, West Midlands B91 1JS,
  UK

J. D. JENKINS

  Department of Chemical Engineering, Aston University, Aston Triangle,
  Birmingham B4 7ET, UK

J. W. PALEN

Heat Transfer Research, Inc., 1000 South Fremont Avenue, Alhambra, California 91802-3900, USA

Chapter 1

INTRODUCTION

D. CHISHOLM

Heat Transfer Research, Inc., Alhambra, California, USA

1. INTRODUCTION

This text concerns primarily the thermal design of industrial heat exchangers, mechanical design only being implicitly discussed. It is not in general the intention of this text to give an overview of current developments in heat transfer, except in so far as they relate to the particular heat exchangers discussed. For a general overview of the field of heat transfer the reader is referred to the *Proceedings of the Sixth International Heat Transfer Conference.*[1]

After discussing the scope of this text the greater part of this Introduction relates to general background developments influencing the design of heat exchanger equipment. It should come as no surprise to the reader that most of these background developments arise from the computer scene.

1.1. Scope of Text

This book starts with the most common industrial heat exchanger, the shell-and-tube, discussing first shell-side heat transfer coefficients in Chapter 2, then in Chapter 3 two-phase flow, again on the shellside of heat exchangers. These topics are more extensively covered here than in the previous volume.

Chapter 4 discusses Fluidised Beds, a topic of interest in a large number of sectors of industry; it is used in the combustion of coal, in incineration, and in the Petro-Chemical Industry to name a few. Dryers and drying is the subject of Chapter 5; this is probably the most common heat and mass transfer process in the Food Industry, but is also of interest to a variety of industrial sectors.

The subject of Agitated Vessels, a topic of great current interest due to its relevance to biotechnology, is discussed in Chapter 6. Chapter 7 concerns Falling Film Evaporation; this is becoming of increasing interest to industry, particularly for boiling processes at vacuum where the available pressure differences are low; evaporators can be designed to have negligible pressure drop.

The greater part of the heat transfer literature concerns flow and heat transfer of Newtonian fluids, fluids which have a viscosity independent of the process. There are of course a considerable number of fluids which have non-Newtonian characteristics; heat transfer and flow in these situations is discussed in Chapter 8. The final chapter concerns the design of run-around-coil systems, where a tertiary fluid is used to transfer heat from the primary fluid to the secondary fluid.

1.2. The Design Process

Developments in relation to the computer continue to dominate the scene. Personal Computers which were already creating great interest 10 years ago have become even more increasingly used, as their power and storage capacity have increased. Most design aspects of shell-and-tube heat exchangers, thermal, mechanical and draughting can now readily be carried out on Personal Computers (PCs).

Main frame machines are now essential tools only for complex three-dimensional calculations and the prediction of complex transient phenomena. For most design calculations the PC gives the engineer as much computational power as he needs.

As already stated the present text is primarily concerned with the thermal design of heat exchangers. For information on mechanical design of heat exchangers the reader is referred to reference 2, which has the merit of giving a comprehensive summary of the various national codes related to mechanical design. Mechanical design, unlike thermal design, is subject to national dictate, due to the safety ramifications of mechanical design.

1.3. Software Houses

Computer software supply is now a major industry. In the heat exchanger field the industrial requirement is met by two types of organisation, the software house, and the research and software development organisation.

Discussing first the software houses, software for the thermal and mechanical design is available from organisations like B-jac or Heat Transfer Consultants in a variety of ways:

- license

- purchase
- service bureau

Major engineering organisations such as Lummus and Technip, which developed software for internal use, provide a software service. Technip provide this service through a subsidiary ESIA. Addresses are given in the appendix to this chapter. Other organisations like Cham and Creare provide software for three-dimensional flow analysis and other complex calculations.

1.4. Research and Software Development Organisations

There are two principal R & SD organisations; Heat Transfer Research Inc. and the Heat Transfer and Fluid Flow Service. In the case of these organisations the methods used in their software are supported by extensive testing of heat exchangers; in the case of many software houses the calculation methods are not available to the user.

1.5. Data Base Systems

Major engineering projects involve a vast amount of complex information. The heat exchanger design process is not carried out in isolation, and for optimum design requires to be effectively interfaced with other aspects of design. Engineering database management systems have been created to facilitate the interfacing of software and the accessing of data banks.

Figure 1 illustrates schematically how the 'Process Engineering Database Management System' called Prodabas, marketed by Prosys Tech Inc., is structured. Prodabas 'offers an integrated approach to design by enabling all the complex information for major projects to be stored, updated and retrieved on a consistent basis with full facilities for document production'.

1.6. Expert Systems and Artificial Intelligence

There is increasing interest in the application of 'expert systems' and 'knowledge engineering' (references 3–5). Expert systems are a branch of artificial intelligence. In place of the database discussed above expert systems use a knowledge base containing data, rules, goals and explanatory text. Like a database system the most important characteristic of the system is the base. The program is driven or controlled by a 'shell' containing an 'inference engine' which uses languages such as LISP, for list processing, or PROLOG, for programming in logic.

Figure 2 illustrates the architecture of an expert system. The system is constructed such that the knowledge base can be developed as required, whereas the driving program is as stable as possible. Once the system is

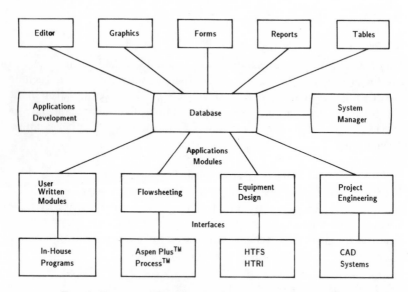

FIG. 1. Process engineering database management system.

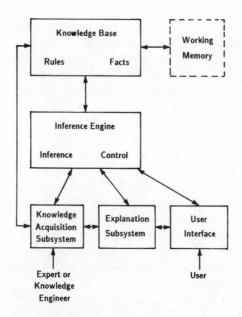

FIG. 2. Expert system architecture.

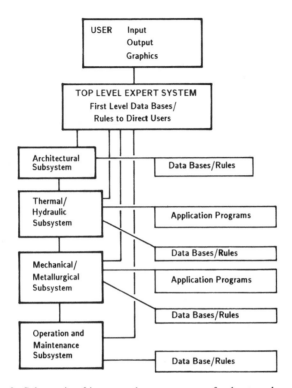

FIG. 3. Schematic of integrated expert system for heat exchangers.

written, its development does not require, in theory, the attention of a software specialist.

These systems are directed at complex problem solving, and are well able to tackle the problem of 'total design' of heat exchangers. A detailed discussion of an expert system for the design of shell-and-tube heat exchangers is given in reference 6. Figure 3 shows the architecture for such a system.

The design process may be divided into four stages

- Geometrical
- Thermal
- Mechanical-metallurgical
- Operation and maintenance

At present there is little interaction between these stages. Each is optimised individually. An expert system however, such as illustrated in Fig. 3, would optimise the overall process in arriving at the recommended design.

1.7. Energy Conservation Technology

The area of technology dealing with the optimisation of heat exchanger networks has blossomed in the last few years. Major saving in running costs, and also reduction in capital outlay can be obtained by these techniques.

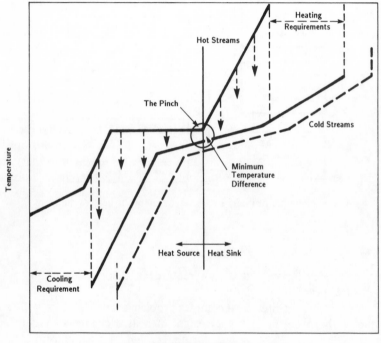

FIG. 4. Determination of the 'pinch'.

The description 'Pinch Technology' is used to describe a basic concept in this technology. Having determined the minimum temperature difference between the hot and cold streams in the plant, as shown in Fig. 4, the following guidelines can be applied:

- do not transfer heat across the pinch;
- do not heat below the pinch;
- do not cool above the pinch;
- design the process in two halves; each time start at the pinch.

Centres of expertise in this new technology are:

- The Process Integration Research Consortium, UMIST
- The Energy and Process Integration Service, Harwell
- Simulation Sciences Inc., California/Stockport
- Tensa Services, Houston.

1.8. Future Heat Exchanger Developments

Looking to the future there are a number of significant developments.

Heat pipes, a novelty twenty years ago, have been finding an increasing number of applications (reference 7). Sales in America have doubled over the period 1982–1986 (reference 8). Incidently the two other areas in which sales expanded were plate heat exchangers (see volume 1), and heating and cooling coils, which expanded by 45% and 12% respectively.

Printed Circuit Heat Exchangers, miniaturised heat exchangers, are being adopted in some industries (reference 9). They are made from flat metal plates which have flow passages chemically 'milled' into them. The plates are diffusion bonded together. They are perhaps the 'ultimate' compact heat exchanger. Using a large number of these units in parallel can avoid 'scale-up' problems encountered in some processes. The following advantages are also claimed for these units:

- less fluid inventory;
- more sophisticated processing routes;
- wide range of material choice;
- surfaces tailored to suit both primary and secondary fluids;
- Suitable for 'aggressive' chemical cleaning.

Ceramic heat exchangers for high temperature application are the subject of extensive development programmes. Babcock & Wilcox supported by the US Department of Energy have a development programme on ceramic Bayonet-type Heat Exchangers for delivering air at 1400 K to a steel mill soaking pit. Thermo Electron, also supported by the US Department of Energy, are developing Ceramic Composite Heat Exchangers to operate at temperatures in excess of 1400 K in corrosive and fouling industrial waste streams.

There is little doubt that there will continue to be significant developments in the future in industrial heat exchangers.

REFERENCES

1. *Proceedings of the 6th International Heat Transfer Conference, San Francisco,* August, 1986, Hemisphere Publishing Corporation, New York.
2. *Heat Exchange Design Handbook, Volume 4, Mechanical Design of Heat Exchangers,* 1983, Hemisphere Publishing Corporation, New York.
3. RICH, E. *Artificial Intelligence,* 1983, McGraw-Hill, New York.
4. HARMON, P. and KING, D. *Expert Systems: Artificial Intelligence in Business,* 1985, John Wiley, New York.
5. MOORE, A. Design/construct decision support using expert systems, *Process Engineering,* January 1987, 27–8.
6. SOLER, A. I. Expert system for design integration-application to the total design of shell-and-tube heat exchangers, ASME Winter Meeting, December 7–12 1986. Thermal/Mechanical Design—Karl Gardner Memorial Session, PVP-Vol. 118, HTD-Vol. 64, 1986, ASME, New York, 135–9.
7. CHISHOLM, D. *Heat Pipes,* Chapter 3.10. *Heat Exchange Design Handbook,* 1983, Hemisphere Publishing Corporation, New York.
8. Anon. *The American Market for Heat Exchangers,* 1987, Frank and Sullivan Inc., New York.
9. JOHNSTON, T. Miniturized heat exchangers for chemical processing. The Chemical Engineer, December 1986, (431), 36–8.

APPENDIX: ADDRESSES

1. B-jac Computer Services Inc, 5000 Village Green, Midlothian, Virginia 23113, USA.
2. Babcock & Wilcox, 1562 Beeson Street, PO Box 835, Alliance, Ohio 44501, USA.
3. Cham Ltd, Bakery House, 40 High Street, Wimbledon, London SW19 5AU, UK.
4. Creare R & D Inc., Etna Road, PO Box 71, Hanover, New Hampshire 03755, USA.
5. Energy and Process Integration Systems, Harwell Laboratory, Harwell, Oxfordshire, OX11 0RA, UK.
6. ESIA, 1 rue des Herons, Montigny-le-Bretonneux,78184 Saint-Quentin-Yvelines, Cedex, France.
7. Heat Transfer Consultants Inc., 1985 Maybelle Drive, PO Box 23525, Pleasant Hill, California 94523, USA.
8. Heat Transfer and Fluid Flow Service, Harwell Laboratory, Harwell, Oxfordshire, OX11 0RA, UK.
9. Heat Transfer Research Inc., 1000 South Fremont Avenue, Alhambra, California 91802-3900, USA.

10. Lummus Heat Tansfer Systems B V, Treubstraatt 16, PO Box 1925, 2280 DX Rijswijk Z H, The Netherlands.
11. Lummus Heat Transfer Systems B V, 1515 Broad Street, Bloomfield, New Jersey 07003, USA.
12. Process Integration Research Consortium, Department of Chemical Engineering, Institute of Science and Technology, University of Manchester, PO Box 88, Manchester, UK.
13. Prosys Technology Ltd, Sheraton House, Castle Park, Cambridge, CB3 0AX, UK.
14. Prosys Tech Inc., 30 Vreeland Road, Florham Park, New Jersey 07932-1986, USA.
15. Simulation Sciences Inc., 1051 West Bastanchury Road, Fullerton, California 92633, USA.
16. SimSci International, Regent House, Heaton Lane, Stockport, Cheshire SK4 1BS, UK.
17. Thermo Electron Coorporation, Waltham, Massachusetts, USA.
18. Tensa Services, 18300 Saturn Lane, Suite 113, Houston, Texas 77058, USA.

Chapter 2

SINGLE-PHASE COEFFICIENTS ON THE SHELLSIDE OF BAFFLED HEAT EXCHANGERS

J. D. JENKINS

Department of Chemical Engineering, Aston University, Birmingham, UK

SUMMARY

This chapter relates single phase shellside coefficients to flow patterns and ideal tube bank behaviour, before discussing the present degree of knowledge as to the dependence of shellside coefficients on geometry and flowrate. To this end, experimental data on the no-leakage and leakage cases are discussed, and their relative paucity pointed out. Finally, an interim geometry-independent correlation is presented, restricted in validity by being based only on small-exchanger data.

NOTATION

A Area (usually that for flow) (m^2)
A_L Total leakage area, $= A_{TB} + A_{SB}$ (m^2)
A_M Minimum area of flow at centre line of shell (m^2)
A_{SB} Shell-to-baffle leakage area (m^2)
A_{TB} Tube-to-baffle leakage area (m^2)
C_p Specific heat at constant pressure (J/kg)
L_c Baffle overlap (m)
L_s Baffle spacing (m)
Z Orifice shape factor, $= 2 \times$ baffle thickness/diametrical clearance
d Diameter (m)
j j-factor of Chilton and Colburn, $= (\beta/u)Sc^{2/3}$
u Linear velocity (m/s)

11

Subscripts

H	Heat transfer
I	Related to area for flow at baffle edge
L	Leakage
M	Related to minimum flow area at middle line of shell
M	Mass transfer
NL	No leakage
SB	Shell-to-baffle
TB	Tube-to-baffle
c	Related to baffle overlap
new	Corrected by correlation of (46, 79)
o	Uncorrected or uncorrelated
s	Related to baffle spacing
t	Tube

Greek

α	Heat transfer coefficient (W/m^{2}K)
β	Mass transfer coefficient (m/s)
δ	Diffusion coefficient (m^2/s)
η	Dynamic viscosity (N s/m^2)
λ	Thermal conductivity (W/m K)
ρ	Mass density (kg/m^3)
ϕ	Angle by which flow angle to tube bank differs from right angle (-)

Dimensionless

Nu	Nusselt number, $= \alpha d_t / \lambda$
Pr	Prandtl number, $= \eta C_p / \lambda$
Re	Reynolds number, $= u d_t \rho / \eta$
Sc	Schmidt number, $= \eta / \rho \delta$
Sh	Sherwood number, $= \beta d_t / \delta$

1. INTRODUCTION

Many processes in the chemical and process industries require inputs and outputs of energy in the form of heat, as does any engine producing work from heat. Typically, the requirements of heat exchanger design for these energy transfers are different for each type of application. For a prime mover such as a car engine, a light compact exchanger with a large surface area per unit volume is required, but which transfers heat energy between essentially clean fluids (air, coolant). In contrast, in the chemical and process industries, one or other (or both) of the fluids may be liable to cause fouling of the heat transfer surfaces, and the design has to reflect this fact. Often, too, the overall area of the exchanger is very large, the design has to be robust, and yet economical and straightforward in construction. The traditional solution has been the use of shell-and-tube heat exchangers, in which one fluid flows through the tubes in a tube bundle, and the other passes across the outside of the tubes, being deflected by baffles (through which the tubes pass) so as to cross the tubes at approximately right angles. Clearly, the number of possible arrangements is large, since the tube-side fluid can either pass once through the exchanger (single-pass) or do so more than once (two, three, four times and even more), and the number and arrangement of the baffles can be varied to give the best heat transfer and pressure drop characteristics on the shellside.

This form of construction has been adopted since the mechanical design of the exchanger can be such that the ends of the exchanger can be removed to allow cleaning of the insides of the tubes, and some designs allow the whole exchanger bundle to be withdrawn so that the outsides of the tubes can be cleaned. This latter arrangement is only required for situations where both hot and cool streams are potentially liable to produce fouling on the heat transfer surface.

As might be expected there are many feasible shellside arrangements, but in practice those used are the variants identified by TEMA.[1] These are (i) the basic E-type, with inlet and outlet at the opposite ends, having only one pass on the shellside, (ii) the 'divided-flow' J-type, with one central inlet and two outlets (one at each end of the shell), (iii) the 'split-flow' G-type, having a central longitudinal baffle along the shell, with opposed inlet and outlet, (iv) the pure-cross flow X-type, with no cross baffles and inlet and outlet opposed, and (v) the F-type with two shell passes since it has a longitudinal baffle, with inlet and outlet at the same end of the shell.

Of these various types, that usually selected for theoretical and experimental study is the E-type. In this design, the segmental cross-baffles deflect the flow sinusoidally from inlet nozzle to outlet nozzle. But this simple view of the nature of the flow has to be modified considerably because of the leakage flows introduced by the mechanical requirements of the heat exchanger design. These arise from the design of the tube bundle. While again a large number of possible tube arrangements are possible, in practice triangular and rotated square pitch arrangements are most commonly used, with the in-line arrangement reserved for special low pressure drop cases. In a typical tube layout, the necessary clearance close to the shell wall provides an easier path for fluid flow. Similarly, the tubes forming the bundle have to pass through the various segmental baffles, and require a clearance between the edge of any hole in the baffle, and the tube passing through it. Again, there needs to be a clearance gap between the edge of any baffle and the shell wall. Since fluid can flow through these clearances, the simple picture above of flow through the shell has to be modified.

In order to make subsequent discussion more straightforward, the following standard terminology will be used. We regard the shellside of a baffled cylindrical exchanger as being divided into a series of compartments, the first of these in the direction of flow being the inlet compartment and the last the outlet compartment, the remainder being the internal compartments and referred to by their position in the sequence (e.g. third of five). Each compartment is bounded by the shell itself and the two baffles forming the other walls, and is divided into three zones, defined as the inlet window, crossflow and outlet window zones. The crossflow zone comprises the volume lying between the baffle overlap, i.e. where the tubes pass through both baffles. The various leakage areas are identified as the shell-to-baffle leakage area and the tube-to-tube leakage area. The baffle cut (i.e. the dimension determining the area for flow between the edge of any baffle and the extreme part of the shell opposite it) is defined in terms of the diametrical percentage cut down, i.e. a 25% baffle cut (or 25% BC) provides a smaller area for flow than a 45% baffle cut. Note that since at least one row of tubes must pass through all the baffles, the most extreme baffle cut is about 47·5%. The baffle spacing is defined in the literature either as the distance between baffle centre-lines or between their opposed faces. As far as possible, baffle spacing (or BS) will here be the distance between the opposed faces, this being the most useful for correlation purposes. The area available for flow between the baffle edge and the shell is the window area.

1.1. Flow on the Shellside of Shell-and-Tube Exchangers

Qualitatively the nature of the flows on the shellside of shell-and-tube heat exchangers is well known, and can be related to the general geometrical proportions of the tube bundle and its baffles. Recent experimental studies are those of Perez and Sparrow,[2] Berner[3] and Murray.[4] The two key parameters are baffle cut and baffle spacing. When the window area is small in proportion to the area for flow between the baffles (as happens for low baffle cuts with moderate to large baffle spacings), then the flow 'jets' across the baffle compartment and a large eddy forms behind the baffle edge. For low Reynolds numbers, or where the area of flow remains relatively constant as between the window and the crossflow zone, then the flow sweeps most of the available volume. For the case of large baffle cut and relatively close baffle spacing, the main flow by-passes much of the compartment, which is filled with eddies.

Superimposed on these general flows is the effect of leakage flow; (i) around the bundle, (ii) through the baffle-to-shell clearances and (iii) through the tube-to-baffle clearances. The first schematic approach to the analytical description of these complex flows is due to Tinker.[5]

1.1.1. Stream Analysis Models

In this analysis the shellside flow is regarded as consisting of a set of individual streams identified as follows.

Stream A is the combined leakage flows through the annular orifices formed by the tubes in the baffle holes.

Stream B is the main crossflow stream, often analysed by reference to ideal tube banks, and regarded as the most effective stream for heat transfer.

Stream C is the stream by-passing the tube bundle through the gap between the bundle and the shell wall.

Stream E is the leakage stream through the gap between the edge of the baffle and the shell wall.

In this model stream B, considered to be the dominant stream, by its flow through the exchanger compartment, creates the pressure drop which in turn causes Streams A, C, D and E. The Tinker model was later restated in terms of an equivalent piping or node diagram by Palen and Taborek.[6] They first added an additional stream, Stream F, the pass-partition stream, analogous to Stream C, but allowing for flow along channels caused by omitting tubes as required in shell-and-baffle arrangements necessary for multipasses on the tube side.

Stream B (the crossflow stream), Stream C (the bundle by-pass stream) and Stream F (the pass-partition stream) are considered to flow in parallel through the crossflow zone, joining in the window zone, and separating again at the next crossflow zone entrance. Streams A and E (the tube-baffle leakage flow and the shell-baffle leakage flow) are considered to flow in parallel from a hypothetical node in one crossflow zone to the corresponding node in the next. The virtue of this approach is that the resulting network can be solved by standard techniques for pipe networks (closely analogous to the use of Kirchoff's Laws for electrical networks). For each stream we may write the pressure drop as a flow resistance for each stream times the linear velocity. The flow resistance is itself a function of the velocity. From these fundamental equations, an equation set suitable for iterative solution can be set up, iterative because the resistance are functions of Reynolds number, itself dependent on the flows created by the various pressure drops, themselves in turn dependent on flow and resistance. A modified form of this approach has been presented by Grant.[7]

These models are used both to calculate pressure drops, and the flows in the various streams, for a given geometry, and then to calculate the heat transfer for that geometry. This last step assigns effectiveness factors for heat transfer to each stream, and so calculates the overall heat transfer. But for both stages experimental data are needed, first to derive the resistances, effectiveness factors and heat transfer correlations for each stream, but then also to check the accuracy of the predictions and so refine the model. We return to this point below.

Despite their complexity, the models as such are still only approximate, for example the pressure drop across a given baffle, creating the tube-baffle leakage and shell-baffle leakage streams, drops from inlet to outlet of the crossflow zone, so that modelling the flows by a single node-to-node channel is clearly inadequate, especially for small baffle-cut situations.

Even with their limitations, these models have found extensive use in commercial heat exchanger design computer programs, but because of their iterative nature are not suitable for hand calculation. Their effectiveness comes from the careful use of the results of both flow visualisation studies (see above) and of extensive experimental data, largely from the Delaware project, supplying values for the Stream A and Stream E orifice resistance coefficients, on small-scale baffled exchangers, and on ideal tube banks in laminar and transition flow. The first use of these data was by Bell [8-10] in developing a non-iterative method suitable for manual calculation. He used the insights of the Tinker flow model to produce a 'semi-analytical' model, based on ideal tube bank data, which takes into account the effects of leakage and by-pass streams but perforce has to ignore their interaction. The method also allowed for the effect of baffle cut and adverse temperature gradient build-up in laminar flow. A recent variant of the method is presented in Taborek.[11]

Palen and Taborek[6] developed their model into a full-blown 'stream analysis method' and did so not only using the Delaware data, but also with a very extensive proprietary data set on commercial size exchangers. Development of the Grant[7] method is on parallel lines, again with extensive data generated by the Heat Transfer and Fluidflow Service (e.g. Macbeth[12]) in the UK. Both these methods are only available through the respective commercial services (Heat Transfer Research Inc. for the Palen and

TABLE 1
BREAK-DOWN OF FLOWS IN A SHELL-AND-TUBE EXCHANGER

Stream	Turbulent (%)	Laminar (%)
Main crossflow (B)	40–70	25–50
Bundle bypass (C + F)	15–20	20–30
Shell-to-baffle leakage (E)	6–20	6–40
Tube-to-baffle leakage (A)	9–20	4–10

Taborek method). The stream analysis method, when applied to data for industrial size exchangers obtained from the HTRI data bank gave, for the various streams, the flow fractions set out in Table 1 quoted from Taborek.[11]

1.1.2. Porous Body Models

One of the early porous body approaches to heat (and mass) transfer in tube bundles is due to Whitaker[14] who sought to establish common correlations for packed beds and tube bundles. In such an approach the tube bundle is regarded as a porous body of rather large voidage, with either the same resistance to flow in all directions (an isentropic viewpoint) or with different resistances along the principal axes. Butterworth[15,16] made the former assumption and was able to show fair agreement between calculated and experimental values (the latter from the rectangular shell-and-tube heat exchanger in the Delaware project[18]). His analysis was hampered by the non-availability of a computer package able to solve the finite difference equations of his complete model. As part of his work he required a direction-free equation for heat release into the flowing fluid, and so sought a relationship giving the heat transfer coefficient. From his fundamental analysis he obtained

$$\left[\frac{\alpha}{\alpha_1^1}\right]^n = \cos^2 \phi_1 + \left[\frac{\alpha_2^1}{\alpha_1^1}\right]^n \sin^2 \phi_1$$

α_1^1, α_2^1 are heat transfer coefficients along two of the three principal axes (one perpendicular to the tubes and two parallel). ϕ is the angle between the flow direction and a line perpendicular to the tubes. A comparison of this equation with experimental data is made below. His approach may be compared to that of the ESDU manual[19] for heat transfer in tube banks. With recent advances in computation (notably the advent of the array processor) more complex porous models (which, *inter alia*, incorporate different resistances along the principal axes) have been devised (e.g. references 20–22). Full discussion of these models is outside the scope of this chapter, but they are of great importance since, while too complex for routine design use, they offer the prospect of testing the simple stream analysis models in a rigorous way.

1.1.3. Complete Flow Models

An alternative approach to flow and heat transfer in tube banks is the detailed numerical solution of the continuity, momentum and energy differential equations by finite-difference methods for the volumes in the bundle and around the tubes, that is, a truly point-to-point approach in complete contrast to the porous body models. However, even the most developed attempt [24,25] has been limited to the ideal tube bank, although for all angles of approach to the bundle. Again detailed discussion is beyond the scope of this chapter. For fully developed turbulent flow predicted heat transfer coefficients agree well with experiment, although data were only available for axial flow and cross flow. These predictions are discussed further below.

2. IDEAL TUBE BUNDLES IN CROSSFLOW

As already noted, the Bell and related methods for the prediction of heat transfer coefficients on the shellside of shell-and-tube heat exchangers use as a starting point data on ideal tube banks. Further, as we have seen, flow in a single compartment of a baffled shell-and-tube heat exchanger approximates to ideal tube bank flow in the crossflow zone. To understand the more complex situation presented by the shellside as a whole requires a consideration of this simpler situation. Experimental work on ideal tube bundles has always been intended as a step to the understanding of real exchangers.

Early work (e.g. Huge,[26] and of Pierson[27]) was carried out using air on banks of heated tubes in wind tunnels and the extensive data obtained have been correlated (Grimison[28]). In all, 22 staggered and 16 in-line tube arrangements, ten rows deep, were studied over the Reynolds number range 200–40 000 and the correlated results conveniently presented by McAdams.[29] The Delaware project expanded data collection to fluids other than air, (notably oils of various specification) and so extended the Reynolds number range down into the laminar region. Data have been reported[30] on overall pressure drop and heat transfer coefficients for laminar flow through a triangular pitch bank; further work on in-line and rotated square pitch banks has been reported (Bergelin et al.[31]) for tube banks of various sizes and discussed and correlated in reference 32. The project also obtained data for the three geometries studied[34] in the subcritical regime, up to a Reynolds number of 105, and the results were well summarised on a single plot. Other work has been carried out[35] on water flow with Reynolds numbers up to 12×10^6, across a staggered tube bank. Recently Jenkins and Noie-Baghban[36] have obtained pressure drop results, and heat transfer results using an electrochemical mass-transfer modelling technique. In this technique, mass transfer coefficients can be related to heat transfer coefficients through the use of the Chilton–Colburn analogy.[37] These data, obtained in two sets of runs for a single tube bank configuration, in general agree well with those of the Delaware programme. They cover, however, a wider range of Reynolds number than any single Delaware investigation and help to resolve some of the anomalies of the Delaware work; in particular, their results show a smooth variation of coefficient with Reynolds number, with no dip in the Reynolds number range $30 \leqslant Re_M \leqslant 300$.

Other work on rectangular ideal tube banks has been summarised by Zukauskas[38,39] and Achenbach.[40] Only the Delaware project data have been discussed in any detail because of their close relation to the cylindrical exchanger data from the same project.

2.1. Inclined Flow across Ideal Tube Banks

The discussion of flow patterns above shows that for some configurations, the principal flow in the crossflow zone is not at right angles to the tube bundle but is at some lesser angle.

To date, only a few experimental studies of this situation have appeared in the literature, the earliest being that of Ornatski,[41] the only data available to Butterworth[15−17] in his analysis of inclined flow. More recently, Groehn[42] has investigated such flows at Reynolds numbers above 10 000, and Jenkins and Noie-Baghban[36] extended their ideal bundle work to such flows. The importance of these data is that they cover the whole Reynolds number from the (pseudo) laminar, through the transition zone to the fully developed turbulant ($0.5 \leqslant Re_M \leqslant 12\,600$). At lower Reynolds number, the data for the different inclinations virtually coincide, through the transition zone they diverge, and the fully developed turbulent region shows a variation similar to that of earlier workers. However, if for this region we plot the variation for a given Reynolds number as a function of inclination, we find that the variation is not as Butterworth[15-17] (and the ESDU report[19]) supposed. In common with the numerical predictions of Antonopoulos,[24] data for inclinations close to the perpendicular flow situation show little variation from the ideal tube bank. As the angle varies more from this, the data show a marked effect, but one which tends (correctly) asymptotically to the axial flow experimental data. The Butterworth and ESDU relationships do not meet this criterion. Jenkins and Noie-Baghban[36] have also reported row-by-row variation of coefficients, as well as pressure drop data for the inclined tube situations.

3. SHELLSIDE COEFFICIENTS

As already noted, there are numerous geometrical parameters whose value can affect the shellside performance of shell-and-tube heat exchangers. Their relative importance can be judged in some measure from the flow-studies and calculations outlined above, but the effects can only be quantified through experimental work on heat transfer. Clearly the greater benefit is to be obtained from schematic studies such as the Delaware project[9] and the programme at Aston[36,43-51] and the related one at Winfrith.[12,13] In general the work can be divided into two classes, (i) whole exchanger bundle work (heat transfer proper) and (ii) measurement of local heat transfer coefficients, usually by the use of a mass transfer analogue and the Chilton–Colburn relationship in either its original form[37] or the Nusselt form using $NuPr^{-1/3}$ (or $ShSc^{-1/3}$) as opposed to the j-factor forms. Both classes are briefly reviewed before any detailed discussion is attempted.

3.1. Whole Bundle Studies Outlined
Early work can be conveniently referred through the paper by Donohue[52] in which he correlated earlier data (e.g. Short,[53] Gardner and Siller[54] and Tinker[55]) for both bored and unbored shells over a range of Reynolds numbers from 100 to 40 000. These investigations were for either actual exchangers or models reflecting the design and construction of such exchangers. The results were used in the development of 'whole exchanger' correlations (e.g. references 52, 56), while Kern[57] used 'industrial data' to the same end. As already noted, Tinker's analysis of the flow streams present led to a change of emphasis in experimental work, reflected in the Delaware project. This covered not only ideal tube banks, and rectangular tube banks with by-passing (i.e. no dummy row of half tubes on the wall),

but also rectangular exchangers with a single baffle, and a range of cylindrical heat exchangers, with and without leakage streams. The emphasis was on seeking to separate the effects of the various streams and establish the necessary effectiveness terms, resistance and transfer coefficients necessary for the successful application of the stream analysis models (see above).

Whole exchanger heat transfer data were obtained on a number of geometries:

- a small rectangular exchanger with a single baffle (so designed that it approximated two adjacent compartments in a cylindrical exchanger, the effects of baffle cut and of tube-to-baffle leakage were investigated[18,58]),

- a small cylindrical heat exchanger with a shell of 5·25 in (133·4 mm) internal diameter with eighty 3/8 in (9·52 mm) diameter tubes in a staggered square arrangement with a 1·25 pitch-to-diameter ratio (both for no-leakage[59] and leakage cases[9,60]), the effects of baffle-cut and spacing were studied, the leakage cases were for shell-to-baffle, then tube-to-baffle, and finally combined, all with bundle by-passing reduced to a minimum), and

- a larger cylindrical heat exchanger[9,60] with an initial shell internal diameter of 8·378 in (212·8 mm) having 470 1/4 in (6·4 mm) diameter tubes in an equilateral triangle arrangement with a 1·375 pitch-to-diameter ratio (initial runs were for no-leakage, then with a range of shell-baffle and tube-baffle clearances, and finally with larger shell internal diameters to give increasing by-pass effects).

The case for localised heat transfer studies was restated by Sparrow and Perez[61] who noted that in addition to the need for definitive compartment-average experimental results to validate candidate design procedures, more localised heat transfer and pressure drop information were needed to define the path toward improved performance of shell-and-tube heat exchangers.

3.2. Tube-by-Tube Studies Outlined

The various early flow studies referred to above, by identifying the existence of three zones of flow, longitudinal, true crossflow, and eddy or dead zones, showed the need for localised measurements of the heat transfer coefficient. Ambrose and Knudsen[62] were the first to make detailed measurements of local heat transfer coefficients in a cylindrical baffled unit for leakage conditions at five baffle spacings and two tube pitches using an electrically heated probe for tube increments at various positions in the bundle, while

Gurushankariah and Knudsen[63] continued with more detailed investigations in a single baffle compartment. They showed marked variations along
the tubes at the centre of the crossflow zone from baffle to centre line, the
coefficients were higher in the longitudinal flow portion of the window
zone, and the coefficients confirmed the presence of a large eddy zone in the
lee of each baffle, but whole coefficients were not inferior due to the jetting
of the leakage flow through the tube-to-baffle leakage area. This is in
contradiction to the later work of Stanchiewicz and Short[64] from studies in
a rectangular no-leakage exchanger, who had found lower coefficients in
these eddies. A similar contrast can be seen in the later model exchanger
results. Similar work was later carried out by Narayanan[65] using an 18-
tube bundle as opposed to the four- and twelve-tube bundles of Ambrose
and Knudsen. Comparison of the results of these workers and between
themselves and later work is difficult because large leakage and bundle by-
passing flows existed and their significance was not recognised. Subsequent
work has consistently used one form or other of the mass transfer technique.

The first work of note was that of Williams[66,67] who used a model
exchanger virtually identical to the 80-tube small cylindrical exchanger of
the Delaware project (see above).[9,59,60] As for that model, rubber seals were
used to give a 'no-leakage' situation, and bundle by-passing was reduced by
careful location of tubes and tie-bars. Individual tube coefficients were
found by a mercury evaporation technique, and were averaged to give
window, crossflow zone, and overall bundle coefficients. These latter
agreed reasonably well with the earlier whole exchanger results.[9,59] Gay
and Roberts[68] used the tube-by-tube data of Williams to determine the
distribution of local velocities within the bundle, by examination of the
exponents of the Reynolds number in the correlation of the data for each
tube. This method has been returned to recently by Sparrow and Perez[61] in
their interpretation of results obtained by a sublimation technique. The
work of Williams was both restricted in its Reynolds number range (54–
1625) and that it was for the 'no-leakage' case. Mackley[43] showed that the
ferri-ferrocyanide redox couple provided an accurate method of determining heat transfer coefficients through the Chilton–Colburn analogy. The
initial work of Mackley at Aston led to a HTFS programme at Winfrith, of
which only a part has been reported in the open literature,[12,13] and a
parallel programme at Aston.[43-51] Recently, Sparrow and Perez[61] have
carried out similar local coefficient determinations using a naphthalene
sublimation technique in an exchanger similar in proportion to those of
Mackley and Nibber, save that the bundle is composed of 92 tubes on an

equilateral triangular pitch. The different geometries covered in all these studies are summarised in Table 2. They include both leakage and no-leakage cases.

3.3. Detailed Discussion of Experimental Studies

In this and subsequent sections we turn from a review of the experimental work that has been carried out to a discussion of the experimental results obtained. Clearly, some degree of selectivity has to be exercised, and in general, the reader is referred to the original papers and reports for the actual numerical results. Here the preferred method of reporting the data graphically is in the form due to Nusselt rather than in the j_H or j_M form. This choice of presentation makes the formulation of correlations and the handling of the effects of geometrical factors more straight forward.

3.3.1. No-leakage Studies

Traditionally, any programme of studies on heat transfer in shell-and-tube exchangers always started with investigation of the no-leakage situation, since it was felt that this provided the obvious basis for subsequent correlation of leakage data as well as a basis for theoretical studies. However, we note that the Bell method (as given in references 8–10, and in revised form, in reference 11) uses as a basis heat transfer data obtained for an ideal rectangular tube bank, and 'corrects' these values for the effects of the various leakage streams (see above). On the other hand, the recent development of complex porous body models (see discussion above) offers the opportunity to calculate flow patterns and local velocities in the shell-side of shell-and-tube exchangers, which can then be related to local values of heat transfer coefficients if these are available. The early attempt by Gay and Roberts[68] already noted was not particularly successful simply because such computational tools were not available. Clearly, a no-leakage case should prove to be capable of being modelled in a more straightforward way than a case with leakage flows. But porous-bed models are far too complex for use in routine design computer codes (for rapid solution an array processor is required) and, for this purpose, as already noted, the stream analysis models have been developed. For these, the no-leakage case provides a 'boundary-condition' situation, since if the leakage flows are set at zero in the stream analysis model, it should yield the no-leakage results. Ideally, both types of model should interact with each other, since insights gained from the porous-bed models (especially for the leakage situation) should enable improvements to the stream analysis model to be made.

TABLE 2

SUMMARY OF MODEL CYLINDRICAL EXCHANGERS USED IN EXPERIMENTAL STUDIES

Shell internal diameter (mm)	Number of tubes and diameter (mm)	Tube layout	Pitch-to-diameter ratio	Baffle spacing (face-to-face) (mm)	Baffle cut (diametrical) (%)	Diametrical clearances		Compartment studied	Notes
						Shell-to-baffle (mm)	Tube-to-baffle (mm)		
Delaware project									
No-leakage studies									
133	80 × 9·52	RSP[a]	1·25	94·5[c]	18·4	3·38	—	whole exchanger studies	'Model 9' 9 BC-BS combinations studied
133	80 × 9·52	RSP	1·25	48·4[c]	31·0 ×	—	—		
133	80 × 9·52	RSP	1·25	24·8[c]	43·7	—	—		
133	80 × 9·52	RSP	1·25	12·7[c]		—	—		
Leakage studies									
133	80 × 9·52	RSP	1·25	48·4	18·4	3·38	—	whole exchanger studies	'Model 9'
133	80 × 9·52	RSP	1·25	50·0	18·4	—	0·15		
133	80 × 9·52	RSP	1·25	50·0	18·4	—	0·33		
133	80 × 9·52	RSP	1·25	48·4	18·4	1·60	—		
133	80 × 9·52	RSP	1·25	48·4	18·4	0·53	—		
133	80 × 9·52	RSP	1·25	50·0	18·4	3·38	0·33		
133	80 × 9·52	RSP	1·25	50·0	18·4	1·60	0·33		
133	80 × 9·52	RSP	1·25	50·0	18·4	0·53	0·33		
213	470 × 6·35	ETP[b]	1·375	65·5	17·56	—	0·55		'Model 10'
213	470 × 6·35	ETP	1·375	65·5	17·56	2·16	0·33		
216	470 × 6·35	ETP	1·375	65·5	17·56	2·03	0·33		
222	470 × 6·35	ETP	1·375	65·5	17·56	2·03	0·33		
232	470 × 6·35	ETP	1·375	65·5	17·56	2·03	0·33		
232	470 × 6·35	ETP	1·375	66·9	20·4	2·03	0·25		several cases

No.	Tube size	Pitch	Ratio	Length	Spacing			Leaky compartments	Notes
133	80 × 9.52	RSP	1.25	97.0c	18.4 ⎫			3rd of 5 and 5th of 9	Earlier Aston models virtually identical with 98.8 mm BS model
133	80 × 9.52	RSP	1.25	48.5c	25.0 ⎬ ×				
					37.5 ⎭				
Leakage studies									
133	80 × 9.52	RSP	1.25	48.4	18.4	1.40	0.33	all	
133	80 × 9.52	RSP	1.25	46.8	18.4	2.67	0.66	5th of 9	
133	80 × 9.52	RSP	1.25	46.8	25.0	2.67	0.66		
133	80 × 9.52	RSP	1.25	46.8	37.5	2.67	0.66		
249	300 × 9.53	RSP	1.25	97.0	18.4				
					25.0			many cases, all proprietary, summarised in Macbeth[12]	
					37.5				
Aston									
No-leakage studies									
133	80 × 9.52	RSP	1.25	47.6	18.4	0.5	—	1 to 4 of 8	all end compartments 47.6 mm long except as
133	80 × 9.52	RSP	1.25	47.6	18.4	—	—	1 to 4 of 8	
133	80 × 9.52	RSP	1.25	47.6	18.4	—	—	5 to 8 of 8	
133	80 × 9.52	RSP	1.25	149.2	18.4	—	—	1 to 2 of 4	
Leakage studies									
134	80 × 9.52	RSP	1.25	47.6	18.4	2.2	0.5	1 to 4 of 8	shown below
134	80 × 9.52	RSP	1.25	66.6	18.4	2.2	0.5	1 to 6 of 6	
134	80 × 9.52	RSP	1.25	97.0	18.4	2.2	0.5	1 to 4 of 4	97 mm
134	80 × 9.52	RSP	1.25	97.0	18.4	2.2	0.5	1 to 5 of 5	
134	80 × 9.52	RSP	1.25	149.2	18.4	2.2	0.5	1 to 4 of 4	
Sparrow and Perez									
No-leakage studies									
104	92 × 6.35	ETP	1.5	62.4	22.3	—	—	5th of 9	
104	92 × 6.35	ETP	1.5	62.4	30.2	—	—	3rd of 7	
104	92 × 6.35	ETP	1.5	62.4	46.0	—	—	3rd of 7	

a Rotated square pitch.
b Equilateral triangular pitch.
c All spacings were studied at all cuts.

There is here, too, an interaction with the flow-pattern and velocity distribution studies now being carried out)[4] as well as with work on pressure drop prediction and measurement.

Clearly the direct heat transfer data of the Delaware project form the bedrock of subsequent experimental work, since they are the basis against which the quicker and more detailed indirect mass-transfer studies have to be validated. But by their very nature (studies on a complete heat exchanger) they do not provide the more detailed information required to test the various theoretical models (see above). When Gay et al.[43,44] turned to the electrochemical method using the ferri-ferrocyanide redox couple, their first concern was to validate the method. For this they compared the heat transfer data of the Delaware project, the mercury evaporation mass transfer data of Gay and Williams,[66,67] and their own obtained in a preliminary investigation at Aston University. The model exchangers in each of these studies were virtually identical.

The comparison of the different results is not altogether straightforward. The data of Gay and Williams and of Gay et al. are equivalent to isothermal data, while those from the Delaware project (Brown[9,69] and Tompkins[9,70]) are necessarily non-isothermal. Discrepancies exist for runs carried out at the lower flow rates of both workers where the temperature rises through the Delaware exchanger are greatest (of the order of 14 K) and negligible for the high flow-rate runs where the temperature rises are small (of the order of 3 K). But these low flow-rate runs are also the ones with the greater uncertainty in he heat balances.[59] The original investigators noted that below $Re = 150$, their data for this small exchanger deviated from the Bergelin et al.[33] correlation for the equivalent ideal tube bundle. They attributed this to either, as already noted, poor heat balances or to bundle by-passing. But comparison of the friction-factor plot for the two situations shows no comparable discrepancy. Hence bundle by-passing can be eliminated as a cause. Further, as already noted, the Delaware data are for a complete exchanger, the other data were obtained in a single baffle compartment. Mackley summarised that one possible cause of this discrepancy might be due to the different contributions of natural and forced convection in the two situations. Jenkins and Noie-Baghban[36] have shown that for both situations the contribution of natural convection is not significant, and so the discrepancy is probably attributable to experimental error (the error-bands for the Delaware and Aston data still overlap in this region).

A similar comparison for data obtained for a different geometry in the subsequent programme at AEE Winfrith confirmed the general agreement but with the same reservations.[45] In a much later programme, Nibber *et al.*[50,51] obtained results by the same technique for a range of geometries, and did so along the whole length of the exchanger, thus providing a better case for comparison. They found a considerable variation in coefficient along the exchanger length (see below), but fortuitously, the average value (obtained by summing the individual compartment results and dividing by the number of compartments) is close to that for the fifth compartment, the compartment investigated by Gay *et al.*[45] The discrepancies observed are in line with those already noted. As part of their work Gay and his co-workers (Jenkins *et al.*[44]) investigated the validity of using the Schmidt number to the 0·66 power to both account for the effect of the changes in physical properties and in the heat-and-mass transfer analogy in its *j*-factor form due to Chilton and Colburn. They found its use justified. In the $Nu/Sc^{1/3}$ form, the $-0·33$ power is thus confirmed. This may be compared with the recommendation of Zukauskas[38] of the use of the $-0·34$ power on the Prandtl number to correlate data for heat transfer in ideal tube banks, a conclusion based on a narrower range of Prandtl number than the range of Schmidt number considered by Jenkins *et al.*[44] and with the use of the $-0·36$ power in the computational study noted above on ideal rectangular tube banks.[24,25] Confirmation may also be found in the recent work of Jenkins and Noie-Baghban[36] whose ideal rectangular bundle results (obtained by the same mass transfer technique) agree closely with the heat transfer data of the Delaware project. It is also of interest to note here that their wide range of Reynolds number show a monotonic variation of transfer coefficient with Reynolds number whereas the equivalent results from the Delaware project (obtained in separate investigations) show a discontinuity akin to that for the different cylindrical model exchanger studies considered here. Thus the discrepancies discussed above may be an artifact of the Delaware techniques. That the flow conditions in the various experimental programmes are alike can be seen by a comparison of the pressure drops (in the form of friction factors) obtained, which are similar.[36,43]

Nibber[50] was able to summarise the results of the Delaware project for the no-leakage work on their smaller cylindrical model as shown in Fig. 1. In this and subsequent figures, the characteristic Reynolds number is based on the area not occupied by tubes at the edge of the baffle. This choice removes many of the effects of geometry since all the cases fall on one of three straight lines.

The early data of Gay *et al.*[46] can also be shown on such a plot (Fig. 2). For these data, the scatter of the data is reduced to less than 10% if the

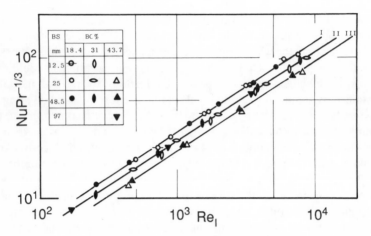

FIG. 1. Summary of Delaware project data for the small cylindrical exchanger (Nibber[50]).

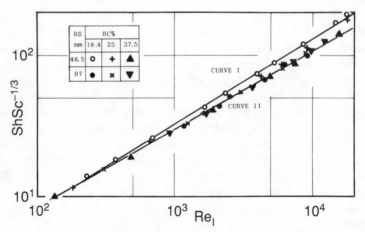

FIG. 2. Summary of Mackley's data for a small cylindrical exchanger (Nibber[50]).

extreme 18·4% baffle cut (BC) and 48·5 mm baffle spacing (BS) case is omitted. A comparison with the data of Brown is instructive. For Reynolds numbers greater than 1500 the curve for the 18·4% BC/48·5 mm BS case falls close to the upper curve in Fig. 1. The lower line in Fig. 2 is coincident with the middle curve in Fig. 1, while the lower line in Fig. 2 represents smaller baffle spacings at a larger (43·7%) baffle cut. The comparison below a Reynolds number of 1500 is hampered by the considerations discussed above. An interim conclusion reached by Nibber[50] was that the lower line in Fig. 2 and the equivalent line in Fig. 1 represented a correlation of the configurations likely to be used commercially (but, be it noted, for the no-leakage case).

Nibber's own experimental work[50,51,71,72] concentrated on investigating lengthwise variation of transfer coefficients for both no-leakage and leakage cases. (His leakage case gave results for a situation not studied by Mackley.) Both covered only a single baffle cut (18·4%), two baffle spacings for the no-leakage (and four for the leakage case).

In this work, in the exchanger model, similar to that of Bergelin *et al.*,[9,59,69,70] and Gay *et al.*,[45,46] as already noted, only twenty composite electrodes were used, placed to provide maximum information. Each electrode spanned half the length of the exchanger and was made up of six nickel tubular elements, four 25·4 mm long and two 50·8 mm long. This potentially enabled the investigation of baffle spacings of 25 mm, 50 mm, 75 mm and 100 mm. Complete bundle information could be obtained by reversing the flow direction.

Figure 3 gives the compartment-by-compartment variation of transfer

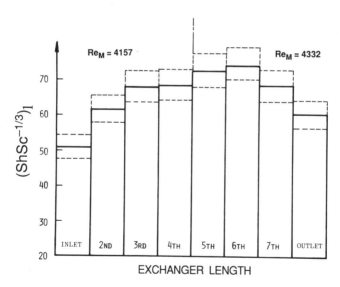

FIG. 3. Length-wise compartment-by-compartment variation of transfer co-efficients for a no-leakage case.

coefficient along the length of the exchanger for the no-leakage 18·4% BC, 47·6 mm BS case investigated. The compartment-by-compartment variation is quite marked and shows some support for the observation of Perez and Sparrow[2] that the flow is fully developed after the first compartment. But no explanation is forthcoming for the decrease after the sixth compartment. These data present a severe challenge for any modelling of shellside flow.

If we consider the experimental evidence for the inlet and outlet compartment from Prowse and Nibber, the following points arise.

Whilst the data of Prowse are inaccurate in absolute terms, he was able to obtain consistency within his data set.[47] Repeat runs gave virtually identical results. Further his inlet and outlet compartment data show the same lowering of coefficients as do Nibber's data, i.e. they are both low, with the outlet compartment being slightly higher. Prowse studied a range of inlet and outlet compartment configurations. Here we note that Jenkins et al.[77] have reported that his data show very little mean transfer coefficient performance differences between the Delaware rectangular ports, circular ports of typical industrial proportions, and the same ports fitted with an impingment baffle for both with a horizontal baffle-cut and with a vertical one. These, as already noted, were all no-leakage cases. Nibber[50] showed that inlet compartments did not show a significant drop in performance between no-leakage and leakage cases, but that the outlet compartment did show a drop. Hence Prowse's comparison for the inlet case probably holds for the leakage case, and since the major effect of leakage is to reduce the performance, the same probably holds for the exit compartment.

Sparrow and Perez,[61] as already noted, used the naphthalene sublimation technique to determine tube-by-tube transfer coefficients in a method akin to that of the electrochemical method, although the main thrust of their work was on flow visualisation and pressure drop determination. Their work was for a no-leakage case (guaranteed to be so by the method of construction used) and (effectively) for a single internal compartment, initially the fifth compartment and later the third. Their flow visualisation work[2] showed that hydrodynamically developed flow was achieved rapidly, i.e. after only one compartment, for experimental convenience they therefore reduced the length of the model exchanger. Their model had an inside diameter of 4·100 in (104·1 mm) but used 92 one-quarter inch (6·25 mm) OD dummy tubes on a 1·5 pitch-to-diameter ratio equilateral triangular pitch, and a baffle spacing of 62·4 mm. Only three Reynolds numbers were used. Direct comparison of these results with those of the earlier work reported above is not straightforward but can be attempted since their Reynolds number was based on the minimum flow area at the centre line of the bundle (i.e. equivalent to A_M as defined above). This choice has been shown to provide a convenient basis for the correlation of both rotated square pitch (as in the Delaware project and Aston/Winfrith programmes) and triangular pitch data. The Delaware project obtained data on both an equilateral triangular pitch of P/D ratio of 1·5 and a rotated square pitch of P/D ratio 1·25. When the data (in the form of $NuPr^{-0.33}$) for these cases are plotted for the Reynolds number range of interest here, the triangular pitch data lie about 7% above the rotated square pitch data. The Sparrow and Perez case (22·3%, 30·2%, 46·0% baffle cuts and a 61·5 mm baffle spacing) does not correspond to any one case in the earlier programmes, but an attempt at comparison was made by plotting their data on a plot of Mackley's no-leakage data. Their data were plotted as both uncorrected for the different tube arrangement, and corrected as outlined above. The positive features are that the dependence on Reynolds number is very similar, tending to confirm Mackley's slope as against that of Brown in the Delaware project. Also, the effect of increasing baffle cut is the same. However, overall the coefficients are significantly higher, since one would expect the slightly larger baffle cuts at the larger spacing to yield lower coefficients. The discrepancy is of the order of 20%. No attempt was made by Perez-Galindo[73] to carry out any such comparison.

One feature of the work of Gay et al.[43–51] is that since data were acquired initially tube-by-tube they were able to report zone coefficients as well as overall coefficients. For the crossflow compartment the no-leakage data they reported had the characteristics that all the data at the larger 98 mm spacing, and those at 37·5% BC on the shorter spacing, fell within ± 5%. The data from the 18·4% and 25·0% BCs fell on separate lines above these data. They noted that the geometry of the crossflow zone could be expressed by the ratio L_c/L_s, where L_c and L_s are the baffle overlap and baffle spacing, respectively. High values of this ratio (1·78 for 49 mm and 18·4% BC, 1·48 at 49 mm BS and 25·0% BC) correspond to conditions close to true crossflow. Commercial heat exchangers tend to have L_c/L_s values of less than 1·0, a baffle spacing equal to the shell diameter giving $L_c/L_s = 0.5$. The well-correlated data correspond then to situations of industrial significance, albeit for the no-leakage situation. Gay et al.[46] attempted correlation of both compartment and zonal data by various methods using the j-factor approach without great success.

3.3.2. The Leakage Case
Despite the great importance of the leakage case, since this represents

virtually all industrial heat exchangers, there is a surprising lack of reliable experimental data for such situations. As already noted, much of the earlier complete exchanger results are not of great value because of uncertainty over the clearances present in the exchanger bundle between tubes and baffles, and baffles and shells. The Delaware project sought to remedy this, with detailed studies not only of heat transfer but also of flows and pressure drops. This included experimental investigations[74] into annular orifice flow, to elucidate the magnitude, and if possible the effect, of leakage flows through the clearances between baffles and shell. Similar measurements were made for an annular orifice formed by a tube in a baffle,[18] and have been incorporated into the various stream models.

The Delaware project's work on exchangers with leakage was, as already noted, on a single-baffle rectangular exchanger (tube-to-baffle leakage study, building on the various orifice studies noted above) and on a small exchanger with 80 3/8 in (9·52 mm) OD tubes, (on a 1·25 P/D ratio, rotated square pitch) and on a larger unit with 470 1/4 in (6·25 mm) OD tubes. The tubes in this unit were on an equilateral triangular (1·375 P/D ratio) pitch. The larger unit was more representative of industrial practice, except for the rather large pitch-to-tube diameter ratio. The Aston programme as already noted used a model virtually identical with the small unit of the Delaware project. The Winfrith programme[12,43] also used a rotated square pitch of 1·25 P/D ratio, but detailed data from this are proprietary and not in the public domain.

The Delaware project investigated first the no-leakage case (see above),

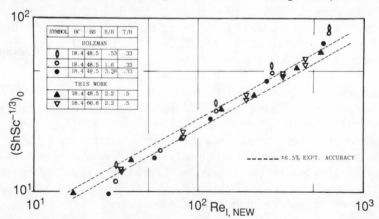

FIG. 4. Comparison of leakage data for the Delaware and Aston programmes (Nibber[50]).

then a series of controlled leakage situations—first shell-baffle, next tube-baffle, and finally combined shell-baffle and tube-baffle situations. Bundle by-passing was reduced as far as possible by placing tubes as near the shell wall as construction practices permitted.

The Delaware project leakage work was reported in references 9 and 60. That for the small exchanger was reported in full but the larger exchanger work in a more limited way. Discussion of the Delaware results alongside those from the Aston programme is made difficult by the fact that no real agreement exists between them. Both sets, as will be seen below, are self-consistent, but differ from each other. Figure 4 compares the results for the situation most alike in the two programmes. It can be seen that the major feature is the discrepancy in the variation of the Nusselt group with Reynolds number. Because of this, the two sets of data will be discussed first separately and then together.

3.3.3. Delaware Project Data

The data from the Delaware project are reported in tabular form in reference 9 and graphically in a smoothed form in reference 60. One feature of both exchangers used is the large rectangular entry ports, designed to avoid entrance or exit pressure losses. (Prowse[47] showed that the heat transfer results from such an entry port are similar to those for a conventional circular port.) A convenient way to report their data is to reproduce Table 3 from reference 60. Note the restricted Reynolds number range reported ($1000 \leqslant Re \leqslant 10\,000$). In reference 60, the authors presented a correlation in terms of a resistance factor, based on the work of Sullivan and Bergelin[18] but in reference 9, a simpler correlation in terms of A_L/A_M was presented, and this is shown in Fig. 5. The term

$$\left[1 - \left[\frac{\alpha_L}{\alpha_{LO}} \right] \right]_0$$

is obtained from the experimental

$$\left[1 - \left[\frac{\alpha_L}{\alpha_{LO}} \right] \right]_{exchanger}$$

by the use of a correlation term, i.e.

$$\left[1 - \frac{\alpha_L}{\alpha_{LO}} \right]_{exchanger} = \left[1 - \frac{\alpha_L}{\alpha_{LO}} \right]_0 \left[\frac{A_{TB} + 2A_{SB}}{A_L} \right]$$

where A_{TB} is the tube-to-baffle leakage area, A_{SB} that for shell-to-baffle and

TABLE 3
EFFECT OF INTERNAL LEAKAGES UPON PRESSURE DROP AND HEAT TRANSFER

Diametrical leakage clearance between		Percentage of non-leakage case					
		Pressure drop			α_o		
Tube and Baffle (in.)	Shell and Baffle (in.)	$Re=1\,000$ $u_M=0{\cdot}82$	$Re=3\,500$ $u_M=2{\cdot}8$	$Re=10\,000$ $u_M=8{\cdot}2$	$Re=1\,000$ $u_M=0{\cdot}82$	$Re=3\,500$ $u_M=2{\cdot}8$	$Re=10\,000$ $u_M=8{\cdot}2$ (ft/s)
Model No. 9							
0·000	0·000	100	100	100	100	100	100
0·013	0·000	66	58	50	87	83	80
0·000	0·021	63	61	61	80	82	80
0·013	0·021	58	51	50	83	82	80
0·000	0·063	44	42	40	70	70	70
0·013	0·063	38	35	32	66	69	70
0·000	0·133	27	27	27	55	59	60
0·013	0·133	27	26	24	61	64	63
Model No. 10							
0·000	0·000	100	100	100	100	100	100
0·013	0·080	31	28	26	54	54	54
0·0218	0·086	19	18	18	47	48	48

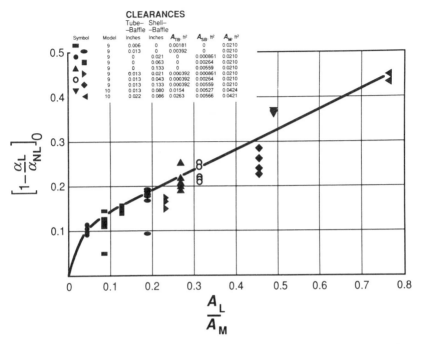

FIG. 5. Effect of baffle leakage on overall shellside heat transfer coefficient (Bell[9]).

A_L is the total leakage area $(A_{TB} + A_{SB})$. The use of this factor allows for the greater negative effect of shell-to-baffle leakage on the heat transfer based on the discussion that follows. (Bell[9] presents a similar argument and correlation for pressure drop; for recent discussions on pressure drop, see references 75 and 76.)

Bell[9] set out the effect of baffle leakage on both pressure drop and heat exchanger thus. Noting that the baffle leakages will be greatest at the baffle root (where, as already noted, the pressure drop is greatest) and minimal at the baffle tip (since here the pressure drop is smaller), he observes that a number of mechanisms alter the shellside characteristics. These include the following:

1. The short-circuiting of a substantial fraction (up to, say, one-half) of the flow reduces the velocity of the flow normal to the tubes and hence reduces the pressure drop and the local heat transfer coefficient.

2. Since the short-circuiting fluid does not undergo the same change in

temperature as the fluid that follows the sinusoidal path, the 'ideal' temperature profile of the shellside fluid is distorted, and to a degree not readily determinable since the leakage stream does not mix immediately and completely with the crossflow stream it enters. Further this fact changes the driving force as well as the coefficient.

3. Shell-to-baffle leakage flows are not effective for heat transfer whereas tube-to-baffle leakage flows at high velocity parallel to heat transfer surface, and is significantly changed in temperature.

Clearly the situation is complex and this in turn creates difficulty in the analysis of the data produced.

Bell drew attention to the contrast in behaviour of heat transfer and pressure drop effects. In the small exchanger work, test on a situation with a 3·4 mm shell-baffle clearance and no tube-and-baffle clearance could be compared with a case which had the same shell-baffle clearance but also tube-baffle clearance at 0·33 mm. The second showed a slightly lower pressure drop but had 5% higher heat transfer coefficients. The lower cross-flow velocities were compensated for by the higher local velocities close to the baffle. (It is this effect which accounts for the effectiveness of the orifice baffle heat exchanger.)

Another point made by Bell is that α_L (i.e. the heat transfer situation) for the leakage case is necessarily derived from a logarithmic mean temperature difference (LMTD) using terminal temperatures, as is the case for α_{NL}, so any correlation of α_L/α_{NL} includes the effect of distortions on the LMTD as well as changes in the heat transfer coefficient.

This discussion may also provide an explanation for the discrepancy between the leakage data of the Delaware project and those of the Aston programme. The Aston data are essentially isothermal, since the bulk concentration of the reacting ion is scarcely altered in the experiment. Hence they give the actual effect of leakage on the heat transfer coefficients. But the Delaware project data have both the temperature gradient distribution and the effect on the heat transfer coefficient. Since the leakage flows do not behave in the same way as the crossflow with increasing pressure drop, there will be an effect which varies with Reynolds number, thus changing the slope of the dependence of $NuPr^{-1/3}$ (or $ShSc^{-1/3}$) on Re. Further discussion is deferred to after discussion of the later results.

3.3.4. The Aston Programme

Mackley[43] included in his extensive programme, work on the leakage situation. In designing his exchanger for this work, he used the TEMA

TABLE 4
DETAILS OF THE ACTUAL CLEARANCES BETWEEN SHELL AND BAFFLES, AND TUBES
AND BAFFLES FOR THE WINFRITH SMALL EXCHANGER MODEL

Shell internal diameter (mm)	Baffle thickness (mm)	Baffle clearances (diametrical)		Orifice shape factor	
		S-B (mm)	T-B (mm)	Z_S	Z_T
133·4	1·63	1·40	0·33	2·33	9·85
133·4	3·10	2·67	0·66	2·32	9·38

standards as a guide for the values of shell-to-baffle and tube-to-baffle diametrical clearance, close to the TEMA recommended orifice shape factor values for tube-to-baffle clearance of 8·0 and shell-to-baffle of 2·5. The actual values used, and other details, are given in Table 4. The tubes were allowed to lie on the bottom of the baffle holes, and the baffles to lie on the floor of the shell, giving eccentric baffle clearance areas typical of commercial exchangers.

The model was used both with the baffle-cut horizontal (up-and-down flow) and with it vertical (side-to-side flow, closest to the industrial situation). For the horizontal baffle cut, results were obtained for fluid entering the compartment containing the test electrodes at both the top and the bottom, since the leakage flows and crossflow interactions are different and were expected to give different results. Seven cases were investigated in all; two with thin baffles (top entry, bottom entry) at a 18·4% BC and 48·4 mm BS; the rest with the thick baffles at a 46·8 mm BS, and successively 18·4%, 25·0% and 37·5% BC. The 18·4% BC was investigated for top entry, bottom entry and side entry cases, the remainder side entry only.

A plot of compartment average j-factors for both baffle thicknesses at the 18·4% BC, showed that top and bottom entry results were virtually identical. Despite the identical Z-factors the data for the thick baffles lie below those for the thin ones (see Fig. 6). Sullivan and Bergelin[18] have shown that the eccentric discharge coefficient was a function of the orifice shape factor Z and the orifice Reynolds number; for a given pressure drop the flow through the baffle clearances would be a function of the leakage channel flow area as well. The thin baffles have a Z close to that for the thick baffles, but only about half the leakage channel flow area, hence the greatest contribution seems to be from the greater area for leakage flow. As for the

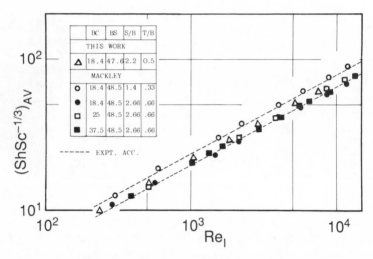

FIG. 6. Comparison of the leakage data of Mackley[43] and Nibber.[50]

no-leakage case, Gay et al.[46] reported zonal results as well as compartment results. These show less variation than in the no-leakage case, see the discussion below on the tube-by-tube results. The very good agreement they obtained for the crossflow data suggested that the net upstream and downstream flows are the same for both top and bottom entry, these compartments need not be distinguished in a general analysis. The effects of baffles resting on the shell bottom can be seen in their data in that enhanced coefficients were obtained in the window zones at the bottom. Comparison of the side-to-side flow case with the two correspondingly top-to-bottom cases gave about 8% higher results for the side-to-side case, not thought to be a significant variation. Gay et al.[46] gave a correlation of their data along the lines suggested by Bell.[9]

Nibber,[50] as already noted, extended his work to the investigation of coefficient values along the length of the exchanger. He investigated five leakage situations, all at a baffle cut of 18·4%, at orifice shape factors of 2·75 (shell-to-baffle) and 12·75 (tube-to-baffle); diametrical clearances were 2·3 mm and 0·5 mm respectively. This work was done with top-to-bottom flow, save for one side-to-side case. Figure 6 gives a partial comparison of the data of this work and of those of Mackley. The data are in good agreement, note that the Reynolds number used here is that defined for the flow area available at the baffle edge. Nibber[50] had shown that this choice gave a good correlation of no-leakage data. The coefficient variation along the length of the exchanger is small. The maximum difference in similar sized compartments is $\pm 10\%$, not markedly higher than the estimated overall experimental accuracy. The lack of variation in the leakage case means that data from one internal compartment give the bundle average coefficient. End compartments in runs with internal compartments of varying baffle spacing have very similar coefficients. Sparrow and Perez[61] from their no-leakage results drew attention to a compartment-by-compartment periodic variation of coefficient for a singletube and discussed the implications for design. But clearly the results obtained by Nibber show that for the leakage situation this effect does not exist at any significant level.

3.4. Localised Heat Transfer Coefficients

As noted above, both Mackley and Nibber, by virtue of the electrochemical technique used, were able to obtain localised mass (and so, by analogy, heat) transfer coefficients at each electrode used. For Mackley this gave tube-by-tube coefficients and, since one half of his compartment was filled with electrodes, a complete picture of the coefficient distribution. Nibber did not investigate as many tube positions, but was, for some configurations studied, able to obtain information on variation along the tube length between baffles. Mackley, in his preliminary Aston work, had also been able to do this for one or two cases. Prowse also obtained partial tube-by-tube data for a number of inlet compartment situations. However, his data as already noted were vitiated by an error in his activation technique, which gave uniformly low transfer coefficients (Nibber[50]). But since they were uniformly low, the distribution results are still of interest, as has been pointed out recently (Jenkins et al.[77]). Data recently reported[77] have been available for some time but were not published in the general literature since no straightforward way of making use of them existed.

Further, since the leakage results (those most relevant to the industrial situation) showed a fairly uniform coefficient distribution, tube-by-tube information for the no-leakage situation did not appear to be very relevant. However, the picture has changed with the development of the complex porous body and other models noted above. For these, the no-leakage situation represents a 'boundary condition', and the correct representation of the variations in flows and local coefficients presents a formidable challenge to any model.

In this review, we report some of the data of Mackley and of Nibber, and compare their results with those of Sparrow and Perez.[61] For this purpose, the most convenient representation is given by normalising the tube-by-tube coefficients, whereby each tube coefficient is divided by the mean coefficient for that compartment.

3.4.1. The No-leakage Case—Internal Compartment

A comparison of the distributions obtained by Mackley *et al.* for Reynolds numbers close to each other (the distribution does not vary much with flow rate) showed that the results of Mackley and Nibber are, in general, in good agreement. Figure 7 gives distributions from Mackley for the Reynolds numbers 123, 1678, 8599. A similar plot, prepared from Perez-Galindo,[73] is

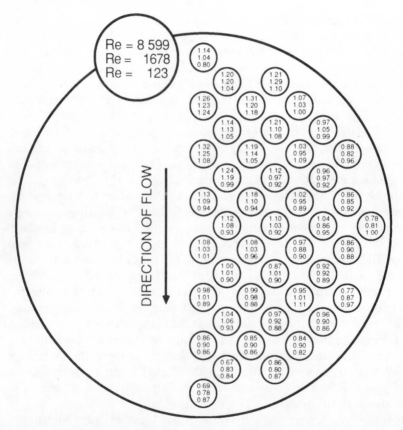

FIG. 7. Comparison of individual tube-by-tube transfer coefficients for three Reynolds numbers for the data of Mackley.[43]

given in Fig. 8 for his three Reynolds numbers of 1350, 2850 and 5750 for the baffle cut close to that for the other cases. Nibber noted that the spread of his data and those of Mackley were respectively 20% and 30%, while those of Williams show a spread of 48%. However, the data of Perez-Galindo for the case shown show a spread of the same order of magnitude. Since the maldistribution is largely due to jetting as the fluid sweeps round the baffle, this difference may be typical of the different viscosities, since this will affect the velocity gradients. Similarity of Reynolds number may not be a sufficient criterion for modelling this effect. If this distinction is real, rather than due to inherent drawbacks in the techniques of Williams, and of Sparrow and Perez, then reproducing it will provide another extreme test for the different models.

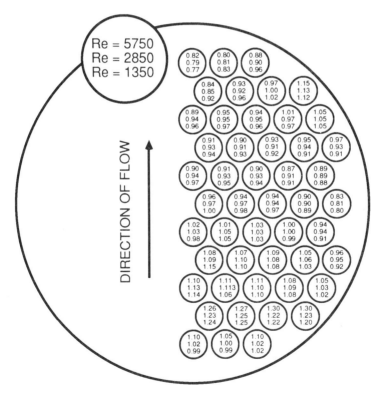

FIG. 8. Individual tube coefficients compared for the results of Perez-Galindo.[73]

But in general, the distributions are very similar where a direct comparison is possible ($1000 \leqslant Re \leqslant 6000$). The coefficients are higher in the inlet window and lower in the outlet window, with a tendency for a central penetration region in the crossflow zone. For the higher Reynolds numbers,[43,77] both inlet and outlet zones show reduced normalised coefficients, with the higher coefficients in the crossflow zone. Nibber,[50] following Gay and Roberts,[68] attempted a tube-by-tube analysis to deduce the flow direction at each tube by examining the dependence on Reynolds' number for the coefficient at each tube, but this approach is at best inexact, especially in light of the between-baffle variation on single tubes noted below, and proper analysis is only possible through the various flow models.

3.4.2. The No-leakage Case—Inlet Compartment

As noted above, Nibber showed that the inlet compartment data of Prowse were in error, but consistently so. Hence it is feasible[77] to use his normalised data to give an indication of coefficient distribution in the inlet–outlet compartments. Both no-leakage and leakage situations were investigated. Prowse investigated a number of different configurations (different inlet ports, with and without impingement baffles) and these are reported in reference 77.

3.4.3. The Leakage Case

When we turn to the leakage case, one feature is clearly apparent. The leakage data show a much reduced variation (see discussion in reference 12). Since only leakage cases are of industrial interest, this uniformity has led to a lack of interest in such data—they do not seem to add to our knowledge of heat transfer on the shellside. But what is overlooked is the existence of variation in transfer coefficient along the between-baffle tube length. The uniformity is more apparent than real. Some limited data on lengthwise variation between baffles are available from the work of Mackley and of Nibber.

As already noted, overall the different configurations have very similar coefficients. The local distributions are, however, different. As would be expected, the results show higher coefficients immediately opposite the inlet ports. For the cases with horizontal baffle cut, the lower coefficients are at the two sides, with the circular port showing a very similar distribution to the rectangular port of the Delaware project. For the vertical baffle cut, again the two parts show a similar distribution, but now with the lower coefficients in the 'corner' away from the lower part of the window zone.

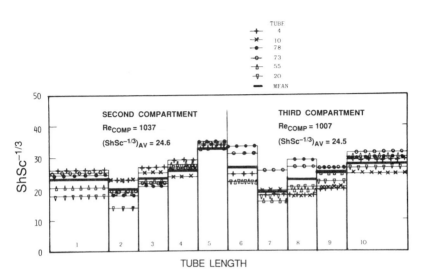

FIG. 9. Variation of transfer coefficients along individual tubes in two adjacent compartments for an exchanger with leakage (Nibber[50]).

When an impingement baffle was used, the lower coefficients were (as would be expected) behind the baffle, but those at the sides were average. Exit compartments showed similar characteristics.

3.4.4. Between-Baffle Lengthwise Variation

Mackley[43] in his development work at Aston obtained limited data from a segmented multi-electrode spanning a single compartment. Nibber[50] with his segmented electrodes spanning half an exchanger, also produced a limited amount of data showing the lengthwise variation in a single compartment. A typical data set is graphed in Fig. 9. This is for a leakage case, at 149·2 mm baffle spacing. As compared with the no-leakage situation, the tube segment just behind the baffle shows an increased coefficient, attributable to the leakage stream through the baffle-tube clearance area. But as noted above there is still a marked variation along the tube length, between the baffles. Thus the picture of nearly uniform tube-by-tube coefficients, for the no-leakage case, conceals considerable localised variations. The data sets reported in reference 77 can only be regarded as fragmentary, but were reported since modern computer models (see above) are capable of providing estimates of such variations. The existence of these variations make much of the analysis of the tube-by-tube (or row-by-row) coefficients extant in the literature suspect. In particular, comparison between ideal banks and the crossflow zones is invalidated, since clearly the uneven lengthwise flow/coefficient distribution in the crossflow zone does not exist in the ideal tube bank.

4. A GEOMETRY-INDEPENDENT CORRELATION

How may localised heat transfer coefficients be related to complete exchanger coefficients? This problem has been discussed by Bell[9]. In his discussion, he distinguished between window and crossflow zones, and summed for each along the length of the exchanger, for each zone, in each compartment, a term of the form (heat transfer coefficient) × (area available for heat transfer) × (local temperature difference between shellside fluid and fluid in the tubes) and thus obtained the various contributions to the total quantities of heat transferred. For work such as his on no-leakage situations, such a discussion is relevant but for the leakage case, the coefficients, at least as averaged across one tube segment in one compartment, are very nearly uniform and so the summation reduces to the simple situation where (logarithmic mean temperature difference) × (area) × (overall coefficient) gives the total quantity of heat transferred.

We know that the localised coefficients vary significantly along the length of the exchanger for the no-leakage case. One virtue of the electrochemical procedure is that the driving force is virtually constant, thus derivation of localised zone whole compartment and whole exchanger coefficients is fairly easy. The relative uniformity suggests that correlation of leakage results among themselves rather than by reference to the no-leakage case may provide a straightforward manual design procedure. This is in contrast to the Bell method, which seeks to relate the leakage case to the no-leakage case and to the ideal tube-bank data. But such an approach to the correlation of leakage coefficients implies that a suitable method must be available. Jenkins[78] combined the approach of Nibber[50] which used the area for flow at the baffle-cut edge to account for variations in baffle spacing and baffle cut, and the correlation of Gay et al.[48] by which they had correlated one geometrical configuration studied by Mackley for a number of different leakage cases. Sullivan and Bergelin,[18] from a study of pressure drop across a single baffle with clearances, as already noted, have shown that the discharge coefficient is a function of the orifice shape factor Z and the orifice Reynolds number. For a given pressure drop the flow through the baffle clearances would be a function of the leakage channel flow area as well. Gay et al.[48] (who, as already noted above, carried out tests for baffle thickness and clearance combinations with the same Z-factor) noted that their thinner baffles had a Z-factor close to that for their thicker baffles, but had only about half the leakage flow area. They attributed the lower mass transfer performance of the thick baffles to a greater leakage flow, reducing the amount of fluid cross flow, and sought a correlation for the effect of greater leakage flows in terms of the ratio of the total leakage area, A_L, to the area available for the flow at the middle of the bundle, A_M.

To carry out the correlation, they used the two leakage cases available to them of the same general geometry, and the low Reynolds number data from the no-leakage data of the same geometry. They then related the leakage j-factors to the no-leakage ones by the expression

$$j_{M\,leakage} = (1\cdot0 - 0\cdot6(A_L/A_M)^{0\cdot9})j_{M\,no\text{-}leakage}$$

(unfortunately this equation was misreported in reference 48). In practice it is easier to invert this correlation and express all j_M factors in terms of a corresponding 'no-leakage' factor. It is of interest to note that Bell[9] also used the parameter A_L/A_M, albeit in a different way. Gay et al.[48] observed that a degree of correlation resulted. In a suitable plot the two leakage cases were brought together and lay along part of the no-leakage curve. They noted that more leakage data would be required before this correlation could be tested further.

The basis for their attempted correlation was that the crossflow in the compartment is rendered less effective by the portion of the flow that can pass through the leakage area. Taking this 'lost' flow away completely would not be appropriate and it retains some effectiveness for mass (and heat) transfer; the form of the correlation shows this. They also showed that this correlation (as would be expected) correlates the zonal coefficients well.

Jenkins[78] re-expressed this correlation in the Nusselt form and also, as noted above, introduced Nibber's redefined flow area, i.e. that at the baffle-cut edge, into the Reynolds number. Since Nibber et al.[51] had shown that this correlates the effect of baffle cut and baffle spacing, it was now feasible to attempt the simultaneous correlation of all the Mackley and Nibber leakage data. The results are shown in the two plots, given as Figs. 10 and 11.

In Fig. 10 the results of using this correlation method on the leakage data from both Nibber and Mackley are shown for the 18·4% BC and (approximately) 48 mm BS cases. The data plotted include the thin and thick baffle leakage data of Mackley, and two cases from Nibber, the first is his case with both tube-to-baffle and shell-to-baffle leakage, the second a

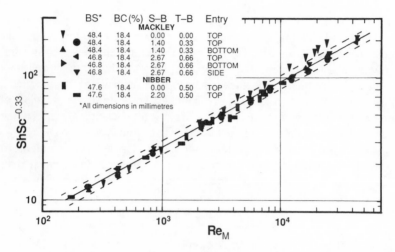

FIG. 10. Correlation of Aston programme leakage data (Jenkins[78]) for a single geometry.

case where he had only shell-to-baffle leakage. This last case lies very well on the correlating line

$$NuPr^{-1/3} \text{ (or } ShSc^{-1/3}) = 0.689 \, Re_M^{0.531}$$

Since all the geometries are identical, the Reynolds number used is based on the minimum area for flow at the centre line. For the Nibber cases, the data used are for the fifth compartment, this being the compartment Mackley investigated.

Figure 11 shows the correlation extended to the other geometries investigated by Nibber and Mackley. This was done by defining the flow area for the Reynolds number Re_I, as being that at the baffle edge. The straight line is that in the previous figure, transposed by use of Re_I rather than Re_M. Essentially, Fig. 11 shows correlation of both baffle spacing and baffle cut, baffle cut from the data of Mackley and baffle spacing from those of Nibber. The Mackley data for 18·4% BC and 25·0% BC are well represented by the line, but one of the larger baffle-spacing data (18·4% BC, 97 mm BS) and the 37·5% BC case of Mackley falls further from the line. For the larger spacings, the data used had to be for that compartment more distant from the inlet, since this most nearly approximates the situation investigated for the narrow spacing. This may account for some of the

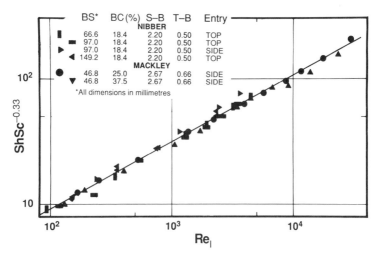

FIG. 11. Correlation of remaining leakage cases, including variation in baffle cut and baffle spacing (Jenkins[78]).

discrepancy, but note that the widest compartment data (149·2 mm BS) lie close to the line. The 37·5% BC data still lie in the ± 20% band drawn in the previous figure. One drawback of all the experimental work on small exchangers is that the leakage areas are proportionally large compared with commercial exchangers and so the effect of leakage flows is magnified. Since this correlation projects all the data back to an idealised no-leakage case, real exchanger data will lie 'between' the cases studied and the 'ideal no-leakage' line. This is illustrated well by the low leakage case of Nibber, with only shell-to-baffle leakage. Bell's discussion of the relative contribution of shell-to-baffle and tube-to-baffle leakages, in which the shell-to-baffle leakage is assumed not to contribute to heat transfer, whereas the tube-to-baffle leakage is assumed to contribute, would suggest that this case ought not to be correlatable on the same basis as cases with tube-to-baffle leakage. But because the leakage area is small, even giving this flow some effectiveness for heat transfer (i.e. equivalent to the same flow through the tube-to-baffle leakage area) does not outweigh the advantage of deducting it from the crossflow. It must be stressed that this correlation has been derived from data on a very small exchanger, and should be used only with reservations for large exchangers.

5. CONCLUSION

One major drawback of the work described in this chapter is the relatively
small scale of the model exchangers on which the various experimental
studies have been carried out. How far, therefore, can results obtained on
these be used as a basis for industrial design? Bell[9] commented that a
primary emphasis on size is misleading and only serves to divert attention
from the significant point, namely the question 'Are the phenomenological
models and dimensionless correlations consistent with the partial differential equations governing an isothermal flow in the flow regimes of interest?'.
Then no conclusive answer could be given, for the then accepted basic
equations were under suspicion, particularly for turbulent flow, and there
were (and are) problems about consistency in scaling all the dimensions (in
the broadest sense) of a model. The best way out of these problems is the
application of recent numerical methods to the models, and then to the real
situations. But the real problem with using small-scale exchangers with
relatively few tubes is that the flow distribution in them may not be typical.

This point was given emphasis by the work of Murray[4] who in carrying
out a detailed study of pressure drops in shell-and-tube exchangers found
that the relative split of pressure drop between window and crossflow zones
differed as between the small model used in the Delaware project, and the
Aston and Winfrith programmes, and his own more typical exchanger. He
attributed this to the very small number of tubes in the window zone of the
small exchanger, thus giving an atypical hydraulic resistance pattern and so
flow pattern. This may also be linked with the differences noted in the tube-
by-tube coefficient distributions discussed above as between air and water
flows. A preliminary attempt to correlate the large exchanger leakage
results from the Winfrith programme showed that the leakage effects could
be accounted for quite well by a correlation of similar form to that proposed
in reference 78, but the geometrical effects only less well. Thus the Nibber
use of Re_1 does not correlate the large exchanger data, thus pointing to
a difference in flow patterns.

This conclusion, if valid, leads to some unfortunate deductions. These
are:

(i) The bulk of the Delaware/Aston programme results, while of
    interest in themselves, may not in fact be relevant to the larger
    exchangers in commercial use.

(ii) How does this conclusion affect the validity of the design procedures
    in common use? No answer to that question is attempted here.

(iii) Despite 30 years of experimental work, we still have no firm body of precise, reliable experimental data for exchangers of industrial proportions available in the open literature.

(iv) In particular, there remains a query over the relationship between the actual heat transfer leakage data of the Delaware project and the 'isothermal' data of the Aston/Winfrith programmes, which only further experimental work can resolve.

However, the commercial designer can take comfort from the fact that exchangers designed using current techniques meet the duties required of them. This is partly due to the fact that available methods for the shellside coefficient are probably accurate to about 30%, that both the better-known wall resistance and tube-side coefficients effectively reduce the error in the overall coefficients, and the designer's friend, the dirt factor, gives a valuable safety margin. Further, problems associated with assigning flows correctly on the tubeside contribute as much to the uncertainty, as well as problems about allowing for multipass effects, as does our lack of understanding of shellside heat transfer.

Refinement of current design procedures will require more experimental work, and a considerable body of simulation work using the latest techniques directed towards the improvement and parameter assignment of design models, both current and future.

REFERENCES

1. *Standards of the Tubular Exchanger Manufacturers Association* (TEMA), 6th edn., 1978, Tubular Exchanger Manufacturers Association, New York.
2. PEREZ, J. A. and SPARROW, M. Patterns of fluid flow in a shell-and-tube heat exchanger, *Heat Trans. Engng*, 1984, **5**(3,4), 56–69.
3. BERNER, C., DURST, F. and McELIGOT, D. M. Flow around baffles, *J. Heat Trans.*, 1984, **106**(11), 743.
4. MURRAY, P. M. Flow and Pressure Drop on the Shellside of Cylindrical Exchangers, PhD Thesis, 1988, Aston University, Birmingham.
5. TINKER, T. Shell side characteristics of shell and tube heat exchangers, *General Discussion on Heat Transfer*, 1951, Proc. Inst. Mech. Engrs, London, 89–116.
6. PALEN, J. W. and TABOREK, J. Solution of shell-side flow pressure drop and heat transfer by the stream analysis method, *Chem. Engng Prog. Symp. Ser.*, 1969, **65**(92), 53–63.
7. GRANT, I. D. R. Divided flow method of calculating shell-side pressure drop for segmentally baffled shell and tube heat exchangers, CAD'74, *Proc. Int. Conf. Computers in Eng. Build. Design*, 1974, London, 25–27 September; GRANT, I. D. R. Shell-and-tube exchangers for single-phase application. In: *Developments in*

Heat Exchanger Technology — 1, 1981, D. Chisholm (ed.), Applied Science, London, 11–40.

8. BELL, K. J. Exchanger design based on the Delaware research program, *Petro/Chem. Engr*, 1960, **32**, C-26–C-40c.

9. BELL, K. J. Final Report of the Co-operative Research Program on Shell and Tube Heat Exchangers, Bulletin No. 5, 1963, University of Delaware Engineering Experiment Station, Newark, Delaware.

10. BELL, K. J. Delaware method for shell-side design. In: *Heat Exchangers, Thermal-Hydraulic Fundamentals and Design*, S. Kakac, A. E. Bergles and F. Mayinger (eds.), 1981, Hemisphere, Washington DC, 581–618.

11. TABOREK, J. Shell-and-tube heat exchangers. In: *Heat Exchanger Design Handbook*, 1983, Hemisphere, Washington DC.

12. MACBETH, R. V. Shell-and-tube heat exchanger data produced by an electrochemical mass transfer modelling technique, Paper HX7, *Proc. Sixth Int. Heat Trans. Conf.*, Vol. 4, 1978, 225–30.

13. MACBETH, R. V. Heat exchanger design and practices. In: *Heat Exchangers: Theory and Practice*, J. Taborek, G. F. Hewitt and N. H. Afgan (eds.), 1983, Hemisphere, Washington DC, 615–29.

14. WHITAKER, S. Forced convection heat transfer correlations for flow in pipes, past flat plates, single cylinders, single spheres, and for flow in packed beds and tube bundles, *AIChE J.*, 1972, **18**(2), 361–71.

15. BUTTERWORTH, D. *A Model for Heat Transfer During Three-dimensional Flow in Tube Bundles*, UKAEA Report No AERE-R-8822, 1977, UKAEA, Harwell.

16. BUTTERWORTH, D. A model for heat transfer during three-dimensional flow in tube bundles, Paper HX6, *Proc. Sixth Int. Heat Trans. Conf.*, Vol. 4, 1978, 219–24.

17. BUTTERWORTH, D. The development of a model for three-dimensional flow in tube bundles, *Int. J. Heat Mass Trans.*, 1978, **21**, 253–6.

18. SULLIVAN, F. W. and BERGELIN, O. P. Heat transfer and fluid friction in a shell-and-tube exchanger with a single baffle, *Chem. Engng Prog. Symp. Ser.*, 1956, **52**(18), 85–94.

19. Engineering Sciences Data Item Number 73031, *Convective Heat Transfer during Cross-Flow of Fluids over Plain Tube Banks*, 1973, Engineering Science Data Unit, London.

20. SHA, W. T., YANG, C. I., KAO, T. T. and CHO, S. M. Multi-dimensional numerical modeling of heat exchangers, *J. Heat Trans.*, 1982, **104**(3), 417–25.

21. SHA, W. T. Numerical modelling of heat exchangers. In: *Handbook of Heat and Mass Transfer*, Vol. 1, Chapter 26. *Heat Transfer Operations*, N. P. Cheremisinoff (ed.), Gulf Publishing, New York, 815–52.

22. ZIJL, W. and DE BRUIJN, H. Continuum equations for the prediction of shell-side flow and temperature patterns in heat exchangers, *Int. J. Heat Mass Trans.*, 1983, **25**(3), 411–24.

23. PATANKAR, S. V. and SPALDING, D. B. A calculation procedure for the transient and steady-state behaviour of shell-and-tube heat exchangers. In: *Heat Exchangers: Design and Theory Sourcebook*, H. N. Afgan and E. V. Schlunder (eds.), 1974, McGraw-Hill, New York, 155–76.

24. ANTONOPOULOS, K. A. Prediction of Flow and Heat Transfer in Rod Bundles, PhD Thesis, 1979, Imperial College, London.

25. ANTONOPOULOS, K. A. Heat transfer in tube banks under condition of turbulent inclined flow, *Int. J. Heat Mass Trans.*, 1985, **28**(9), 1645–56.
26. HUGE, E. C. Experimental investigation of effects of equipment size on convection heat transfer and flow resistance in cross-flow of gases over tube banks, *Trans. ASME*, 1937, **59**(7), 573–80.
27. PIERSON, O. L. Experimental investigation of the influence of tube arrangement on convection heat transfer and flow resistance in crossflow of gases over tube banks, *Trans. ASME*, 1937, **59**(7), 563–72.
28. GRIMISON, E. D. Correlation and utilisation of new data on flow resistance and heat transfer for crossflow of gases over tube banks, *Trans. ASME*, 1937, **59**(7), 583–94.
29. MCADAMS, W. H., *Heat Transmission*, 3rd edn., 1954, McGraw-Hill, New York.
30. OMOHUNDRO, G. A., BERGELIN, O. P. and COLBURN, A. P. Heat transfer and fluid friction during viscous flow across banks of tubes, *Trans. ASME*, 1949, **71**, 27–34.
31. BERGELIN, O. P., DAVIS, E. S. and HULL, H. L. A study of three tube arrangements in unbaffled tubular heat exchangers, *Trans. ASME*, 1949, **71**, 369–74.
32. BERGELIN, O. P., COLBURN, A. P. and HULL, H. L. *Heat Transfer and Fluid Friction during Flow across Banks of Tubes*, Bulletin No 2, 1950, University of Delaware Engineering Experiment Station, Newark, Delaware.
33. BERGELIN, O. P., BROWN, G. A., HULL, H. L. and SULLIVAN, F. W. Heat transfer and fluid friction during viscous flow across banks of tubes—III A study of tube spacing and tube size, *Trans. ASME*, 1950, **72**, 881–88.
34. BERGELIN, O. P., BROWN, G. A. and DOBERSTEIN, S. C. Heat transfer and fluid friction during flow across banks of tubes—IV A study of the transition zone between viscous and turbulent flow, *Trans. ASME*, 1952, **74**, 953–60.
35. DWYER, O. E., SHEEHAN, T. V. and SCHOMER, R. T. Cross flow of water through a tube bank at Reynolds numbers up to a million, *Ind. Engng Chem.*, 1956, **48**, 1836–46.
36. JENKINS, J. D. and NOIE-BAGHBAN, H. Transfer coefficients and pressure drop for ideal tube banks in cross flow at differing angles of attack, In preparation.
37. CHILTON, T. H. and COLBURN, A. P. Mass transfer coefficients, *Ind. Engng Chem.*, 1934, **26**, 1183–7.
38. ZUKAUSKAS, A. Heat transfer from tube bundles in cross flow, *Advances in Heat Transfer*, 1972, **8**, 93–160.
39. ZUKAUSKAS, A. Air cooled heat exchangers. In: *Heat Exchangers: Thermal-Hydraulic Fundamentals and Design*, S. Kakac, A. E. Berles and F. Mayinger (eds.), 1981, Hemisphere, Washington DC, 49–83.
40. ACHENBACH, E. Total and local heat transfer and pressure drop of staggered and in-line tube bundles. In: *Heat Exchangers: Thermal-Hydraulic Fundamentals and Design*, S. Kakac, A. E. Berles and F. Mayinger (eds.), 1981, Hemisphere, Washington DC, 85–96.
41. ORNATSKI, A. P. Heat transfer in tube-banks with differing angles of attack of gas in cross-flow, *Sovetskoe Kultoturbostroenie*, 1940, **2**, 48–52.
42. GROEHN, H. T. Thermal hydraulic investigation of yawed tube bundle heat exchangers. In: *Heat Exchangers: Thermal-Hydraulic Fundamentals and Design*,

S. Kakac, A. E. Berles and F. Mayinger (eds.), 1981, Hemisphere, Washington DC, 97–110.

43. MACKLEY, N. V. Local Shell-Side Coefficients in Shell-and-tube Heat Exchangers—the Use of a Mass Transfer Technique, PhD Thesis, 1973, Aston University, Birmingham.

44. JENKINS, J. D., MACKLEY, N. V. and GAY, B. The influence of property numbers in forced convection heat and mass transfer correlations, Letters Heat Mass Trans., 1976, 3, 105–10.

45. GAY, B., MACKLEY, N. V. and JENKINS, J. D. Shell-side heat transfer in baffled cylindrical shell-and-tube exchangers—an electrochemical mass transfer modelling technique, Int. J. Heat Mass Trans., 1976, 19, 995–1002.

46. GAY, B., JENKINS, J. D. and MACKLEY, N. V. Shell-side heat transfer coefficients in cylindrical heat exchangers. The influence of geometrical factors, I—The non-leakage case, Letters Heat Mass Trans., 1977, 4, 41–52.

47. PROWSE, J. N. Local Heat Transfer Coefficients in a Baffled Shell-and-Tube Heat Exchanger, PhD Thesis, 1977, Aston University, Birmingham.

48. GAY, B., MACKLEY, N. V. and JENKINS, J. D. Shell-side heat transfer coefficients in cylindrical heat exchangers. The influence of geometrical factors. II—The leakage case, Letters Heat Mass Trans., 1981, 8, 437–52.

49. GAY, B., JENKINS, J. D. and MACKLEY, N. V. Shell-side heat transfer in double-segmentally baffled cylindrical shell-and-tube exchangers, Letters Heat Mass Trans., 1982, 9, 39–47.

50. NIBBER, S. P. S. Shell-Side Transfer in Shell-and-Tube Heat Exchangers, PhD Thesis, 1981, Aston University, Birmingham.

51. NIBBER, S. P. S., GAY, B. and JENKINS, J. D. Length-wise variation of shell-side coefficients in cylindrical exchangers, IChemE Symp. Ser., No 94, 1985, 57–66.

52. DONOHUE, D. Heat transfer and pressure drop in heat exchangers, Ind. Engng Chem., 1949, 41, 2499.

53. SHORT, B. E. Heat Transfer and Pressure Drop in Heat Exchangers, University of Texas Publication No 4324, 1943, University of Texas, Austin.

54. GARDNER, H. S. and SILLER, I. Shell-side coefficients of heat transfer in a baffled heat exchanger, Trans. ASME, 1947, 69(6), 687.

55. TINKER, T. Shell-side transfer characteristics of shell and tube heat exchangers, Paper No 47-A-130, 1947, ASME Annual Meeting, New York.

56. British Shipbuilding Research Association, A Correlation of Current Data on Heat Transfer and Pressure Drop in Segmentally Baffled Shell-and-Tube Heat Exchangers, Report No 148, 1955, British Shipbuilding Research Association, London.

57. KERN, D. Q. Process Heat Transfer, 1st edn., 1950, McGraw-Hill, New York.

58. BERGELIN, O. P., BELL, K. J. and LEIGHTON, M. D. Heat transfer and fluid friction during flow across banks of tubes, VII—Bypassing between tube bundle and shell, Chem. Engng Prog. Symp. Ser., 1959, 55(29), 45–58.

59. BERGELIN, O. P., BROWN, G. A. and COLBURN, A. P. Heat transfer and fluid friction during flow across banks of tubes—V: A study of a cylindrical baffle exchanger without internal leakage, Trans. ASME, 1952, 74, 841–50.

60. BERGELIN, O. P., BELL, K. J. and LEIGHTON, M. D. Heat transfer and fluid friction during flow across banks of tubes—VI: The effect of internal leakages within segmentally baffled exchangers, Trans. ASME, 1958, 80, 53–60.

61. SPARROW, E. M. and PEREZ, J. A. Internal, shellside heat transfer and pressure drop characteristics for a shell-and-tube heat exchanger, *J. Heat Trans.*, 1985, **107**, 345–53.
62. AMBROSE, T. W. and KNUDSEN, J. G. Local shell-side heat transfer coefficients in baffled tubular heat exchangers, *AIChE J.*, 1958, **4**(3), 332–7.
63. GURUSHANKARIAH, M. S. and KNUDSEN, J. G. Local shell-side heat transfer coefficients in the vicinity of segmented baffles in tubular heat exchangers, *Chem. Engng Prog. Symp. Ser.*, 1959, **55**(29), 29–36.
64. STANCHIEWICZ, J. W. and SHORT, B. Local shell-side heat coefficients in a leak-proof heat exchanger. In: *International Developments in Heat Transfer*, 1961, American Society of Mechanical Engineers, New York, 959–66.
65. NARAYANAN, K. Local and Overall Heat Transfer Coefficients in Baffled Heat Exchangers, PhD Thesis, 1962, Oregon State University.
66. WILLIAMS, T. A. A Mass Transfer Study of Local Transfer Coefficients on the Shell-Side of a Cylindrical Shell and Tube Heat Exchanger Fitted with Segmental Baffles, PhD Thesis, 1962, Manchester University, Manchester.
67. GAY, B. and WILLIAMS, T. A. Heat transfer on the shell-side of a cylindrical shell-and-tube heat exchanger fitted with segmented baffles—I: Bundle and zonal average heat transfer coefficients, *Trans. IChemE*, 1968, **46**, T95–T100.
68. GAY, B. and ROBERTS, P. C. O. Heat transfer on the shell-side of a cylindrical shell-and-tube heat exchanger fitted with segmented baffles—II Flow patterns and local velocities derived from the individual tube coefficients, *Trans. IChemE*, 1970, **48**, T3–T6.
69. BROWN, G. A. Heat Transfer and Fluid Friction during Turbulent Flow through a Baffled Cylindrical Shell and Tube Heat Exchanger, PhD Thesis, 1956, University of Delaware, Newark, Delaware.
70. TOMPKINS, J. F. Jr. Heat Transfer and Pressure Drop in a Cylindrical Baffled Heat Exchanger during Viscous Flow, MChE Thesis, 1953, University of Delaware, Newark, Delaware.
71. JENKINS, J. D., GAY, B. and NIBBER, S. P. S. Shellside heat transfer coefficients in cylindrical heat exchangers. Variation along the exchanger length, I—The no-leakage case. Paper submitted to: *Int. Commun. Heat Mass Trans.*
72. JENKINS, J. D., NIBBER, S. P. S. and GAY, B. Shellside heat transfer coefficients in cylindrical heat exchangers. Variation along the exchanger length, II—The leakage case. Paper submitted to: *Int. Commun. Heat Mass Trans.*
73. PEREZ-GALINDO, J. A. Internal Heat Transfer and Pressure Drop Measurements in a Variously Baffled Shell and Tube Heat Exchanger, PhD Thesis, 1984, University of Minnesota, Minneapolis.
74. BELL, K. J. and BERGELIN, O. P. Flow through annular orifices, *Trans. ASME*, 1957, **79**, 595–603.
75. Engineering Sciences Data Item Number 83038, *Baffled Shell-and-Tube Heat Exchangers: Flow Distribution, Pressure Drop and Heat Transfer Coefficient on the Shellside*, 1983, Engineering Science Data Unit, London.
76. JOHNSTON, D. and WILLIS, M. J. W. The prediction of shellside flow distribution and pressure drop in a shell-and-tube heat exchanger, *IChemE Symp. Ser.*, No. 84, 1984, 1163–74.
77. JENKINS, J. D., GAY, B., MACKLEY, N. V., PROWSE, J. N. and NIBBER, S. P. S.

Shellside heat transfer coefficients in cylindrical heat exchangers—local values
of the transfer coefficients, in preparation.

78 JENKINS, J. D. Shellside heat transfer coefficients in cylindrical heat exchangers—
a geometry-independent correlation, in preparation.

Chapter 3

TWO-PHASE FLOW IN SHELL-AND-TUBE HEAT EXCHANGERS

D. Chisholm

Heat Transfer Research, Inc., Alhambra, California, USA

SUMMARY

Methods are presented for predicting the following in shellside and tubeside flow in shell-and-tube heat exchangers:

Friction and form drag.
Gravitational pressure gradient.
Pressure gradient associated with momentum flux changes.
Flow patterns.
Phase distribution.

Also discussed is the application of these methods to some aspects of horizontal reboiler design.

NOTATION

A	Flow cross-section (m^2)
A_{sL}	Flow cross-section of separated liquid (eqn. (39))
A_{sG}	Flow cross-section of gas or vapour and entrainment (eqn. (41))
B	Coefficient (eqn. (10))
b	Baffle spacing (eqn. (47)) (m)
C	Coefficient (eqn. (12))
C_d	Drag coefficient (eqn. (93))
c	Coefficient (eqn. (23))($m^2 s/kg)^{2-n}$
D	Derivative with respect to displacement

d Diameter (eqn. (69)) (m)

e_c Entrainment parameter (eqn. (25))

Fr_{Lo} Froude number if mixture flows as liquid

G Mass velocity or flux ($kg/(m^2 s)$)

I Integral (eqn. (50))

K Phase velocity ratio

K_e Phase velocity ratio, effective (eqn. (79))

MF Momentum flux (N/m^2)

m Mass flow rate (kg/s)

m_L Mass flow rate of liquid

m_{Le} Mass flow rate of liquid entrained in gas

N Tube rows normal to flow direction

n Blasius exponent

p Static pressure (N/m^2)

R Coefficient (eqn. (19))

Re Reynolds number when liquid flows alone

s Exponent (eqn. (55))

u Velocity (m/s)

u_G Velocity of gas or vapour

u_L Velocity of liquid

u_{Gs} Velocity of gas when flowing alone

u_{Ls} Velocity of liquid when flowing alone

v Specific volume (kg/m^3)

v_G Specific volume of gas

v_H Specific volume, homogeneous, $xv_G + (1-x)v_L$

v_L Specific volume of liquid

We Weber number, (eqn. (75))

We_c Weber number, critical value (eqn. (93))

w Entrainment, proportion of liquid in gas

X Lockhart–Martinelli parameter

x Mass dryness fraction

z Length (m)

z_e Length, overall (m)

Greek

α Void fraction

α_{sL} Void fraction of cross-section occupied by separated liquid (eqn. (31))

β Volume flow ratio

Γ Physical property parameter (eqn. (8))

η_1	Coefficient (eqn. (63))
η_K	Coefficent (eqn. (65))
μ	Dynamic viscosity (Ns/m^2)
ρ	Density (kg/m^3)
σ	Surface tension (eqn. (76)) (N/m)
ϕ_L	Two-phase multiplier (eqn. (13))
ϕ_{Lo}	Two-phase multiplier (eqn. (7))
ψ	Dimensionless two-phase multiplier
ψ_F	Dimensionless two-phase multiplier for friction (eqn. (9))
ψ_M	Dimensionless two-phase multiplier for momentum (eqn. (2))

Subscripts

b	Bubble
f	Spray or mist-annular
G	Gas
Ge	Gas with entrained liquid
Gm	Gas velocity at maximum entrainment
Go	Mixture flows as gas
Gs	Gas flows alone
H	Homogeneous
L	Liquid
Lo	Mixture flows as liquid
Ls	Liquid flows alone
s	Stratified
sL	Separated liquid

1. INTRODUCTION

This chapter discusses two-phase flow on the shell-side and tube-side of baffled shell-and-tube heat exchangers. First some basic relationships, then shell-side flow is discussed.

2. MULTIPLIERS AND PARAMETERS

Using a separated flow model, the momentum flux for a flowing two-phase mixture can be expressed as

$$MF = x \cdot G \cdot u_G + (1-x)G \cdot u_L \qquad (1)$$

where G is the mass velocity (or flux), x is the mass dryness fraction, and u_G and u_L are the gas (or vapour) and liquid (average) velocities respectively.

Define[1,2] a normalised two-phase multiplier

$$\psi_M = \frac{MF - MF_{Lo}}{MF_{Go} - MF_{Lo}} \tag{2}$$

where the subscripts Go and Lo refer to conditions where the mixture flows as all-gas or all-liquid, respectively. This multiplier is normalised in the sense that ψ changes from 0 to 1 as X changes from 0 to 1.

Equation (1) can now be expressed approximately[2] as

$$\psi_M = \frac{1}{K}x(1-x) + x^2 \tag{3}$$

where the phase velocity ratio is

$$K = \frac{u_G}{u_L} \tag{4}$$

For the particular case of homogeneous flow $(K = 1)$

$$\psi_M = x \tag{5}$$

For friction in pipes[1] and for cross-flow over tube banks[3] the normalised multiplier is defined as

$$\psi_F = \frac{Dp - Dp_{Lo}}{Dp_{Go} - Dp_{Lo}} \tag{6}$$

where D is used, for convenience, to denote gradient with respect to the flow direction. The static pressure is represented by p.

Define now the two-phase multiplier[4]

$$\phi_{Lo}^2 = \frac{Dp}{Dp_{Lo}} \tag{7}$$

and the physical property parameter[1]

$$\Gamma^2 = \frac{Dp_{Go}}{Dp_{Lo}} \tag{8}$$

Equation (6) can also be expressed

$$\psi_F = \frac{\phi_{Lo}^2 - 1}{\Gamma^2 - 1} \tag{9}$$

Define now a B coefficient by the equation

$$\psi_F = Bx^{(2-n)/2}(1-x)^{(2-n)/2} + x^{2-n} \tag{10}$$

where n is the Blasius coefficient. For processes independent of Reynolds number this equation reduces to

$$\psi_F = Bx(1-x) + x^2 \tag{11}$$

which is a more general statement of eqn (3).
Equation (10) can be transformed to[5]

$$\phi_L^2 = 1 + \frac{C}{X} + \frac{1}{X^2} \tag{12}$$

where the multiplier[6]

$$\phi_L^2 = \frac{Dp}{Dp_L} \tag{13}$$

and

$$X = \left(\frac{Dp_L}{Dp_G}\right)^{1/2} = \left(\frac{1-x}{x}\right)^{(2-n)/2} \frac{1}{\Gamma} \tag{14}$$

$$C = \frac{1}{\Gamma}\left[B(\Gamma^2 - 1) + 2^{2-n} - 2\right] \tag{15}$$

The subscripts G and L indicate conditions where the component flows alone. The transformation results in a remainder which is of negligible magnitude.

Shell-side flows are now discussed.

3. SHELLSIDE HORIZONTAL FLOW

The greater part of the procedures for predicting flow conditions on the shell-side of baffled shell-and-tube heat exchangers discussed here were based on air–water experiments using the models shown[7] in Fig. 1. The 39-tube model was used not only with horizontal flow, as illustrated in Fig. 1, but for flow in the vertical plane.

Four distinct flow patterns can occur in horizontal shell-side flow.

(a) Bubbly flow. The gas flows as bubbles in the liquid. This occurs at void fractions up to about 0·75 at higher velocities.

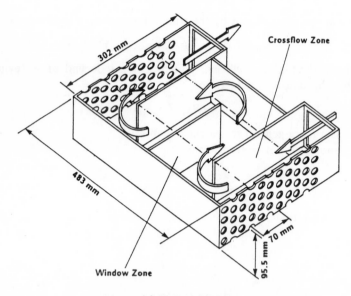

(a) 39-Tube Model

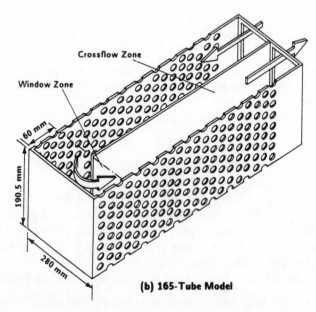

(b) 165-Tube Model

FIG. 1. Heat exchanger models.

(b) Stratified flow. There is a complete separation of the phases, the heavier phase flowing along the lower part of the tube bank. This flow pattern occurs at the lowest flow rates.

(c) Stratified-spray flow. Similar to stratified flow but part of the liquid is now entrained in the gas or vapor as liquid droplets.

(d) Spray flow. Apart from a small amount of liquid wetting the metal surfaces, the liquid is all entrained in the gas.

Methods of predicting the flow pattern are discussed later.

4. HORIZONTAL CROSS-FLOW PRESSURE DROP

As shown in Fig. 2 the following B coefficients for predicting cross-flow pressure drop for horizontal conditions are in good agreement with experiment.[8-11]

4.1. Bubbly Flow

$$B_b = \left[\frac{v_L}{x v_G + (1-x)v_L} \right]^{1/2} = \left(\frac{v_L}{v_H} \right)^{1/2} \tag{16}$$

4.2. Stratified Flow

$$B_s = \frac{2^{2-n} - 2}{\Gamma + 1} \tag{17}$$

4.3. Spray Flow

$$B_f = \left(\frac{\mu_L}{\mu_G} \right)^{n/2} \tag{18}$$

For the transition to spray flow

$$\psi = R x^{2-n} \tag{19}$$

where

$$R = 1 \cdot 3 + 0 \cdot 59 Fr_{Lo} N^2 \left(\frac{\mu_L}{\mu_G} \right)^n \tag{20}$$

Fr_{Lo} is the Froude number based on the velocity at the minimum flow cross-section, if the mixture flows as liquid, and N is the number of tubes in the bank normal to the flow direction. Equations (10) and (16)–(20) allow the flow pattern to be identified for a given mass flow and dryness fraction; this is discussed below in the section on flow patterns in horizontal cross-flow.

The absence of a gas density term in eqn. (20) is a matter of concern. For tube flow, as discussed later, entrainment depends significantly on the gas Weber number, and hence on the gas density. An alternative approach is based on the observation that, at the onset of maximum entrainment with increasing mass dryness fraction, the homogeneous momentum flux

$$G^2 v_H = c(1 - x)v_L \tag{21}$$

where c is a constant. This observation leads to the equation

$$R = 1 + cB_f G^{2-n}\left[\frac{v_G}{v_L}\left\{1 + \frac{1-x}{x}\left(\frac{v_L}{v_G}\right)^{0\cdot75}\right\}\right]^{(2-n)/2} \tag{22}$$

TABLE 1

COMPARISON OF PREDICTED VALUES OF R

G $(kg/m^2 s)$	Tube-rows N	R: equation 20	R: equation 22
17·5	4	1·32	1·06
41·9	4	1·39	1·23
47·25	8	1·57	1·50
59·4	4	1·48	1·39
77·6	4	1·60	1·58
158	4	2·55	2·74
236	8	7·98	8·14
265	4	4·81	4·86

Table 1 compares predictions by eqn. (20) and (22) at the experimental conditions. The density ratio was taken as 769 and the viscosity ratio as 56. The major differences between the two equations is that eqn. (22) does not contain the number of tubes normal to flow, and does contain the gas density. The latter equation is recommended.

From experiment it is found that

$$c = \frac{1}{580\,000}\left(\frac{m^2 s}{kg}\right)^{2-n} \tag{23}$$

Figure 2 shows the comparison with data.

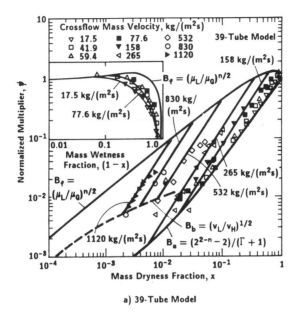

a) 39-Tube Model

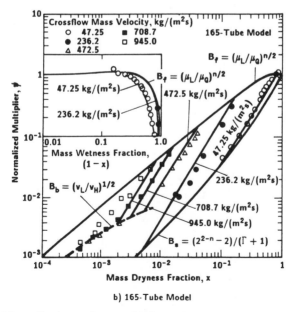

b) 165-Tube Model

FIG. 2. Normalised two-phase multiplier to base of mass dryness fraction.

The pressure drop in the window was[7] given satisfactorily for all the flow patterns, using eqn. (10) with

$$B = \left(\frac{v_{\mathrm{L}}}{v_{\mathrm{H}}}\right)^{1/4} \tag{24}$$

5. SUBMERGENCE, VOID FRACTION AND ENTRAINMENT

With horizontal flow in condensers, for example, it is important to be able to predict the extent to which the tubes are submerged in the condensate. Also the liquid entrainment in the vapour affects the vapour-to-tube heat transfer. An entrainment parameter has been defined[9,10] as

$$e_{\mathrm{c}} = \frac{\psi - \psi_{\mathrm{s}}}{\psi_{\mathrm{f}} - \psi_{\mathrm{s}}} \tag{25}$$

where

$$\psi_{\mathrm{s}} = B_{\mathrm{s}} x^{(2-n)/2}(1-x)^{(2-n)/2} + x^{2-n} \tag{26}$$

$$\psi_{\mathrm{f}} = B_{\mathrm{f}} x^{(2-n)/2}(1-x)^{(2-n)/2} + x^{2-n} \tag{27}$$

and ψ is given by eqn. (19). Equation (25) can also be expressed

$$e_{\mathrm{c}} = \left(\frac{R-1}{B_{\mathrm{f}}-B_{\mathrm{s}}}\right)\left(\frac{x}{1-x}\right)^{(2-n)/2} - \frac{B_{\mathrm{s}}}{B_{\mathrm{f}}-B_{\mathrm{s}}} \tag{28}$$

Define the entrainment as

$$w = \frac{\dot{m}_{\mathrm{Le}}}{\dot{m}_{\mathrm{L}}} \tag{29}$$

where m_{L} is the liquid flow rate and m_{Le} the mass flow rate of liquid entrainment in the vapour.

It has been shown[10] that approximately

$$w = e_{\mathrm{c}}^{1.3} \tag{30}$$

The pressure gradient in the separated liquid can be expressed

$$Dp = \frac{Dp_{\mathrm{L}}(1-w)^{2-n}}{\alpha_{\mathrm{sL}}^{2-n}} \tag{31}$$

where α_{sL} is the cross-section occupied by the separated liquid. Using

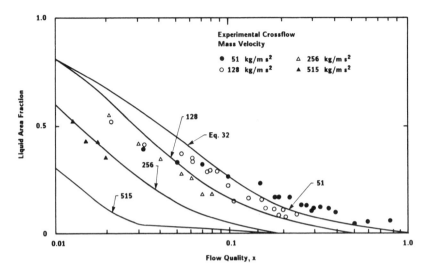

FIG. 3. Liquid fraction holdup in heat exchangers.

eqns. (7) and (13), and rearranging

$$\alpha_{sL} = (1 - w)\phi_L^{2/(2-n)} = (1 - w)(1 - x)\phi_{Lo}^{2/(2-n)} \tag{32}$$

Figure 3 compares this equation with experiment.

The orientation of the inlet and outlet nozzles has a slight effect on the submergence.[12] The above methods are shown to give good agreement with experiment when the outlet flows downward; where it flows upward, the submergence is increased by about 10%.

6. FLOW PATTERN BOUNDARIES IN HORIZONTAL CROSS-FLOW

The terms x_s, x_b, and x_f are defined as the mass dryness fractions at the stratified transition point, the bubble transition point, and the spray transition point, respectively. The mass dryness fractions are evaluated using the following equations obtained by combining eqns. (10) and (19)

$$\frac{1 - x_s}{x_s} = \left(\frac{R - 1}{B_s}\right)^{2/(2-n)} \tag{33}$$

$$\frac{1-x_b}{x_b} = \left(\frac{R-1}{B_b}\right)^{2/(2-n)} \tag{34}$$

$$\frac{1-x_f}{x_f} = \left(\frac{R-1}{B_f}\right)^{2/(2-n)} \tag{35}$$

Where α_b is the void fraction corresponding to x_b, the flow patterns are determined as follows:

$\alpha_b < 0.75$

$x < x_b$ bubble flow

$x_b < x < x_f$ bubble-spray transition

$\alpha_b > 0.75$

$x < x_s$ stratified flow

$x_s < x < x_f$ stratified-spray transition

All α_b

$x > x_f$ spray flow

The void fraction α_b is evaluated using[13] a velocity ratio

$$K_o = \left(\frac{v_H}{v_L}\right)^{1/2} \tag{36}$$

It proves convenient to identify the velocity ratio defined in this way with the subscript o. It should be noted that from eqn. (16)

$$B_b = \frac{1}{K_o} \tag{37}$$

7. BY-PASS EFFECTS: HORIZONTAL FLOW

For convenience let k_1 denote the by-pass pressure loss coefficient and k_2 that in the bank, and assume they are the same for each phase. The by-pass characteristics are denoted by the subscript 1 and the bank by subscript 2. For the liquid

$$k_1 u_{sL1}^2 = k_2 u_{sL2}^2 \tag{38}$$

and

$$A_{sL1}u_{sL1} + A_{sL2}u_{sL2} = (1-w)\dot{m}_L v_L \tag{39}$$

Hence the separated liquid mass flow rate through the bank is

$$\dot{m}_{sL2} = \frac{(1-w)\dot{m}_L}{1 + \left(\dfrac{k_2}{k_1}\right)^{1/2}\dfrac{A_{sL1}}{A_{sL2}}} \tag{40}$$

Similarly for the gas or vapour phase with entrained liquid

$$\dot{m}_{Ge2} = \frac{\dot{m}_G + w\dot{m}_L}{1 + \left(\dfrac{k_2}{k_1}\right)^{1/2}\dfrac{A_{sG1}}{A_{sG2}}} \tag{41}$$

The appropriate total mass flow rate when using the 'ideal bank' equations is

$$\dot{m}_2 = \dot{m}_{sL2} + \dot{m}_{Ge2} \tag{42}$$

and the mass dryness fraction

$$x_2 = \frac{\dot{m}_{Ge2}}{\dot{m}_2} \cdot \frac{\dot{m}_G}{\dot{m}_G + w\dot{m}_L} \tag{43}$$

An iterative solution is necessary, the first iteration calculating A_{L1}/A_{L2} neglecting by-pass flow. A major factor affecting k_2/k_1 is that for certain tube layouts the number of restrictions in the by-pass will be half that in the bank.

8. HORIZONTAL REBOILERS

It is relevant here to discuss how the above equations for flow patterns influence the design of horizontal reboilers with vertical baffle cuts; the merits and disadvantages of vertical baffle cuts are discussed later.

It is essential that the unit does not operate in the stratified flow regime as all the tube surfaces would not be wetted with liquid. At low mass dryness fractions it is desirable to operate in the bubble flow regime. On the basis that the maximum void fraction for bubble flow is 0·75 and x_1 is the corresponding mass dryness fraction, the minimum mass velocity to ensure bubble flow, rather than stratified flow is, by combining eqns. (10) (using

B_b), (19) and (22) approximately

$$G = (1 - x_1)^{1/2} B_b^{(3-n)/(2-n)} \left(\frac{5 \cdot 8 \times 10^5}{B_f} \right)^{1/(2-n)} \tag{44}$$

Maintaining this mass velocity through the transition to fully entrained spray flow will ensure adequate tube wetting. The approach is conservative as it is derived from adiabatic tests; boiling will facilitate the distribution of the liquid phase.

Combining again eqns. (10) (now with B_f), (19) and (22) gives approximately

$$G = (1 - x)^{1/2} \left(\frac{v_L}{v_H} \right)^{1/2} (5.8 \times 10^5)^{1/(2-n)}$$

$$\doteq \left(\frac{1-x}{x} \right)^{1/2} \left(\frac{v_L}{v_G} \right)^{1/2} (5 \cdot 8 \times 10^5)^{1/(2-n)} \tag{45}$$

This gives the relation between G and x at the onset of maximum entrainment

Denote the mass dryness fraction at the onset of fully entrained flow by x_2 and at exit from the reboiler by x_3 then, from eqn. (45), to maintain full entrainment the associated mass velocities are related by

$$\frac{G_3}{G_2} = \left(\frac{1-x_3}{x_3} \cdot \frac{x_2}{1-x_2} \right)^{1/2} \tag{46}$$

Once fully entrained flow has been achieved the mass velocity can be reduced by opening up the baffle spacing. The corresponding ratio for baffle spacing is then

$$\frac{b_2}{b_3} = \frac{G_3}{G_2} = \left(\frac{1-x_3}{x_3} \frac{x_2}{1-x_2} \right)^{1/2} \tag{47}$$

9. HORIZONTAL CONDENSERS

In the case of horizontal condensers the flow pattern is less critical than in the case of a reboiler. It is preferable that stratified flow rather than bubble flow should occur, and it can be preferable to maintain significant convection to avoid gas pockets.

The pressure drop can however be important in condensers particularly at vacuum operation. It is relevant therefore to illustrate the use of these equations to predict the overall pressure drop.

Where Dp_{Go} is the pressure gradient due to friction and form drag an average two-phase multiplier can be defined as

$$\bar{\phi}_{Go}^2 = \frac{\int_0^2 D_p dz}{Dp_{Go} z} \tag{48}$$

For a constant B coefficient, an initial value of mass dryness fraction of x_1 and a final value of x_2, and a linear variation of x, the average two-phase multiplier is[9] shown to be

$$\bar{\phi}_{Go}^2 = \frac{1}{\Gamma^2} + \left(1 - \frac{1}{\Gamma^2}\right) \frac{1}{x_1 - x_2} \left[B(x_1 I_{x_1} - x_2 I_{x_2}) + \frac{x_1^{2-n} - x_2^{2-n}}{3-n} \right] \tag{49}$$

where

$$\left[I_{x_1} = \frac{1}{x_1} \right] \int_0^{x_1} x^{(2-n)/2} (1-x)^{(2-n)/2} \, dx \tag{50}$$

and

$$I_{x_2} = \frac{1}{x_2} \int_0^{x_2} x^{(2-n)/2} (1-x)^{(2-n)/2} \, dx \tag{51}$$

Values of the integrals are given in Table 2.

If the dryness fraction x_2 is that at the beginning of transition from spray to stratified flow and x_3 that at the beginning of stratified flow, the average multiplier where the mass velocity is kept constant during the transition (constant baffle spacing) is

$$\bar{\phi}_{Go}^2 = \frac{1}{\Gamma^2} + \left(1 - \frac{1}{\Gamma^2}\right) \frac{R}{x_1 - x_2} \left[\frac{x_1^{3-n}}{3-n} - \frac{x_2^{3-n}}{3-n} \right] \tag{52}$$

In the stratified region eqns. (17) and (49) can be used.

It can also be convenient to use a normalised average two-phase multiplier

$$\bar{\psi} = \frac{\bar{\phi}_{Go}^2 - 1}{\Gamma^2 - 1} \tag{53}$$

For the case where the Blasius exponent n is taken as zero analytic solutions

TABLE 2

$$\text{VALUES OF } \frac{1}{x_2} \int_0^{x_2} x^{(2-n)/2}(1-x)^{(2-n)/2}\,\mathrm{d}x$$

x_2	n	0·25	0·20	0·10
0·01		0·009 43	0·008 29	0·006 42
0·02		0·017 20	0·015 38	0·012 32
0·03		0·024 38	0·022 02	0·017 99
0·04		0·031 17	0·028 36	0·023 49
0·05		0·037 67	0·034 46	0·028 85
0·06		0·043 93	0·040 36	0·034 08
0·07		0·049 97	0·016 08	0·039 19
0·08		0·055 82	0·051 64	0·044 21
0·09		0·061 51	0·057 06	0·049 12
0·1		0·067 04	0·062 34	0·053 92
0·2		0·115 40	0·108 95	0·097 14
0·3		0·153 66	0·146 21	0·132 42
0·4		0·183 48	0·175 40	0·160 36
0·5		0·205 62	0·197 11	0·181 22
0·6		0·220 37	0·211 59	0·195 13
0·7		0·227 88	0·218 93	0·202 13
0·8		0·228 17	0·219 15	0·202 23
0·9		0·221 01	0·212 09	0·195 36
1·0		0·205 62	0·197 11	0·181 22

can be obtained for a number of different situations, including the case where the mass flux varies as

$$\frac{x - x_2}{x_1 - x_2} = \left(\frac{z}{z_2}\right)^s \tag{54}$$

It can be shown[9] that for complete condensation of a vapour at a constant B coefficient

$$\bar{\psi} = \frac{Bs + 2s^2}{(1+s)(1+2s)} \tag{55}$$

and when also $B = 1$

$$\bar{\psi} = \frac{s}{1+s} \tag{56}$$

10. SHELL-SIDE FLOW: VERTICAL

Using the baffled model shown in Fig. 1 Grant and Murray[14] observed the following three flow patterns

(a) Bubble flow. As for horizontal flow, bubbles of gas in liquid.
(b) Spray flow. As for horizontal flow, all the liquid entrained in the gas, except for small amounts wetting the walls.
(c) Intermittent flow. Slugs of liquid followed by slugs of gas. The liquid accumulates at the lower baffle windows until it is blocking the flow path, then a slug of liquid flows upwards.

An approximate method of predicting the occurrence of these flow patterns is to use the methods described above for horizontal flow, assuming that intermittent flow occurs at the flow rates at which stratified flow occurs in horizontal flow. Alternatively a flow pattern map can be used.[9,14]

For vertical upflow with air–water mixtures close to atmospheric pressure Grant, et al.[15] obtained the data shown in Fig. 4. The upper data in this figure are data obtained with an 'ideal' bank, one with half tubes at the

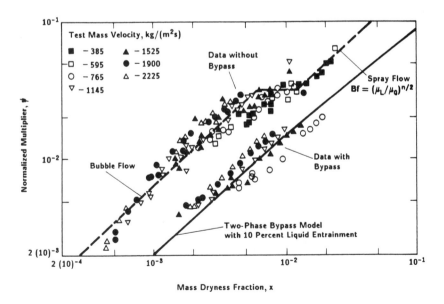

FIG. 4. Two-phase pressure drop for ideal bundle and bundle with by-pass.

wall to prevent by-passing. The lower data were obtained with the half tubes removed; the effects of by-pass at the walls can be seen to be significant.

For the ideal bank the discontinuity at a mass dryness fraction of about 0·006 (a void fraction of about 0·67 for air–water mixtures close to atmospheric pressure) is believed to be associated with the limit of bubble flow. For mass dryness fractions up to this the data are approximated by

$$B = \left(\frac{\mu_L}{\mu_G}\right)^{1\cdot25n} \tag{57}$$

At higher mass dryness fractions where spray flow occurs the corresponding equation is eqn. (18). The latter equation is also that for horizontal flow; it is to be expected that for spray flow the pressure gradient due to friction and form drag is more or less independent of flow direction.

Grant and Murray[14] in working out the gravitational component of the total pressure gradient used the Armand equation which gives the void fraction as a function of the volumetric flow ratio

$$\beta = \frac{xv_G}{xv_G + (1 - x)v_L} \tag{58}$$

The Armand equation is

$$\beta \leqslant 0\cdot9 \qquad \alpha = 0\cdot833\beta \tag{59}$$

and

$$[\beta > 0.9 \qquad \alpha = 2\cdot92\beta - 1\cdot92] \tag{60}$$

For $\beta < 0\cdot9$ eqn. (59) is closely approximated using eqn. (36) for the velocity ratio.

For vertical downflow, data of Barbe and Roger[16] can be approximated by the stratified flow eqn. (17); at higher mass dryness fractions this means that the pressure drop approximates that of the gas flow alone. These data are for higher void fractions. For bubble flow it is to be expected that in downflow the B-coefficient will be larger than for upflow, as the bubble will move slower relative to the liquid than in upflow, resulting in the liquid moving faster, with increase in friction.

For vertical flow in the baffled geometry of Fig. 1 Grant and Murray[14] combined the pressure gradients in two successive passes. The pressure drop was approximated by eqn. (10), with B taken as unity; at low flow rates this procedure will underestimate the pressure drop.

11. BY-PASS EFFECTS: VERTICAL FLOW

Polley and Grant[17] studied the maldistribution of phases associated with by-pass lanes. In vertical flow the tendency is for the liquid to flow in the by-pass. There are two effects on the flow through the bank; the mass velocity decreases relative to the ideal bank, and the mass dryness fraction increases.

Polley and Grant[17] obtained good agreement with experimental data for vertical upflow through banks with by-pass lanes with the following assumptions:

- the pressure drop through bank and by-pass are the same;
- the liquid and gas distribute themselves to give minimum pressure drop.

They found on this basis that the minimum (theoretical) minimum pressure drop was obtained either when the by-pass flow was almost all liquid, or almost all gas. As a result of experimental observations they concluded that the 'almost all liquid' situation was that which occurred in practice. On this basis they were able to predict their pressure drop to within 20%.

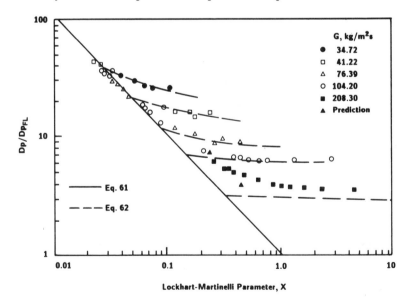

FIG. 5. Dp/Dp_L to base of the Lockhart–Martinelli parameter for an air–water mixture at a pressure of 1 bar.

Barbe and Roger[16] observed that their experimental data were well represented using whichever is the greater of

$$Dp = Dp_G \qquad (61)$$

and

$$Dp = -g/v_L \qquad (62)$$

The first of these equations, which holds at lower mass dryness fractions, indicates that the by-pass lane is full of slowly moving liquid, and the second that at higher mass dryness fractions dry gas flows through the bank, with all the liquid in the by-pass. Figure 5 compares these equations with experiment. For the highest flow rate the equations underpredict the gradient. Chisholm[18] has allowed for the effect of friction in the by-pass lane; predictions on this basis are also shown in Fig. 5.

12. FLOW PATTERNS IN HORIZONTAL TUBES

The flow patterns in horizontal flow may be classified and described as follows.

Bubble flow. Bubbles of gas in a continuous liquid phase.

Stratified flow. Liquid flow along the bottom of the pipe; no significant interfacial waves.

Wave flow. As stratified flow but now waves at interface. There may be liquid entrained in the gas.

Separated flow. Covers both stratified and wave flow.

Plug flow. Plugs of gas, formed from many bubbles coalescing, flow in continuous liquid phase.

Slug flow. The waves in 'wave flow' now large enough to touch upper surface of tube.

Intermittent flow. Covers both plug and slug flow.

Annular flow. The liquid forms a film round the wall. The gas core may contain liquid droplets.

Extending the Kelvin–Helmholtz analysis for the stratified-intermittent transition[19] by allowing for the relative motions of the phases[20] leads to the equation

$$u_{Gs}^* = \frac{\eta_1 \cdot \alpha^{3/2}}{1 - \dfrac{1}{K}} \qquad (63)$$

where[21]

$$u_{Gs}^* = \frac{u_{Gs}}{\left[gD\left(\dfrac{v_G}{v_L} - 1\right) \right]^{1/2}} \tag{64}$$

The introduction of the relative motion becomes of importance as the thermodynamic critical point is approached and the phase density ratio approaches unity. The phase velocity ratio in stratified flow is

$$K = \eta_K \left(\frac{v_G}{v_L}\right)^{(1-n)/(2-n)} \left(\frac{\mu_L}{\mu_G}\right)^{n/(2-n)} \tag{65}$$

where, in an approximation of the theoretical analysis[20]

$$X > 0.385 \qquad \eta_K = \frac{0.666}{X^{0.27}} \tag{66}$$

$$X < 0.385 \qquad \eta_K = \frac{0.766}{X^{0.11}} \tag{67}$$

The equations are sufficiently sensitive to the value of K to warrant the following empirical correction to eqn. (63).

$$u_{Gs}^* = \frac{\eta_1 \cdot \alpha^{3/2}}{1 - \dfrac{0.9}{K}} \tag{68}$$

The coefficient η_1 is given by

$$\eta_1 = \left(1 - \frac{\Delta\alpha}{\alpha}\right)\left(\frac{dh}{d \cdot d\alpha}\right)^{1/2} \tag{69}$$

In this equation $\Delta\alpha$ is the reduction in voidage due to a wave, relative to the upstream condition, and h is the depth of liquid. They also assume

$$1 - \frac{\Delta\alpha}{\alpha} = 1 - \frac{h}{d} \tag{70}$$

However, better agreement is obtained[20] with experiment using

$$\frac{h}{d} > 0.382 \qquad 1 - \frac{\Delta\alpha}{\alpha} = \frac{1 - \dfrac{h}{d}}{\left(\dfrac{h}{d}\right)^{1/2}} \tag{71}$$

$$\frac{h}{d} < 0.382 \qquad 1 - \frac{\Delta\alpha}{\alpha} = 1.0 \qquad (72)$$

From geometric considerations

$$d \cdot \frac{d\alpha}{dh} = \left(\frac{8}{\pi}\right)\left[\frac{h}{d}\left(1 - \frac{h}{d}\right)\right]^{1/2} \qquad (73)$$

The coefficient η_1 can be evaluated using the above equations for a given ratio of h/d. These equations are compared with Weisman's[22] flow pattern map for air–water mixtures at atmospheric pressure in Fig. 6, and Pearce's data[23] for R12 at a pressure of 30 bar[23] in Fig. 7.

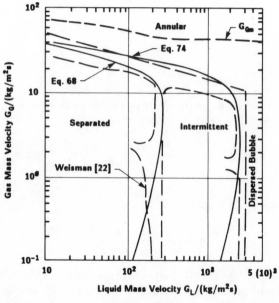

FIG. 6. Flow pattern map for air–water mixture at 1 bar; diameter 51mm.

An interesting development is the extension[20] of the Kelvin–Helmholtz analysis to the intermittent transition to annular and dispersed bubble flow. It is assumed that the difference between the transition from stratified flow and the transition from intermittent flow is that the phase velocity ratio is different; for intermittent flow, the velocity ratio is assumed given by eqn. (36), while for stratified flow eqn. (65) is assumed to apply. Also, assuming

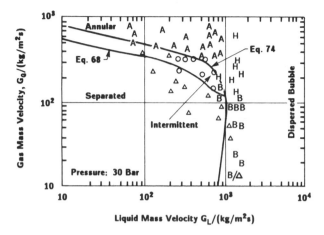

FIG. 7. Flow pattern map for R12. Diameter 40·9 mm. A, annular; B, bubble; H, homogeneous; X, stratified.

entrainment w, the following equation results for the intermittent-annular and intermittent-dispersed bubble transitions

$$u_{Gs}^* = \frac{\eta_1 \alpha^{3/2}}{1 - \dfrac{1}{K}} \left[\frac{x + w(1-x)v_L/v_G}{x + w(1-x)} \right]^{1/2} \tag{74}$$

Predictions using this equation are also shown in Figs. 6 and 7 assuming $w = 0·015$; there is satisfactory agreement with Weisman's map[22] in Fig. 6 and with experimental data in Fig. 7.

13. MAXIMUM ENTRAINMENT IN TUBES

Ishii and Mishima[24] have developed a correlation for entrainment for fully developed flow conditions in vertical pipes, which can be approximated,[25] for convenience, to

$$w = 7·25 \times 10^7 \, We^{1·25} \, Re_L^{0·25} \tag{75}$$

where

$$We = \frac{G_G^2 v_G d}{\sigma} \left(\frac{v_G}{v_L} - 1 \right)^{1/3} \left(1 - \frac{1}{K} \right)^2 \frac{1}{\alpha^2} \tag{76}$$

and

$$Re_L = \frac{G_L d}{\mu_L} \qquad (77)$$

In defining the Weber number, the velocity of the vapour relative to the liquid has been taken as the relevant velocity; for the range of the data used in developing the equation there is little difference between absolute and relative velocities of the vapour.

The vapour or gas mass velocity at the onset, with increasing mass dryness fraction, of maximum entrainment, G_{Gm} can now be obtained. This can be estimated by rearranging the above equations; Ishii and Mishima[24] give an equation for the maximum entrainment. Values predicted in this way are given in Table 3. It is convenient to define 'mist-annular' flow as the pattern occurring after the onset of maximum entrainment.

TABLE 3
GAS MASS VELOCITY AT ONSET OF MAXIMUM ENTRAINMENT

x	G_{GM} $(kg/m^2 s)$	$\dfrac{1}{0.001\,223\Gamma}$	G_{GM} $(kg/m^2 s)$	$\dfrac{1}{0.001\,223\Gamma}$
	Air–water $\Gamma^2 = 341$ 46.7 mm i.d.		Refrigerant 11 $\Gamma^2 = 97$ 46.7 mm i.d.	
0.9	75	44.1	103	83.2
0.5	63	44.1	85	83.2
0.1	51	44.1	70	83.2
0.05	48	44.1	67	83.2
0.01	44	44.1	67	83.2

Figure 8 shows the predicted mist-annular boundary obtained by this procedure. The discontinuous line is obtained using the vapour absolute velocity, the continuous line, using the relative velocity. If the relative velocity is not used, the maximum entrainment is predicted as occurring during stratified flow. The mist-annular boundary is also shown in Fig. 6; there is negligible difference in this case between using the absolute or relative velocity.

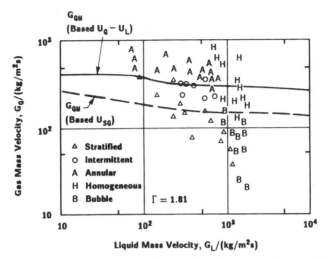

FIG. 8. Flow pattern map with curves of onset of maximum entrainment. R12 at 30 bar.

14. MOMENTUM PRESSURE CHANGES IN TUBES

The pressure change due to change in the momentum flux of the mixture can be expressed[9] as

$$\Delta p_M = G^2(v_{e2} - v_{e1}) \tag{78}$$

where v_e is the effective specific volume of the mixture. Unlike single-phase flow this specific volume is not the reciprocal of the density associated with the gravitational pressure gradient.

It is incorrect to refer to eqn. (78) as an energy equation as the momentum equation is used to predict pressure gradient in two-phase flow, rather than the energy equation. The energy equation is used to determine the thermodynamic flow path.

For a separated flow

$$v_e = [xv_G + K_e(1-x)v_L]\left[x + \frac{1-x}{K_e}\right] \tag{79}$$

where K_e is the 'effective' velocity ratio. It should be noted that the effective velocity ratio K_e is not that associated with the prediction of void fraction, due to the variation of liquid velocity across the flow cross-section. Morris[26] shows excellent agreement with experiment using the following equation

$$v_e = [xv_G + K_o(1-x)v_L]\left[x + \frac{1-x}{K_o}\left\{1 + \frac{(K_o-1)^2}{\left(\dfrac{v_G}{v_L}\right)^{1/2} - 1}\right\}\right] \tag{80}$$

A more approximate treatment[9] uses eqn. (79) with the following effective velocity ratio

$$K_e = K_o^{0.28} \tag{81}$$

Under stratified flow conditions as there is no entrainment in the gas the effective velocity ratio will correspond to that from continuity considerations, which for a zero interfacial model is

$$K = \left(\frac{v_G}{v_L}\right)^{(1-n)/(2-n)}\left(\frac{\mu_L}{\mu_G}\right)^{n/(2-n)} \tag{82}$$

This corresponds to the velocity ratio from eqn. (65), with $\eta_K = 1.0$.

For fully entrained spray flow it is to be expected that the effective velocity ratio is

$$K = 1.0 \tag{83}$$

It is recommended in the transition region to use

$$K_e = \frac{1}{\left(\dfrac{v_L}{v_G}\right)^{(1-n)/(2-n)}\left(\dfrac{\mu_G}{\mu_L}\right)^{n/(2-n)}(1-w)+w} \tag{84}$$

Procedures for predicting pressure changes at tube inlet and outlet are described in reference 9.

15. FRICTION PRESSURE DROP IN TUBES

Figure 9 shows schematically a ψ–x plot similar to Fig. 2, but now for tube friction, and with linear coordinates. For simplicity curves corresponding to eqn. (20) are shown as straight lines.

Stratified flow is again represented by eqn. (17), however the bubble and

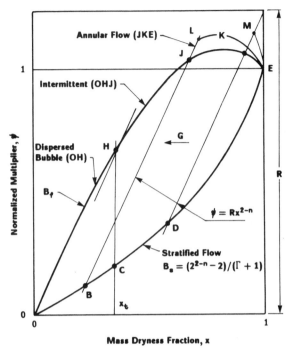

FIG. 9. The normalised multiplier ψ to a base of mass dryness fraction x: pipe flow.

spray or mist flow patterns are no longer represented by eqns. (16) and (18). The annular, intermittent, and bubble regimes are covered by the B-coefficients given in Table 4 (reference 9) which is reproduced here for convenience.

In reference 27 the hypothesis was examined that the turning point L, for example, in Fig. 9 corresponds to the onset of annular flow. This assumption was found to overestimate the mass velocities at transition. An alternative hypothesis[26] is that the turning points are associated with the onset of mist-annular flow. Defining x_m as the mass dryness fraction at the onset of mist-annular flow then, using eqns. (10) and (19),

$$Rx_m^{2-n} = B_f x_m^{(2-n)/2}(1-x_m)^{(2-n)/2} + x_m^{2-n} \tag{85}$$

Values of B_f for pipe flow are given in Table 4. For pipe flow[28]

$$R = 1 + 0.001\ 223\ \Gamma G \tag{86}$$

TABLE 4
VALUES OF B FOR SMOOTH TUBES

Γ	$G(kg/m^2s)$	B
$\leqslant 9\cdot5$	$\leqslant 500$	$4\cdot8$
	$500 < G < 1\,900$	$2\,400/G$
	$\geqslant 1\,900$	$55/G^{0\cdot5}$
$9\cdot5 < \Gamma < 28$	$\leqslant 600$	$520/(\Gamma G^{0\cdot5})$
	> 600	$21/\Gamma^a$
$\geqslant 28$		$\dfrac{15\,000}{\Gamma^2 G^{0\cdot5}}$

[a]This B corresponds to the Lockhart–Martinelli curve.

This equation was developed using air–water mixtures and Refrigerant 11 at the conditions shown in Table 3. However, as shown in Table 3, approximately

$$0\cdot001\,223\Gamma = \frac{1}{G_{Gm}} \tag{87}$$

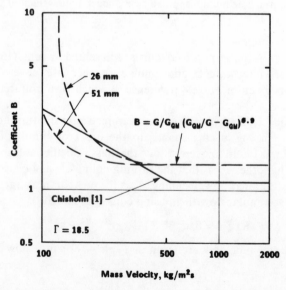

FIG. 10. Coefficient B to a base of mixture mass velocity: horizontal flow in tubes.

Hence eqn. (86) can be expressed[11] as

$$R = 1 + \frac{G}{G_{Gm}} \tag{88}$$

Combining eqns. (85) and (88) gives

$$B_f = \frac{G}{G_{Gm}} \left(\frac{x_m}{1 - x_m} \right)^{(2-n)/2}$$

$$= \left(\frac{G}{G_{Gm}} \right) \left(\frac{G_{Gm}}{G - G_{Gm}} \right)^{(2-n)/2} \tag{89}$$

Figure 10 compares values of B_f on this basis, with values from Table 4. This comparison gives a measure of confirmation that the onset of mist-annular flow is associated with turning points in ϕ against x plots. Some recent data[29] suggest that at high mass dryness fractions and liquids more viscous than water these methods may underestimate the pressure gradient.

16. FLOW PATTERNS IN VERTICAL TUBES

In vertically upwards flow in tubes five flow patterns can be defined:

Bubble flow. Bubbles of gas in a continuous liquid phase.

Finely dispersed bubble flow. As for bubble flow, except that now the bubbles are finely divided.

Slug flow. Bullet-shaped slugs of gas in a continuous liquid phase. The bullet-shaped bubble is known as a 'Taylor' bubble.

Churn flow. A highly oscillatory flow. A tendency for each phase to be continuous with irregular interfaces.

Annular flow. The liquid forms a film round the wall. The gas core may contain liquid droplets.

Taitel *et al.*[30] recommend the following equations for these various boundaries.

Bubble-slug

$$u_{Ls} = 3u_{Gs} - 1 \cdot 15 \left[g(v_G - v_L) \frac{v_L}{v_G} \sigma \right]^{1/2} \tag{90}$$

Bubble — finely dispersed bubble

$$u_H = u_{Ls} + u_{Gs}$$

$$= \frac{4d^{0.429}(\sigma v_L)^{0.089}}{(\mu_L v_L)^{0.072}} [g(v_G - v_L)]^{0.446} \tag{91}$$

Finely dispersed bubble-slug/churn

$$\alpha = 0.52 \tag{92}$$

Transition to annular

$$u_G = \left(\frac{4We_c}{3C_d}\right)^{1/4} \left[g\sigma(v_G - v_L)\frac{v_G}{v_L}\right]^{1/4} \tag{93}$$

where We_c, the critical Weber number is taken as 30, and C_d the drag coefficient is taken as 0·44.

Slug-churn

$$\frac{z_e}{d} = 40.6\left(\frac{u_H}{\sqrt{gd}} + 0.22\right) \tag{94}$$

z_e is the length over which churning will occur prior to the onset of slug flow.

17. PRESSURE GRADIENT DUE TO GRAVITY

Predicting the mixture density requires knowledge of the relative movement of the phases. There are a number of ways of introducing this movement into the calculation. One method uses the Armand Coefficient (see eqn. (59))

$$\alpha = C_A \beta \tag{95}$$

C_A is the Armand coefficient. The mixture density is then

$$\rho_m = \frac{1}{v_m} = \frac{1}{v_L}\left[1 - \alpha\left(1 - \frac{v_L}{v_G}\right)\right] = \frac{1}{v_L}\left[1 - C_A\beta\left(1 - \frac{v_L}{v_G}\right)\right] \tag{96}$$

Except near the thermodynamic critical point $C_A = 0.8$ approximates experiments for $\beta < 0.9$. Equations for calculating C_A are given in reference 9.

Alternatively the velocity ratio can be evaluated. The mixture density is then

$$\rho_m = \frac{1}{v_m} = \frac{x + K(1-x)}{xv_G + K(1-x)v_L} \tag{97}$$

For $\beta < 0.9$ the larger velocity ratio from the following two equations should be used[13]

$$K_o = \left(\frac{v_H}{v_L}\right)^{1/2} \tag{36}$$

or[31]

$$K = 1\cdot2 + 0\cdot2\frac{x v_G}{(1-x)v_L} + w_D\frac{u_b}{u_{Ls}} \tag{98}$$

The bubble velocity is u_b, u_{Ls} is the velocity if the liquid flows alone, and w_D is the drift correction factor given by

$$w_D = 1\cdot4\left(\frac{v_G}{v_L}\right)^{1/5}\left(1-\frac{v_L}{v_G}\right)^5 \tag{99}$$

If the tube diameter is greater than

$$d = 19\left[\frac{\sigma v_L}{g\left(1-\dfrac{v_L}{v_G}\right)}\right]^{1/2} \tag{100}$$

the bubble velocity is obtained from

$$u_b = 1\cdot53\left[g\sigma(v_G - v_L)\frac{v_L}{v_G}\right]^{1/4} \tag{101}$$

For smaller tube diameters

$$u_b = 0\cdot35\left[gd\left(1-\frac{v_L}{v_G}\right)\right]^{1/2} \tag{102}$$

For $\beta > 0\cdot9$, for approximate calculations eqn. (36) can be used, or for more accurate calculations[9,31]

$$K = 1 + \frac{23}{Re_L^{1/2}}\left(\frac{v_G}{v_L}\right)^{1/2}\left(1-\frac{v_L}{v_G}\right) \tag{103}$$

For downflow the sign associated with the bubble velocity term in eqn. (98) is changed, and now the smaller velocity ratio of that given by eqns. (36) and (89) used.

18. FLOW IN INCLINED TUBES

Beggs[32] had developed an equation for the void fraction in inclined tubes which can be written

$$\alpha = \alpha_h + (\alpha_v - \alpha_h)f(\theta) \qquad (104)$$

where the subscripts h and v indicate flow in the horizontal and vertical plane respectively. If the flow is upwards in the tube, α_v is evaluated on that basis, and conversely with downflow. The function is

$$f(\theta) = 3\cdot333[\sin(1\cdot8\theta) + 0\cdot333\sin^3(1\cdot8\theta)] \qquad (105)$$

where θ is the angle of the tube to the horizontal, assumed positive regardless of the flow direction.

19. SUMMARY AND CONCLUSIONS

Procedures for predicting pressure gradients, flow patterns and phase distribution in two-phase flow in baffled shell-and-tube heat exchangers have been outlined.

The methods for friction and form drag in both shell-side and tube-side flow use equations of the following form:

$$\psi_F = Bx^{(2-n)/2}(1-x)^{(2-n)/2} + x^{2-n} \qquad (10)$$

$$\psi = Rx^{2-n} \qquad (19)$$

Procedures for evaluating the B and R coefficients are given.

For predicting the pressure gradient due to gravity in vertical flow, the mixture density is evaluated using the equation

$$\rho_m = \frac{x + K(1-x)}{xv_G + K(1-x)v_L} \qquad (96)$$

Equations (36) and (98) are recommended for the evaluation of the phase velocity ratio K.

The momentum flux can be evaluated using either eqn. (80), or eqns. (79) and (81).

Prediction of the flow pattern and phase distribution is discussed for both shell-side and tube-side flow.

REFERENCES

1. CHISHOLM, D. Pressure gradients due to friction during the flow of evaporating two-phase mixtures in smooth tubes and channels, *Int. J. Heat Transfer*, 1973, **16**(2), 347–58.
2. CHISHOLM, D. Prediction of pressure drop at pipe fittings during two-phase flow, *13th Int. Inst. of Refrig. Cong.*, Washington, 27 August–3 September 1971, Vol. 2, 781–9.
3. GRANT, I. D. R. Two-phase flow and pressure drop on the shell-side of shell-and-tube heat exchangers, heat and fluid flow in steam and turbine plant. University of Warwick, Coventry, 3–5 April 1973, No. CP3, p.244–51. Institute of Mechanical Engineers, London.
4. MARTINELLI, R. C. and NELSON, D. R. Prediction of pressure drop during forced circulation of water, *Trans. Am. Soc. Mech. Engrs*, 1948, **70**(6), 695–702.
5. CHISHOLM, D. and LAIRD, A. D. K. Two-phase flow in rough tubes, *Trans. Am. Soc. Mech. Engrs*, 1980, **80**(2), 276–86.
6. LOCKHART, R. W. and MARTINELLI, R. C. Proposed correlation of data for isothermal two-phase two-component flow in pipes, *Chem. Engng. Progr.*, 1949, **45**(1), 39–48.
7. GRANT, I. D. R., and CHISHOLM, D. Two-phase flow on the shell-side of a segmentally baffled shell-and-tube heat-exchanger, *Trans. ASME*, 1979, **101**, 38–42.
8. GRANT, I. D. R., CHISHOLM, D. and COTCHIN, C. D. Shellside flow in horizontal condensers. ASME/AIChE National Heat Transfer Conference, Orlando, Florida, July 27–30, 1980, ASME Preprint no. 80-HT-52.
9. CHISHOLM, D. *Two-phase flow in pipelines and heat exchangers*, 1983, George Godwin/Institution of Chemical Engineers, Harlow, UK.
10. GRANT, I. D. R., COTCHIN, C. and CHISHOLM, D. Tube submergence and entrainment on the shell-side of heat exchangers, Int. Heat and Mass Transfer Conference, Dubrovnik, September, 1981.
11 CHISHOLM, D. Two phase flow in heat exchangers and pipelines, *Heat Transfer Engineering*, 1985, **6**(2), 48–56.
12. GRANT, I. D. R., COTCHIN, C. D. and HENRY, J. A. R. Submergence in baffled shell-and-tube heat exchangers, First UK National Conference on Heat Transfer, University of Leeds, England, 3–5 July, 1984, Institute of Chemical Engineers, Pergamon Press, Oxford.
13. CHISHOLM, D. Void fraction during two-phase flow, *J. Mech. Engng Sci.*, 1973, **15**(3), 235–6.
14. GRANT, I. D. R. and MURRAY, I. Pressure drop on the shell-side of a segmentally baffled shell-and-tube heat exchanger with vertical two-phase flow, NEL Report No. 500, 1972 National Engineering Laboratory, East Kilbride, Glasgow.
15. GRANT, I. D. R., FINLAY, I. C. and HARRIS, D. Flow and pressure drop during vertically upward two-phase flow past a tube bundle with and without bypass leakage, I. Chem. E./I. Mech. E. Joint Symposium on Multiphase Flow Systems, University of Strathclyde, Glasgow, 2–4 April 1974, Vol. 2, Paper 17, The Institution of Chemical Engineers, London.

16. BARBE, C. and ROGER, D. Echange de chaleur er partes de charge en ecoulement diphasique dans la calandre des exchangeurs bobines, 13th International Institute of Refrigeration Congress, Washington, 27 Aug–3 Sept 1971, Paper No 2.34, Instit. Internat. du Froid, Internat. Instite of Refrigeration, Paris.

17 POLLEY, G. T. and GRANT, I. D. R. Pressure drop prediction for two-phase upward flow through a tube bundle with bypassing. Assoc. Engrs Grad. Univ. Liege (A I Lg), Proc. Int. Meeting, Industrial Heat Exchangers and Heat Recovery; Liege, 14–16 Nov. 1979, Paper A10, A I Lg, Liege Belgium.

18 CHISHOLM, D. Two-phase vertical upflow through tube banks with bypass lanes, Int. J. Heat & Fluid Flow, 1984, 5 (1), 51–3.

19 TAITEL, Y. and DUKLER, A. E. A model for predicting flow regime transitions in horizontal and near-horizontal flow, AIChJ., 1976, 22, 47–55.

20 CHISHOLM, D. Prediction of flow pattern boundaries in horizontal two-phase flow, First UK National Conference on Heat Transfer, University of Leeds, England, 3–5 July, 1984, Vol. 2, Paper 12.1, 761–772. Institution of Chemical Engineers. Pergamon Press, Oxford.

21 WALLIS, G. B. One-Dimensional Two-Phase Flow, 1969, McGraw-Hill, New York.

22 WEISMAN, J. Two-phase flow patterns. In: Handbook of Fluids in Motion, 1983, Ann Arbor Science Publishers, Ann Arbor, Michigan, 409–25.

23 PEARCE, D. L. Two-phase flow regimes in horizontal tubes. Paper no. A2/4, European Two-Phase Flow Meeting, Paris, June 1982.

24 ISHII, M. and MISHIMA, K. Liquid transfer and entrainment correlation for droplet-annular flow, Proceedings of the 7th International Heat Transfer Conference, Vol. 5, 1982, Hemisphere, Washington, D.C., 307–12.

25 CHISHOLM, D. Friction, entrainment, and flow pattern in two-phase horizontal tubes, Second International Conference on Multiphase Flow, London, 19–21 June 1985, BHRA, Bedford, UK.

26 MORRIS, S. D. A simple model for estimating two-phase flow momentum flux, First UK National Heat Transfer Conference, Leeds, 3–5 July 1984, Vol. 2, Paper 12.2, Institution of Chemical Engineers, Pergamon Press, Oxford, 773–84.

27 CHISHOLM, D. Flow pattern maps in horizontal two-phase flow, First Conference on the Physical Modelling of Multi-Phase Flow. paper F1, April 19–21, 1983, BHRA, Coventry, UK.

28 CHISHOLM, D. The turbulent flow of two-phase mixtures in horizontal pipes at low Reynolds number, J. Mech. Engng Sci., 1980, 22(4), 353–4.

29 STEINER, D. Pressure drop in horizontal flows, Proc. Int. Workshop on Two-Phase Flow Fundamentals. Sept. 1985, NBS-Gaithersburg, USA.

30 TAITEL, Y. BARNEA and DUBLER, A. E. Modelling flow pattern transitions for steady upward gas–liquid flow in vertical tubes, AIChE, 1980, 11(26), 345–54.

31 ZUBER, N. and FINDLAY, J. A. Vapor void fraction in subcooled boiling and in saturated boiling systems, Trans. ASME, J. Heat Transfer, 1965, 87, 453–68.

32 BEGGS, H. D. An experimental study of two-phase flow in inclined pipes, Ph.D. Thesis, University of Tulsa, Order No 72-21-615, 1972, University Microfilms, Ann Arbor, Michigan.

Chapter 4

FLUIDISED BEDS

J. R. Howard

HH Associates, Solihull, UK

SUMMARY

Fluidised bed technology has been used widely by chemical engineers to effect processes which depend upon good contacting between solid particles and fluids, especially gases. In recent years the technology has been extended and has enabled gas-to-liquid heat exchangers to be designed and built. This chapter describes the essential features of fluidised beds and presents fundamental subject matter on behaviour, mechanisms and parameters pertinent to present-day fluidised bed heat exchanger design. This is developed and illustrated by means of worked examples, which show the basis upon which shallow fluidised beds, incorporating extended-surface tubing, may be designed for recovering heat from hot waste gases without unacceptable pressure drop. Other aspects and future developments for extending the scope of fluidised beds are discussed briefly and pertinent references provided.

NOTATION

A	Area (m^2)
Ar	Archimedes number $(\rho_f(\rho_p - \rho_f)gd_p^3/\mu^2)$
C_p	Specific heat at constant pressure $(kJ/kg\,K)$
d	Diameter (m)
g	Gravitational acceleration (m/s^2)
h	Heat transfer coefficient $(kW/m^2\,K)$
k	Thermal conductivity $(W/m\,K)$ or $(kW/m\,K)$
L	Length (m)

89

M Mass of particles (kg)

Nu Nusselt number (hd/k)

p Pressure (N/m^2)

Pr Prandtl number ($C_p \mu/k$)

Re Reynolds number ($\rho ud/\mu$)

u Velocity (m/s)

U Fluidising velocity (m/s) or overall heat transfer coefficient (kW/m^2 K)

t Wall thickness (m)

T Temperature (°C)

Greek

ε Voidage

μ Viscosity

ρ Density

ϕ Shape factor

Subscripts

b   Bed

f   Fluidising gas

i   Inner surface

m   Mean diameter

max   Maximum

mf   Minimum fluidisation

mo   Metal at outer surface

o   Outer surface

p   Particle

1. INTRODUCTION

Fluidised beds have been used extensively in the chemical and process industries, most particularly since 1942, when the first full-scale catalytic cracker which was designed to exploit techniques of fluidisation of small solid particles of catalyst came into operation, at an oil refinery in the United States.[1] The principles had however been discovered much earlier and over the years to the present time, considerable research and development effort has produced a vast literature about the subject and its applications. References 1–7 provide some indication of the range. Discussion of the scope of fluidisation will be terminated here because it is more germane to the purpose of this book to describe the underlying phenomena of fluidised beds briefly and show how it has been applied to heat exchanger technology.

2. SOME FEATURES OF A BED OF PARTICLES

Figure 1 shows a quantity of solid particles contained in a vessel having a porous base through which a fluid supplied to the plenum chamber underneath the base can flow and then percolate upwards through the spaces surrounding the individual particles. The fluid can be gaseous or liquid, but this chapter will be concerned with the behaviour of beds of particles through which only gases flow, because fluidised bed heat exchangers have been used most commonly for recovery of heat from hot gas streams.

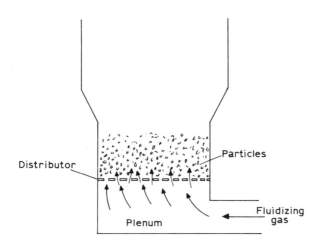

FIG. 1. Fluidised bed.

The first striking feature of a quantity of solid particles is the large surface area of the particles which is available for contact with a fluid flowing among them. For example, a simple estimate shows that a bed of particles having a mean diameter $100\,\mu m$, contained in a vessel of volume $1\,m^3$ has a total surface area of the order of $3 \times 10^4\,m^2$, see reference 4. Such an enormous amount of surface area is potentially available for heat or mass transfer between the solids and the fluid, so that the rates of heat and mass transfer across the interface can be very high. Clearly in any given case, the amount of particle surface area contained within a given bulk volume of particles will vary with the size and shape of the particles, the range of sizes and shapes within the mix and the way in which the particles are packed in the containment, since the latter affects the 'voidage'; nevertheless the amount of surface area will always be very large.

The second feature is that a bed of solids has a large heat capacity per unit volume. The virtue of this is that particulate solids can be used for heat storage and if they can be transported or made to flow from one location to another, they can be a most effective heat carrier. It should also be noted that because of this high heat capacity per unit volume compared with that of gases and the large surface area of contact between the gases and particles, when a hot gas enters a bed of particles it will be cooled to a temperature very close to that of the particles within a very short distance of entering the bed. Thus the temperature of the gas follows the temperature of the particles rather than the converse.

It may be further remarked that the large particle surface area within a given containment volume offers the possibility for relatively rapid heating or cooling of the mass of solids; a feature of importance in regenerators subjected to rapid heat demand or input.

The above features are true whether the bed of particles are simply a fixed bed (sometimes called a packed bed), or a fluidised bed. It is necessary now to distinguish between fixed and fluidised beds.

3. FLUIDISATION PHENOMENA

If gas is introduced into the bed of particles shown in Fig. 1 through the porous base it is normally desirable that the gas be distributed uniformly into the bed. This requires that the porous base be designed to achieve this. Several different designs of distributor have been developed over the years to suit particular situations. Some simple examples are illustrated in Fig. 2.

For example, Fig. 2(a) shows a simple drilled plate, having a number of closely spaced small holes of diameter smaller than the smallest particle in the bed so as to prevent the flow back of solids into the plenum. For uniformity of distribution at the desired rate of gas flow, the pressure drop across the distributor has to be of sufficient magnitude to effect this. On the other hand the pressure drop should not be unnecessarily large because an excessive pressure drop is a penalty, which is paid for through increased running cost due to the additional pumping power and also by increased

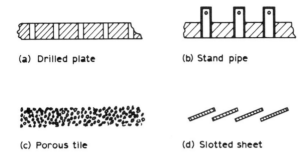

(a) Drilled plate   (b) Stand pipe

(c) Porous tile   (d) Slotted sheet

FIG. 2. Some types of distributor.

capital cost which may arise from the specification of a fan of higher delivery pressure.

Consider now Fig. 3 which shows the pressure drop *across the bed of particles* (the distributor pressure drop is not included), as the gas flow rate through the bed is increased. Note that gas flow rate is specified as a 'fluidising velocity, U,' which is superficial, namely,

$$U = \frac{\text{Volume flow rate of gas}}{\text{Cross-sectional area of bed containment}} \quad (1)$$

Note also that because once in the bed the temperature of the gas becomes essentially that of the bed, the volume flow rate of gas in eqn. (1) is that at bed temperature and pressure.

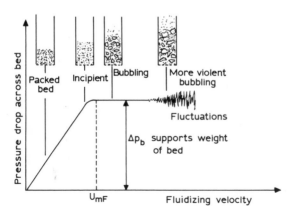

FIG. 3. Variation in pressure drop across bed with fluidising velocity.

Referring to Fig. 3 it will be seen that as the fluidising velocity increases, the pressure drop, Δp_b, across the bed rises until the drag force exerted on the particles is just sufficient to just support the weight of the particles, so that,

$$A\Delta p_b = \frac{M(\rho_p - \rho_f)g}{\rho_p} \qquad (2)$$

Thereafter, any increase in gas velocity is not accompanied by any significant change in pressure drop, until eventually large numbers of the particles start to be transported out of the containment. The latter situation is out of our range of interest here. The interaction between the fluidising gas and the particles over our range of interest is however of profound importance to heat transfer to surfaces immersed in the bed and for mass transfer and mixing.

Visual observation of the bed of particles as the gas flow increases from zero, reveals that initially the particles tend to rearrange themselves so as to accommodate the increasing gas flow, as indicated by the sketches on the upper part of Fig. 3. This results in some expansion of the bed unless it is composed of large particles (> about 1 mm mean size). Expansion increases until a stage is reached when the whole bed exhibits fluid-like properties so that it will flow, solid can either float or sink in it according to their density, etc. This state of the bed is termed one of 'incipient fluidisation' and the gas velocity at which this happens is referred to as the 'minimum fluidising velocity, U_{mf}'.

For simplicity at this stage, we consider the behaviour at ambient temperature and pressure of beds of particles belonging to Geldart's[8] category B; such particles fall into the size and density ranges about 40–500 μm and 1400–4000 kg/m^3 respectively. This category of particles is considered particularly because they have found the most use in fluidised bed heat exchangers. (Geldart's[8] category A powders on the other hand, have particle size and density in the ranges about 20–100 μm and less than 1400 kg/m^3 respectively, behave differently, see reference 8, as do categories C and D.) With category B particles, the gradual expansion of the bed due to particle rearrangement soon ceases as the fluidising velocity increases beyond the minimum fluidising velocity. However as the gas flow through the bed increases beyond the minimum fluidising velocity, the gas tends to form cavities among the particles which look like bubbles of gas and rise through the bed, carrying particles upwards in their wake. This bubbling action, also indicated on Fig. 3, promotes mixing of the particles which in turn promotes uniformity of temperature throughout the bed. On reaching the surface the bubbles of gas burst, throwing particles into the space above the free surface, most of which (at modest fluidising velocities), fall back into the bed. (Some of the finer particles may become entrained in the gas leaving the bed surface and swept out of the systems, but this can be minimised by proper design and operation.)

Determination of minimum fluidising velocity is best done by measuring it experimentally using a simple fluidised bed (a laboratory bench-scale bed can be of sufficient size to obtain an adequate determination), by observing the pressure drop across the bed at gradually increasing fluidising velocity. Minimum fluidising velocity is very sensitive to bed voidage at the point of incipient fluidisation and to particle shape as shown by Ergun's correlation,[10] see eqn. (3) below.

$$Ar = \frac{150(1 - \varepsilon_{mf})}{\phi^2 \varepsilon_{mf}^3} Re_{mf} + \frac{1 \cdot 75}{\phi \varepsilon^3} Re_{mf}^2 \tag{3}$$

Although empirical correlations for estimating minimum fluidising velocity exist, e.g. Wen and Yu,[13] which attempt to average out the effects of particle shape and bed voidage, permit a value to be estimated, the errors can be large and an experimental determination is to be urged. Further discussion can be found in references 2 and 9.

4. FLUIDISED BED HEAT TRANSFER: SIMPLIFIED MECHANISM

If now a surface at a different temperature from the particles is immersed within the fluidised bed, the continual contact and replacement of particles at the surface ensures a high rate of heat transfer between the surface and the bed. The situation is illustrated by the mechanism shown in Fig. 4, in which it will be seen that a particle from the bulk of the bed reaches the immersed surface, resides there for a short time during which heat is conducted from the particle through the gas film between the particle and surface and is then swept away only to be replaced by another particle. (Note that the solid-to-solid contact area is extremely small, so that the heat flow through this path is negligible.[4])

This simple mechanism gives rise to the 'particle convective component of heat transfer' described by Botterill.[2,4] The remaining components of heat transfer, which for simplicity here may be regarded as being additive to the particle convective component, are the 'interphase gas convective component' and the 'radiative component'. The former arises due to the velocity of the gas which passes through the voids and sweeps over the

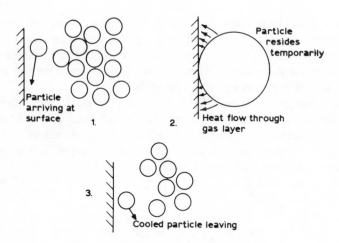

FIG. 4. Particle convective mechanism.

immersed surface. The latter will not be discussed here because of complexity; suffice it to say that the contribution of the radiation component to overall bed-to-surface heat transfer starts to become increasingly significant as the bed temperature increases above about 600°C.

The particle convective component tends to be the dominant one in fluidised bed heat exchangers. The transition between particle convective and interphase gas convective components being dominant occurs at about the following values of Reynolds Number at minimum fluidisation and Archimedes Number[12]

$$Re_{mf} = \frac{\rho_f U_{mf} d_p}{\mu_f} < 12 \cdot 5 \tag{4}$$

$$Ar = \frac{\rho_f (\rho_p - \rho_f) g d_p^3}{\mu_f^2} < 26\,000 \tag{5}$$

It will be apparent that to obtain the highest particle convective component of heat transfer, the particle residence time at the surface should be the shortest, the frequency of replacement of the particles be the greatest, the size of the particles be the smallest, the density of particle contacts over the surface be as great as possible and the thermal conductivity of the interstitial gas be the largest. However, not all these parameters are under the direct control of the designer and practical trials with each fluidised bed are needed to establish the optimum values of its operating parameters to suit the required purpose. The above simple model of the mechanism of heat transfer is not the only one; a more complex one in which the mobile single particle is replaced by a cluster or 'packet' of particles which arrives at the surface, resides there for a time and is then replaced has also been investigated, but the general conclusions about the significant parameters are similar.

The above should provide sufficient initial insight into a highly complex set of interactions for the present purposes; for deeper consideration of heat transfer mechanisms in fluidised beds, the reader is referred to references 2, 4, 8, 11, 12 and 14.

It is now necessary to consider bed-to-immersed-surface heat transfer coefficients for purposes of design of fluidised bed heat exchangers used for gas-to-liquid heat recovery systems or for generation of steam from hot exhaust gases.

5. BED-TO-IMMERSED-SURFACE HEAT TRANSFER COEFFICIENTS

5.1. Single Plain Tube in Beds of Moderate Depth

We proceed now to illustrate how the heat transfer coefficient at the bed-to-surface interface of the tube, immersed in a given fluidised bed of Geldart's category B particles, changes with fluidising velocity. Such a relationship is shown in Fig. 5. It will be seen that as the fluidising velocity increases from zero, the heat transfer coefficient undergoes little change until the minimum fluidising velocity is reached. The heat transfer then rises sharply with fluidising velocity, reaches a maximum and then declines gradually. The values of heat transfer coefficient and corresponding fluidising velocity are affected by the mean size of the particles, the fluidising gas properties, the location of the tube within the bed and the bubbling pattern. However, the fluidising velocity at which the heat transfer coefficient maximises is in the region of about 1·3–3 times the minimum fluidising velocity.

Many empirical correlations for bed-to-immersed-surface heat transfer coefficient have appeared over the years and some can give widely varying and misleading predictions. However, Botterill (see Chapter 1 in reference 2 and also reference 4) has suggested that the simple correlation for the *maximum* heat transfer coefficient, omitting radiation, due to Zabrodsky et al.[11], (see eqn. (6) below) may be used and that a value of about 70% of that

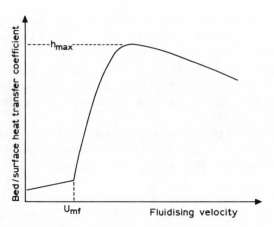

FIG. 5. Influence of fluidising velocity on bed-to-surface heat transfer coefficient.

so predicted may be expected under reasonable operating conditions with category B particles.

Note that the range of validity is as defined by eqns. (4) and (5) and further, that eqn. (6) is *not a dimensionless correlation.* For SI units, the correlation for maximum heat transfer coefficient in W/m^2 K is,

$$h_{max} = 35 \cdot 8 \ \rho_p^{0 \cdot 2} k_f^{0 \cdot 6} d_p^{-0 \cdot 36}$$ (6)

Equation (6) has the merit of simplicity with reasonable predictive accuracy when about 70% of h_{max} is chosen and applies over the range of Archimedes and Reynolds numbers, $Ar < 26\,000$ and $Re_{mf} < 12 \cdot 5$ (see reference 14). Notice however, that eqn. (6) contains no term describing fluidising velocity, so that the predicted value of h_{max} is independent of it; on the other hand eqn. (6) underlines the importance of the thermal conductivity of the interphase gas at bed temperature and particle size. Nothing is said either about the location of the tube in the bed relative to the distributor plate or the effect of bed depth. Such details do however have to be specified by the designer in order that the equipment can be manufactured.

5.2. Fluidised Bed, Gas-to-Liquid Heat Exchanger—Estimate of Plain Cooling Tube Length

For purposes of illustration only, suppose a fluidised bed having a single cooling tube immersed in it is to be used to recover heat from hot, relatively

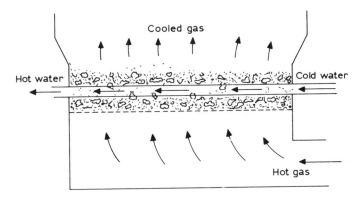

FIG. 6. Simple fluidised bed heat exchanger.

clean gases supplied to the plenum chamber, as shown in Fig. 6. For simplicity, assume that only hot water is generated in the cooling tube. The initial problem is to estimate the amount of tube surface area required to perform the prescribed duty. This duty is likely to be limited by the lowest temperature to which the gases may be permitted to be cooled, e.g. to a value safely above dew point temperature so as to avoid condensation of potentially corrosive liquid. Suppose for the sake of example the relevant data are as given in Table 1.

Although the numerical results of the ensuing estimation is unlikely to produce a commercially acceptable design, the procedure should give insight into some of the considerations that have to be made in order to make engineering decisions and hence the emergence of a satisfactory prototype.

The duty required from the heat exchanger and water flow rate are,

$$Duty = 1 \cdot 2 \times 1 \cdot 04 \times (350 - 200)$$

$$= 187 \, kW$$

$$Water \ flow \ rate = \frac{187}{4 \cdot 18 \times (80 - 20)}$$

$$= 0 \cdot 746 \, kg/s$$

TABLE 1
DATA FOR EXAMPLE ON A FLUIDISED BED, GAS-TO-LIQUID HEAT EXCHANGER

Parameter	Value
Mass flow of gases	1·2 kg/s
Gas inlet temperature	350°C
Gas outlet temperature	200°C
Water inlet temperature	20°C
Water outlet temperature	80°C
Tube material	Copper
Tube bore	25 mm
Tube outside diameter	30 mm
Chosen particles	Silica sand
Particle size	427 μm
Minimum fluidising velocity at 200°C	0·085 m/s
Physical properties	
Particle density	2 640 kg/m^3
Gas mean specific heat	1·04 kJ/kg K
Gas thermal conductivity at 200°C	3·87 × 10^{-2} W/m K
Gas density at 1 atm, 200°C	0·745 kg/m^3
Gas viscosity at 200°C	2·58 × 10^{-5} kg/m s
Water viscosity at 50°C	544 × 10^{-6} kg/m s
Water Prandtl Number at 50°C	3·54
Water specific heat	4·18 kJ/kg K
Water thermal conductivity	634 × 10^{-6} kW/m K
Copper thermal conductivity	380 W/m K

If this water flow is passed through a single tube, the water velocity will be,

$$\text{Water velocity} = \frac{0.746}{\dfrac{\pi}{4} \times (0.025)^2 \times 10^3}$$

$$= 1.52 \text{ m/s}$$

We now proceed to estimate the heat transfer coefficients at the inner and outer surface of the tube using the following empirical correlations:

At the inner surface,

$$Nu = 0.023 \, (Re)^{0.8}(Pr)^{0.4} \tag{7}$$

where Nu, Re and Pr are respectively the Nusselt, Reynolds and Prandtl Numbers.

$$Re = (\rho u d / \mu) = \frac{10^3 \times 1\cdot52 \times 0\cdot025}{544 \times 10^{-6}}$$

$$= 69\,900$$

$$Nu = 0\cdot023 \times (69\,900)^{0\cdot8} \times (3\cdot54)^{0\cdot4}$$

$$= 286$$

At the inner surface, heat transfer coefficient, h,

$$h = (Nuk/d) = \frac{286 \times 643 \times 10^{-6}}{0\cdot025}$$

$$= 7\cdot36 \, \text{kW/m}^2 \, \text{K}$$

At the outer surface, use eqn. (6) after first checking that it is not outside its range of applicability $[Ar < 26\,000$ and $Re_{\text{mf}} < 12\cdot5]$

$$Ar = \frac{(427 \times 10^{-6})^3 \times 0\cdot745 \times 2640 \times 9\cdot81}{(2\cdot58 \times 10^{-5})^2}$$

$$= 2260$$

$$Re_{\text{mf}} = \frac{0\cdot745 \times 0\cdot085 \times 427 \times 10^{-6}}{2\cdot58 \times 10^{-5}}$$

$$= 1\cdot05$$

Using eqn. (6),

$$h_{\text{max}} = 35\cdot8 \times (2640)^{0\cdot2} \times (3\cdot87 \times 10^{-2})^{0\cdot6} \times (427 \times 10^{-6})^{-0\cdot36}$$

$$= 402 \, \text{W/m}^2 \, \text{K}$$

70% of this value gives the heat transfer coefficient at the outer surface of the tube,

$$h_{\text{o}} = 281 \, \text{W/m}^2 \, \text{K}$$

Overall bed-to-liquid thermal resistance $(1/UA)$ is given by,

$$\frac{1}{UA} = \frac{1}{h_o A_o} + \frac{1}{h_i A_i} + \frac{t}{k A_m} \tag{8}$$

where, $A_o = \pi d_o L$, $A_i = \pi d_i L$ and $A_m = 0{\cdot}5\pi(d_o + d_i)L$

Hence,

$$\frac{1}{UA} = \frac{1}{\pi L}\left[\frac{1}{0{\cdot}281 \times 0{\cdot}030} + \frac{1}{7{\cdot}36 \times 0{\cdot}025} + \frac{0{\cdot}005}{0{\cdot}380 \times 0{\cdot}0275}\right] \tag{9}$$

$$= \frac{1}{\pi L}[118{\cdot}6 + 5{\cdot}4 + 0{\cdot}5] \tag{10}$$

$$= \frac{124{\cdot}5}{\pi L}\,K/kW \tag{11}$$

Logarithmic mean temperature difference (LMTD) is based on water inlet and outlet temperature and the assumption that the temperature of the bed of fluidised particles is that of the outlet temperature of the gas, namely 200°C. Thus,

$$(LMTD) = \frac{(200 - 80) - (200 - 20)}{\ln\dfrac{(200 - 80)}{(200 - 20)}}$$

$$= 148\,K$$

Also,

$$\text{Overall thermal resistance} = \frac{(LMTD)}{Duty} \tag{12}$$

Equating eqns. (11) and (12) leads to

$$\text{Tube length, } L, \text{ required} = \frac{124{\cdot}5 \times 187}{148\pi}$$

$$= \underline{50{\cdot}1\,m} \tag{13}$$

5.3. Bed Containment

The bed containment above the distributor must:

(a) Be of sufficient volume to accommodate the 50·1 m length of tubing.
(b) Provide sufficient space around the outside of the tube to allow the particles to circulate freely.
(c) Contain a sufficient quantity of particles to immerse the tube fully at maximum duty.
(d) Be sufficiently shallow so as to avoid excessive pressure drop across the bed.
(e) Provide sufficient height above the bed for particles thrown up by bursting of bubbles to disengage from the gas and fall back into the bed.
(f) Have planform dimensions and proportions appropriate to the particular installation. This will necessitate altering the shape of the tube from a single straight length to a serpentine or spiral or dividing

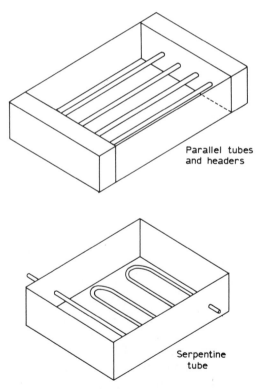

Parallel tubes
and headers

Serpentine
tube

FIG. 7. Alternative arrangement of in-bed tubing.

it into a number of parallel tubes with headers at inlet and outlet as indicated in Fig. 7. (Analysis of the latter arrangement will not be pursued here however, but it is clear that the water velocity through the tubes will be lower, reducing the heat transfer coefficient at the inner surface, while the headers may be exposed to particle contact.)

Consideration (b) is important because interference with particle convection will lead to a reduction in bed-to-tube heat transfer coefficient. On the other hand, if too much space is provided the containment will be unnecessarily large. Reference 15 reported upon the effect of reducing the gap between tubes in tube bundles immersed in fluidised beds on heat transfer coefficients. The reported findings were that the coefficients were about 10% smaller than those obtained with an isolated tube when the gap between the tubes was about 70 mm; reduction of the gap to about 25 mm, reduced the heat transfer coefficient to about 75% of that obtained with an isolated tube.

Since the above calculations were made on the basis of an isolated tube it is clear that the length of tubing required for the duty is increased significantly as the space around the tube is reduced. The situation can be alleviated by using extended-surface tubing; this is discussed in the next section.

5.4. Extended-Surface Tubing

If the bare tube is replaced by extended-surface tubing having integral circular fins on the outside the tube length required for the duty will be reduced. The question which now arises is, 'how closely can the fins be spaced without excessive sacrifice of heat transfer coefficient?' The amount of information on this is comparatively sparse, but some limited experiments have been carried out with extended surfaces in shallow fluidised beds. Al-Ali[16] suggests that if the space between adjacent fins is less than about 20 particle diameters, the bed-to-immersed-surface heat transfer coefficient will start to decline rapidly.

It will be noted that the above experiments were conducted in shallow fluidised beds, circa 50 mm; this is very important on two counts:

1. In shallow fluidised beds, the extent to which bubbles can grow in size and the amount by which the bed expands differs from that encountered in deep beds. This leads to different heat transfer rates,[17] so that the prediction of the bed-to-immersed-surface heat transfer coefficients using correlations obtained from experiments with deep beds can be subject to significant error.

2. The pressure drop across a shallow fluidised bed can be smaller than that required to support the weight of particles in the bed,[18] an important consideration for the heat exchanger designer.

Figure 8 compares some data obtained at the University of Aston by the late Professor Douglas Elliott,[19] in experiments with extended-surface tubing in shallow fluidised beds. It will be noticed that for a given particle size, the heat transfer coefficients obtained with extended surface tubing in shallow beds exceed those obtained with extended surfaces in deep beds and with bare tubes in deep beds.

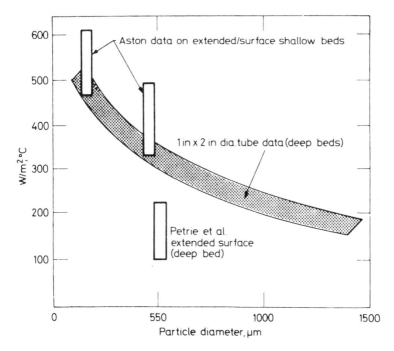

FIG. 8. Comparison of heat transfer coefficients in deep and shallow fluidised beds (reference 19).

5.5. Shallow Fluidised Bed, Extended-Surface Heat Exchanger

If extended-surface tubing of dimensions shown in Fig. 9 is to be used for a shallow fluidised bed heat exchanger to meet the duty prescribed in Table 1, then the length of extended-surface tubing can be calculated as in Section

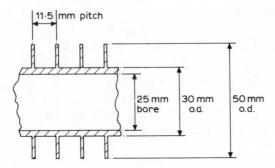

Circular fins 1·5mm thick

11·5 mm pitch

25 mm bore

30 mm o.d.

50 mm o.d.

FIG. 9. Extended-surface tubing.

5.2 above, but however substituting the effective area, A_e, of the external primary and extended surface and the corresponding bed-to-surface heat transfer coefficient, h_e, in place of the bare tube outer area, A_o, and bare tube heat transfer coefficient h_o, in eqn. (8).

For simplicity of analysis, let only the outside area of tube be changed, keeping the value of h_e the same as for the bare tube predicted by eqn. (6), namely, 281 W/m² K. Then it can be shown that[20] the effectiveness of the extended surface, i.e. of the particular circular fins shown in Fig. 9, is about 0·95. When added to the primary area of tube exposed to the particles and the sum is converted to an 'effective diameter' d_e, the entire outer surface has an effective diameter of 0·0923 m.

Inserting these values and the existing values of the remaining parameters into eqn. (8) leads to the first term inside the bracket in eqn. (9), becoming $(1/0\cdot281 \times 0\cdot0923)$ and hence a substantial reduction in the overall thermal resistance, $(1/UA)$, eqn. (11), to

$$\frac{1}{UA} = \frac{44\cdot5}{\pi L} \qquad (14)$$

Hence, using eqn. (13), the tube length required for the duty becomes,

$$\text{Tube length, } L = \frac{44\cdot5 \times 187}{148\pi}$$

$$= 17\cdot9 \text{ m} \qquad (15)$$

If a higher value of bed-to-surface heat transfer coefficient were chosen, then clearly a still shorter length of extended-surface tubing would be predicted. Achievement of values of bed-to-immersed-surface heat transfer coefficient comparable with those shown on Fig. 8 in practice depend upon the design and behaviour of the bed and would have to be confirmed by trials with the actual tubing and bed used.

There is however no doubt that a smaller bed containment vessel is required to contain the necessary length of finned tubing than the necessary length of plain tube. A simple parameter describing the extent to which the bed is being utilised to accommodate heat transfer surface area is the amount of surface immersed per unit volume of bed, known as a 'packing density'. If with both types of tubing the bed depth is 50 mm and a space of 10 mm is provided at the sides, then the packing densities corresponding to the plain and the finned tubing are about $38 \text{ m}^2/\text{m}^3$ and $83 \text{ m}^2/\text{m}^3$ respectively.

5.6. Metal Temperatures and Dew Point

The temperature to which gases can be cooled is often limited in practice by the acid dew point of the gas mixture, because of the high rate of corrosion which can result by acidic vapours condensing on metal surfaces. Accordingly under such circumstances, the temperature of the heat exchanger metal in contact with the gases must not be allowed to fall below the acid dew point temperature and it is common practice to design heat exchangers to maintain metal temperatures everywhere higher than this by an appropriate safety margin.

The metal temperature at the water inlet end of the heat exchanger will be the lowest in the system. For a given duty, the value will depend upon the relative magnitudes of the thermal resistances, $(1/h_oA_o)$, $(1/h_iA_i)$ and (t/kA_m) in eqn. (8). It is obvious however that reduction in thermal resistance on the outside of the tube raises the temperature of the tube metal on the gas side, whether such reduction is brought about by increasing the effective area of the outer surface (changing from bare tube to finned tube), or by raising the heat transfer coefficient by using a shallow fluidised bed heat exchanger instead of a conventional type. This is illustrated by the calculation below which compares the metal temperature at the water inlet end of the heat exchanger required to satisfy the data in Table 1.

The temperature difference between the bed and outer surface of the metal at the water inlet end $(200 - T_{mo})$, is given by,

$$(200 - T_{mo}) = \frac{[1/(h_oA_o)](200 - 20)}{\text{Overall thermal resistance}} \qquad (16)$$

For the case of a plain tube immersed in a fluidised bed, the terms in eqn. (10), are the relevant ones, so that,

$$(200 - T_{mo}) = \frac{118 \cdot 6 \times (200 - 20)}{(118 \cdot 6 + 5 \cdot 4 + 0 \cdot 5)} \tag{17}$$

$$= 171 \cdot 5 \, K$$

which yields a metal temperature,

$$T_{mo} = \underline{28 \cdot 5^\circ C} \tag{18}$$

If the extended-surface tubing, Fig. 9, is employed in the fluidised bed and the heat transfer coefficient on the outside is not changed from the plain tube case, the corresponding metal temperature is $43 \cdot 9^\circ C$.

Both of these metal temperatures are higher than would be the case if a conventional gas convective heat exchanger had been used, because of the much lower gas side heat transfer coefficient and larger surface area involved.

The use of shallow fluidised bed heat exchangers having extended-surface tubing thus opens up the possibility of cooling gases to a temperature closer to the dew point than would be the case with conventional heat exchangers.

6. FLUIDISING VELOCITY, BED EXPANSION AND PRESSURE DROP

When extended-surface tubing is immersed in the bed to form a shallow fluidised bed heat exchanger, the quantity of particles in the bed must be sufficient for the extended-surface tubing to be completely immersed in it at full gas flow. It should be realised that the bed expands as the fluidising velocity is increased and if for example the tubing was located at a level just above the distributor as shown in Fig. 10, then the expansion of the bed could be exploited such that as the gas flow is increased so the amount of heat transfer surface actually immersed in the cloud of highly mobile particles increases and with it the rate of heat removal from the gas. The choice of fluidising velocity at full gas flow needs to be optimised and this requires acquisition of experimental data. On the one hand the velocity should be low enough to avoid unacceptable elutriation of bed particles, while on the other it should be sufficiently high to maintain a high degree of

 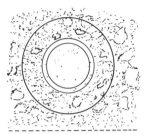

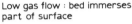

Low gas flow : bed immerses part of surface

Full gas flow : expanded bed immerses entire surface

FIG. 10. Effect of gas flow on immersed extended surface.

particle mobility between the fins and this comes from operation with a high degree of bed expansion, maybe 400%. Relatively little on optimisation has been published, but Virr[19] has suggested that in a large marine steam boiler application where heat was recovered from the exhaust gases of a large marine diesel engine, the gas outlet temperature was 238°C and bed material was aluminium oxide, the optimum fluidising velocity was 1·2–1·5 m/s. This velocity seems to be based upon the flow area between the tubes rather than the 'empty bed' plan area. Tube spacing would have been optimised to obtain the maximum rate of steam generation per unit plan area of bed.

It has already been pointed out that the pressure drop across a shallow fluidised bed can be less than that predicted by eqn. (2). The extent to which this is so has to be established by experiment on the particular bed concerned. There is however a pressure drop across the distributor to be added to that across the bed; the distributor pressure drop increases with gas velocity. The designer however has to ensure that the distributor pressure drop is of sufficient magnitude to achieve uniformity of fluidisation and that taken together with all the other pressure drops in the system the total is within the available discharge pressure of the available fan; the fan characteristic is needed for such an assessment.

The choice of material of the particles has also to be considered carefully because it must resist attrition or other phenomena which may cause breakdown of the particles. Generation of fines from the particles may be sufficient to cause unacceptable rate of loss of bed material by elutriation, with possible consequences downstream and unacceptable changes in the particle size distribution of the bed. Aluminium oxide has been used in preference to some sands, but tests are required to verify performance of the material.

7. OTHER ASPECTS

The above should have provided a little insight into basic design of shallow fluidised bed heat exchangers used for gas-to-liquid or steam generating applications. It is insufficient for an acceptable commercial design, not least because no consideration was made of the environment in which such equipment has to operate. For example, in general most industrial gaseous effluents are not clean; they may contain a troublesome amount of particulates, corrosive gases, condensable vapours or substances which cause extensive fouling of surfaces and loss of effectiveness. Yet such effluents have to be handled and discharged into the environment after suitable treatment to render them safe to do so.

Cooling of high temperature gases is often a necessity before they can be cleaned, irrespective of whether the heat removed is usefully employed. Recovery of heat from such effluents is however highly desirable, and the heat recovery system designer has to find ways of circumventing the worst consequences posed by difficult effluents in a cost-effective manner. Even the best design efforts can be compromised however if the plant from which heat is being recovered is not operated correctly, so that the heat recovery equipment has to cope with factors beyond its capability. In a recent paper, Virr and Williams[21] describe among other things operating experiences with a shallow fluidised bed heat exchanger used for recovery of heat from the exhaust gases of the main propulsion engines of an oil tanker, generating steam. They report an occurrence of oil being ingested into the unit and burnt in the bed causing clinker formation which had to be removed manually; the authors point out that correct operation of the engine could have avoided this.

In normal operating circumstances, the surfaces of immersed finned tubing of shallow fluidised bed heat exchangers are kept clean by the scouring action of the particles. The presence of fine particulates in the gases may tend to block a distributor if allowed to build up; on the other hand such deposits are being confined to one location where they can be dealt with more effectively than if they were more widely dispersed. On the marine waste heat boiler referred to above brushing gear was installed so that the distributor deposits could be removed regularly during normal operation of the plant.

Fouling in any type of process plant or heat exchanger can be a troublesome problem and each set of circumstances is different, calling for differing solutions. Some circumstances may require installation of continuous or semi-continuous cleaning gear, while with others, cleaning during normal maintenance periods may be sufficient. There are however circumstances where the gases are so heavily laden with solids that a different, perhaps more costly solution is needed. One such is the 'falling cloud' system described in references 22 and 23.

However, further progress with shallow fluidised bed waste heat recovery units is to be expected from the evaluation program jointly sponsored by the US Department of Energy and the Aerojet Energy Conversion Co. described in reference 21, where among other things, such a unit is to be installed to recover heat from the exhaust gases of an aluminium melting furnace.

8. FUTURE POSSIBILITIES

The very large surface area, high thermal capacity, and low vapour pressure of a bed of particulate solids, combined with their ability to flow readily when fluidised, makes them potentially attractive as a heat carrier and for high temperature heat storage.

References 24 and 25 show how fluidised solids may be exploited for gas-to-gas heat recovery purposes, while reference 26 discusses their use for heat storage and transport. Further development of such techniques is required to convert their technical promise into commercial reality.

9. CLOSING REMARKS

Invariably, high temperature, dirty, waste gases cost money simply to handle. Properly engineered heat recovery systems, based upon the technology of fluidised solids, may not only recoup such costs, but offer the promise of a good return on the capital invested!

REFERENCES

1. JAHNIG, C. E., CAMPBELL, D. L. and MARTIN, H. Z. History of fluidized solids development at Exxon, Paper presented in *Fluidization*, J. R. Grace and J. Matsen (eds.), 1980, Plenum Press, New York and London.
2. HOWARD, J. R. *Fluidized Beds: Combustion and Applications*, 1983, Elsevier Applied Science, London.
3. DAVIDSON, J. F. and HARRISON, D. *Fluidization*, 1971, Academic Press, London and New York.

4. BOTTERILL, J. S. M. *Fluid-Bed Heat Transfer*, 1975, Academic Press, London and New York.
5. GELDART, D. *Gas Fluidization Technology*, 1986, John Wiley, Chichester, UK.
6. DAVIDSON, J. F., CLIFT, R. and HARRISON, D. *Fluidization*, 1985, 2nd Edn, Academic Press, London and New York.
7. INSTITUTE OF ENERGY, *Proceedings of 3rd International Fluidised Conference*, London, 1984, Institute of Energy, London.
8. GELDART, D. *Powder Technology*, 1973, **7**, 285.
9. BOTTERILL, J. S. M., TEOMAN, Y. and YURIGIR, K. R. *Powder Technology*, 1982, **31**, 101–10.
10. ERGUN, S. *Chem. Engng. Prog.*, 1952, **48**, 889.
11. ZABRODSKY, S. S., ANTONISHIN, N. V. and PARNAS, A. L. *Can. J. Chem. Engng.*, 1976, **54**, 52.
12. BOTTERILL, J. S. M., TEOMAN, Y. and YURIGIR, K. R. Paper 2.4, in *Proceedings of XVIth ICHMT International Symposium Heat and Mass Transfer in Fixed and Fluidized Beds*, Dubrovnik, Yugoslavia, September 3–7, 1984.
13. WEN, C. Y. and YU, Y. H. *AIChE J.*, 1966, **12**, 610.
14. BOTTERILL, J. S. M., TEOMAN, Y. and YURIGIR, K. R. AIChE Symposium Series, Vol. 77, No. 208, 1981, 330–40.
15. ELLIOTT, D. E., HEALEY, E. M. and ROBERTS, A. G. Fluidized bed heat exchangers, *Proc. Conference arranged by The Institute of Fuel* (now The Institute of Energy), and Institut Francais des Combustibles et de L'Energie, Paris, June 1971.
16. AL-ALI, B. M. Ph.D. Thesis, University of Aston in Birmingham, 1976.
17. AL-ALI, B. M. and BROUGHTON, J. *Applied Energy*, 1977, **3** (2), 101–14.
18. PILLAI, K. K. Ph.D. Thesis, University of Aston in Birmingham, 1975.
19. ELLIOTT, D. E. and VIRR, M. J. *Proceedings of 3rd International Conference on Fluidized Bed Combustion*, EPA-650/3-73-053, p. IV-1-14. Also VIRR, M. J. *Fluidized Beds: Combustion and Applications*, J. R. Howard (ed.), 1983, Elsevier Applied Science, London, Chapter 11, p. 348, Fig. 4.
20. KREITH, F. *Principles of Heat Transfer*, 2nd edn, p. 62, Fig. 2.9.
21. VIRR, M. J. and WILLIAMS, H. W. *Chemical Engineering Progress*, July, 1985, 50–6.
22. SANDERSON, P. R. and HOWARD, J. R. *Applied Energy*, 1977, **3**, 115–25.
23. SAGOO, M. S. *Journal of Heat Recovery Systems*, 1981, **1** (2), 133–8.
24. NEWEY, D. C. and HOWARD, J. R. *Journal of Heat Recovery Systems*, 1983, **3** (1), 35–40.
25. HATTORI, H. and HOWARD, J. R. *Journal of Heat Recovery Systems*, 1985, **5** (6), 535–44.
26. BERGOUGNOU, M. A., BOTTERILL, J. S. M., HOWARD, J. R., NEWEY, D. C., SALWAY, A. G. and TEOMAN, Y. *Proceedings of Future Energy Concepts Conference*, IEE London, January 1980, IEE Publication No. 192, 61–4.

in the same direction, the arrangement is termed cocurrent flow. In contrast, counter current flow has the hot fluid and wet material flowing in opposite directions. Counterflow is thermally more effective. In mixed flow the path is a combination of cocurrent and counter current arrangements. When the wet material forms a bed the drying gas passes across it in crossflow.

1.2.2. The Nature of the Material
Individual materials differ widely in their physical and chemical structure, and this influences the manner and rate at which they may be dried. Food products in liquid form, such as milk, are dried by spraying droplets into a heated airstream. Timber must be dried relatively slowly, under controlled conditions, to prevent warping of the manufactured product.

1.2.3. Intermittent or Continuous Operation
The wet solid may be stacked in trays and manually loaded into a drying chamber as a 'batch', at the beginning of a drying cycle. At the completion of drying the dryer is emptied and recharged. In contrast, if the sequence of feeding, drying and removal of dried product is made continuous then this allows mechanisation and automatic control of the plant.

1.2.4. The Handling Characteristics of the Material
The technical difficulties involved in introducing the wet feed stock into the dryer, transporting it through the plant, and removing the dried product may present the designer with even greater problems than the drying process itself. The solution of the handling problem may dictate not only the manner in which the heat is transferred, but also the basic configuration of the dryer.

Considerations such as these suggest the possibility of classifying dryers according to the movement or agitation of the particle as it is being dried. Large objects placed in an oven, or loose material in trays remain stationary. Even when solids are dried on a continuous conveyor the movement within the bed may be negligible. In contrast in spray and pneumatic conveyor dryers the particles move extremely rapidly, with a range of velocities which it may only be possible to define statistically.

A useful methodology, both for design and research, demands some rationalisation of the complex range of drying problems briefly outlined above. Such a structured, scientific approach to dryer design has been proposed by Reay.[10] This proposal will be discussed in more detail later, but in broad outline it consists of separating drying analysis into two complementary fields of enquiry:

(i) Evaluation of the drying characteristics of the material being dried.
(ii) The external environment which is imposed on the material while it is being dried by the particular dryer and its mode of operation.

This is the approach which will be followed in this necessarily brief review of the theory and practice of drying. First the basic heat and mass transfer processes will be presented and related to the process of drying. To avoid repetition, explanations will normally imply the important air/water/solid system and conditions of forced convection. A discussion of the application of theory to design, is followed by a description of some important dryer types. Of necessity, little will be said on the topics of structural design, materials handling, control, safety, etc.

A word of caution to the reader is appropriate at this point. In spite of a great number of tests and trials in industry, together with academic research and investigation, drying theory is still incomplete. Dryers still cannot be designed from theory alone; previous experience is invaluable, both when designing a dryer and selecting one for use. This must be borne in mind when consulting the literature on drying.

In this review, an attempt has been made to present the fundamentals in a simple manner and to provide the necessary background to current developments, so that efforts towards a deeper understanding of this wide ranging and complex subject can be appreciated. An effort has been made to provide references in the open literature to more detailed studies, and to more advanced topics. In this way the informed user can better appreciate the unique and essential contribution made by the dryer manufacturer.

2. GENERAL DESCRIPTION OF THE DRYING PROCESS

2.1. Equilibrium Moisture Content

The liquid in a wet solid, at a particular temperature, generates a vapour pressure. When the vapour pressure produced by the liquid is greater than the partial pressure of the vapour in the surroundings, there is a net transfer of mass (evaporation) from the body and it becomes dry. Evaporation will continue until equilibrium is established when the vapour pressure exerted by the liquid is equal to that of its surroundings. Conversely, for a relatively dry body in humid surroundings, the body may absorb moisture to reach the equilibrium condition.

The term 'bound moisture' refers to that moisture in a material which exerts a vapour pressure which is less than that of the saturated vapour pressure of the pure liquid at the same temperature. This occurs in a hygroscopic material, when some of the liquid enters into physical and/or chemical combination with the solid. Liquid in excess of that which is bound, is said to be unbound.

It can be seen that the equilibrium moisture content of a solid is dependent on the nature of the solid, its temperature and the humidity of the surroundings. The quantity of moisture which it is possible to remove during a drying process is the difference between the initial and equilibrium moisture content; this is called 'free moisture'.

2.2. Definitions of Moisture Content

X = fractional moisture content, dry basis

$$X = \frac{\text{mass of moisture}}{\text{mass of dry solid}} \qquad (2.1a)$$

X' = fractional moisture content, wet basis

$$X' = \frac{\text{mass of moisture}}{\text{mass of moisture} + \text{mass of solid}} = \frac{X}{1+X} \qquad (2.1b)$$

ϕ = fractional free moisture content

$$\phi = \frac{X - X^*}{X_1 - X^*} \qquad (2.1c)$$

X_1 = initial moisture content

X^* = equilibrium moisture content

2.3. Experimental Drying Curves

A drying curve for a particular material is a graph of moisture content against time. It should be established under controlled conditions in a pilot plant or research rig. Accurate measurements of moisture content are required throughout the test period, and this is usually not practical on industrial dryers.

For present purposes let us assume that a sample of the material to be dried can be attached to a weigh-balance in a small wind-tunnel, so that the mass of the sample, moisture plus solid, can be continuously monitored. The state of the drying air, temperature humidity and velocity are maintained constant. Let it be assumed that the air temperature is

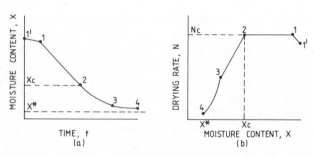

FIG. 1. Typical drying curves.

sufficiently low for radiation to be negligible, and that heat transfer is entirely by forced convection.

A typical driving curve, Fig. 1(a), indicates that the moisture content decreases smoothly approaching the equilibrium moisture content X^* at large values of time. The rate of change of moisture content with time is equal to the drying rate, N. Hence differentiation of curve 1(a), yields the rate of drying curve, 1(b). The drying rate curve is not smooth but exhibits marked discontinuities. Because of this it has become conventional to sub-divide the total drying time into a constant-rate period, (1–2) and a falling-rate period (2–4). After a period of initial adjustment ($1' - 1$), the moisture content decreases linearly with time (1–2) indicating that the material is drying at a constant rate. An explanation of this is that when the body is extremely wet, moisture can reach the exposed surface of the material sufficiently rapidly to maintain it in a wet, saturated, condition. Evaporation of the unbound moisture proceeds unhindered, as if from a free liquid surface, at a rate which depends only upon the external airflow conditions and is independent of the nature of the solid.

When the rate of moisture flow to the free surface is insufficient to keep it saturated, the drying rate begins to fall. The internal structure of the solid now restricts the passage of moisture through it. The critical point, Fig. 1, point 2, has great significance for dryer design. At this point the physical variables which control the drying rate change from the conditions external to the body, to the internal conditions within the body. In the older literature, the critical moisture content X_c was sometimes regarded as a physical constant, characteristic of a particular material. More recent research suggests that X_c is affected by the size and shape of the body, and by the constant-rate period of drying.

The mechanism of falling-rate drying, Fig. 1, 2–4, is sometimes discussed in terms of the first falling-rate period 2–3, and the second falling-rate period, 3–4 (Keey[5]). In the first period, dry areas appear on the surface and continuously increase in size. The fact that constant-rate drying is obtained from a continuously decreasing area explains the linear decrease in drying rate (Treybal[9]). At point 3, sometimes referred to as the second critical point, the surface has become completely dry. From this point, the drying rate is controlled entirely by moisture transfer within the solid, and is essentially independent of external conditions. It should be borne in mind that even though the absolute quantity of liquid to be removed in this period is small, because of the low drying rates, drying times may be protracted.

2.4. Drying Times
The drying rate is defined by the equation

$$N = -\frac{L\,dX}{A\,dt} \tag{2.2}$$

where L = mass of dry solid (kg)
A = surface area of solid (m^2)
N = drying rate (kg/m^2 s)

which may be rearranged to

$$dt = \frac{-L\,dX}{AN} \tag{2.3}$$

To integrate this equation, empirical relations between X and N are obtained from Fig. 1(b).

2.4.1. Constant Rate Region

$N = N_c$ = constant

$$t = \frac{L(X_1 - X_2)}{AN_c} \tag{2.4}$$

2.4.2. First Falling Rate Period

$N = a + bX$, a and b are constants; $b = \dfrac{N_2 - N_3}{X_2 - X_3}$

$$t = \frac{L}{Ab} \int_3^2 \frac{dN}{N} \tag{2.5}$$

$$= \frac{L(X_2 - X_3)}{A\Delta N_m} \qquad (2.5)$$

$\Delta N_m = \log$ mean rate between 2 and 3

$$\frac{N_2 - N_3}{\ln \dfrac{N_2}{N_3}}$$

2.4.3. Entire Falling-rate Period

In some references the entire falling-rate curve is approximated by a straight line

$$N = N_c \frac{(X - X^*)}{(X_c - X^*)}$$

$$t = \frac{L(X_c - X^*)}{A N_c} \int_2^4 \frac{dN}{N}$$

$$\frac{L(X_c - X^*)}{A N_c} \ln \frac{(X_2 - X^*)}{(X_4 - X^*)} \qquad (2.6)$$

Although experimental drying curves can be interpreted with moderate success by the above simple empirical equations, it is unfortunate that a theoretical interpretation of falling-rate drying presents great difficulty. At the microscopic level the physical and chemical structures of industrial materials are extremely complex, and even small changes in this structure markedly affect its drying characteristics.

Realisation of the widespread industrial importance of drying has recently stimulated research in this area. The First International Symposium on Drying was held in Montreal in 1978.[11] This biennial series of International Symposia constitute an important source of information on drying theory.[12,13] In addition, research papers from a wide variety of sources appear in the biennial series edited by Mujumdar.[14-16] For more general articles, reviewing broad areas of drying research and technology, the series *Advances in Drying*[17-19] should be consulted.

3. FORCED CONVECTION—HEAT AND MASS TRANSFER THEORY

3.1. Elementary Description of the Boundary Layer

The process of pure convective drying, introduced in the previous section, will now be examined in greater detail. Let the solid to be dried be a flat sheet of wet material, mounted so that the horizontal airstream flows parallel to its surface. Assume that the air velocity is sufficiently high for flow to be turbulent. Experience shows that the velocity of the fluid decreases from its freestream value V_A to a value of zero at the surface across a thin layer of fluid termed the boundary layer, Fig. 2(a). The nature of the boundary layer will only be briefly described here, for a detailed theoretical analysis the text by Schlichting[20] should be consulted. Although the outer region of the boundary layer is turbulent, the restraining effect of the stationary surface is to damp out turbulence in an extremely thin layer (laminar sub-layer) immediately next to the surface. The reduction of velocity in the boundary layer may be regarded as a loss of momentum to the stationary surface. Loss of momentum (fluid dynamic drag) is manifest as a shearing stress τ which acts on the surface. The velocity gradient may be regarded as the driving force for momentum transfer from the fluid to the surface.

Heat transfer requires that the surface temperature T_s be less than that of the drying air T_A. In a similar manner, mass transfer requires that the surface concentration ρ_s be greater than the moisture concentration in the drying air. Inspection of Fig. 2 shows that the profiles of velocity,

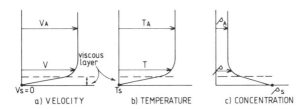

FIG. 2. Boundary layer profiles.

temperature and concentration are similar in shape. This is because momentum, energy and mass are transferred across the boundary layer by essentially the same fluid dynamic mechanisms.

3.2. The Analogy between Momentum, Heat and Mass Transfer in Laminar Flow

When the drying medium is a gas the principal resistance to the transfer of heat and mass across the boundary layer resides in the region of viscous flow near the surface, the laminar sub-layer. In this region the molecular transfer processes can all be expressed by simple linear equations which are identical in their mathematical form; they are analogous.

3.2.1. Momentum Transfer

$$\tau = -\mu\frac{dV}{dy} = -v\frac{d(\rho V)}{dy} \quad \text{(Newton's viscosity law)} \qquad (3.1)$$

3.2.2. Heat Transfer

$$q = -k\frac{dT}{dy} = -D_t\frac{d(\rho C_p T)}{dy} \quad \text{(Fourier's law of conduction)} \qquad (3.2)$$

3.2.3. Mass Transfer

$$j = -D\frac{d\rho}{dy} \quad \text{(Fick's law of diffusion)} \qquad (3.3)$$

The coefficients v, D_t and D are physical properties of the fluid, and all have dimensions (L^2/T), hence their ratios will be dimensionless.

$$\text{Prandtl number} = Pr = \frac{v}{D_t} = \frac{\text{momentum diffusivity}}{\text{thermal diffusivity}} = \frac{\mu C_p}{k}$$

$$\text{Schmidt number} = Sc = \frac{v}{D} = \frac{\text{momentum diffusivity}}{\text{mass diffusivity}} = \frac{\mu}{\rho D}$$

$$\text{Lewis number} = Le = \frac{D_t}{D} = \frac{Sc}{Pr} = \frac{\text{thermal diffusivity}}{\text{mass diffusivity}} = \frac{k}{\rho C_p D}$$

The numerical magnitudes of the above dimensionless groups express the relation of one transfer process to another. For example, in a perfect gas, when the molecular transfer processes are all identical.

$$Pr = Sc = Le = 1 \qquad (3.4)$$

The similarity of the processes of heat, mass and momentum transfer allows them to be studied on a unified basis, see Bird et al.[21] and Rohsenow and Choi.[22] The analogy, which will later be extended to include turbulent flows, is of great use to the dryer designer. Heat transfer data is usually more readily available than mass transfer data. A suitable analogy allows the heat transfer data to be transformed into the desired mass transfer form.

3.3. Heat and Mass Transfer in Turbulent Flow

The transfer coefficients in the rate equations for laminar flow (eqns. (1–3)) were properties of the fluid. The corresponding coefficients for turbulent flow differ from them in a fundamental manner in that they depend upon the fluid dynamic state of the turbulence. Since turbulent velocity fluctuations are random and statistically complex, simple theoretical prediction of the turbulent transfer coefficients is not possible. This has entailed that, in the past, heat and mass transfer coefficients have usually been evaluated empirically from test data.

Heat transfer between a fluid and a surface is expressed in terms of the convective rate equation

$$q = -\alpha(T_s - T_b) \tag{3.5}$$

where q = heat transfer rate (W/m^2)
  α = heat transfer coefficient $(W/m^2\,K)$
  T_s = surface temperature (K)
  T_b = bulk fluid temperature (K)

A simple model of the boundary layer, as a thin film of 'stagnant' fluid next to the surface is sometimes helpful. Resistance to heat and mass transfer resides in this film, and the heat transfer coefficient α, is frequently referred to as a film coefficient. Experiment shows that the magnitude of α depends on a number of variables. Dimensional analysis shows that heat transfer data can be correlated in the general dimensionless form[7]

$$Nu = c\,Re^a\,Pr^b \tag{3.6}$$

where Nusselt number, $Nu = \dfrac{\alpha l}{k}$ dimensionless heat transfer coefficient

Reynolds number, $Re = \dfrac{Vl\rho}{\mu}$ characterises the flow field

The numerical values of the constants, a, b and c are to be determined from tests on a particular geometrical shape of body and flow arrangement. It should be appreciated that the length l in the Reynolds number is used not only as a measure of size or scale, but also to characterise the shape of the flow passage.

For turbulent boundary layer flow parallel to a flat plate[7]

$$Nu = 0.023\,Re^{0.8}Pr^{1/3} \tag{3.7}$$

In a similar manner, mass transfer between a humid gas stream and a wetted surface is expressed in terms of the mass transfer rate equation[9]

$$N = -\beta(\rho_b - \rho_s) \tag{3.8}$$

N = mass transfer rate $(kg/m^2\,s)$
β = mass transfer coefficient (m/s)

ρ_b = vapour concentration in the free stream (kg/m^3)
ρ_s = vapour concentration at the surface (kg/m^3)

One of the difficulties of mass transfer theory is that the concentration of transferred substance may be expressed in a variety of units, which entails that the mass transfer coefficient itself is expressed in a variety of units (Treybal[9]). The form of eqn. (3.8) makes clear the analogy between heat and mass transfer.

However, in industrial practice, the absolute humidity Y (defined in the next section) is frequently used as the driving potential in the mass transfer rate equation

$$N = -k_Y(Y_B - Y_S) \qquad (3.9)$$

k_Y = mass transfer coefficient $(kg/m^2 \, s \, \Delta Y)$
Y = absolute humidity (kg vap/kg dry gas)

The dependency of the mass transfer coefficient upon other variables, may be expressed in dimensionless form

$$Sh = c \, Re^a \, Sc^b \qquad (3.10)$$

where

Sh = Sherwood number $\dfrac{\beta l}{D}$ dimensionless mass transfer coefficient

Sc = Schmidt number $\dfrac{\mu}{\rho D}$ characterises transfer properties

For turbulent boundary layer flow parallel to a flat plate, mass transfer may be correlated by an equation similar in form to (3.7)

$$Sh = 0.023 \, Re^{0.8} \, Sc^{1/3} \qquad (3.11)$$

3.4. The Analogy between Heat Mass and Momentum Transfer in Turbulent Flow

Transfer to or from a surface is enormously enhanced by turbulent eddies, which fluctuate in a direction normal to the direction of the mean flow. The same eddies which transport momentum to the wall and produce drag, are also extremely effective in transferring heat and mass. The analogy between the processes of heat and mass transfer is readily apparent by comparing eqns. (3.7) and (3.11), and is conveniently expressed in terms of the Stanton number, St. Dividing eqn. (3.7) by $Re Pr$

$$\frac{Nu}{RePr} = St = 0.023 \, Re^{-0.2} \, Pr^{-2/3} \tag{3.12}$$

The Stanton number may be regarded as an alternative form of the dimensionless heat transfer coefficient. Rearranging eqn. (3.12)

$$St \, Pr^{2/3} = j_H = 0.023 \, Re^{-0.2} \tag{3.13}$$

j_H = Colburn j factor for heat transfer.

Similarly for mass transfer, divide both sides of the equation by $ReSc$

$$St' \, Sc = j_D = 0.023 \, Re^{-0.2} \tag{3.14}$$

St' = Stanton number for mass transfer (β/V)
j_D = Colburn j-factor for mass transfer

Recall that the friction factor for flow in a smooth duct is given by

$$f = 0.046 \, Re^{-0.2} \tag{3.15}$$

Use of the Colburn j-factors allows the analogy between heat mass and momentum to be expressed in an extremely compact form for this case

$$j_H = j_D = \frac{f}{2} \tag{3.16}$$

This relation is applicable to boundary layer type flows where the drag arises from viscous and turbulent shear. A restricted form of the analogy remains useful even in separated flows.

$$j_H = j_D = f(Re) \tag{3.17}$$

giving

$$\frac{\alpha}{\beta} = \rho C_p Le^{2/3} \tag{3.18}$$

where

$$Le = \text{Lewis number } (Sc/Pr)$$

The analogy between the processes of heat and mass transfer highlights the fundamental connection between the two processes. These relations are particularly important for calculations in the constant-rate period of drying when both processes occur simultaneously. Because of their theoretical importance, analogies have received considerable attention, particularly from boundary layer specialists. For the background to the development of the various analogies, see Sherwood.[23]

3.5. Application to Dryer Design

Heat and mass transfer correlations appropriate to a particular dryer geometry and flow arrangement are a prerequisite of design. Although some simple geometries have been well investigated (references 8, 9) these relate only approximately to the complex flow distributions encountered in practice. Where necessary these standard correlations should be supplemented by appropriate experimental test work. The following remarks are intended for general guidance.

When flow is directed parallel to a surface, the boundary layer thickness increases as it traverses the surface; the thicker the boundary layer the greater the barrier presented to heat and mass transfer. Boundary layer build-up leads both to low transfer coefficients and to marked variations in drying in the constant-rate period. Thick boundary layers may be avoided by interrupting the flow so that the flow separates from the surface. Heat and mass transfer are enhanced by fluid dynamic turbulence. Usually this is promoted by an increase in velocity, but turbulence is induced in the wake which forms after boundary layer separation. Turbulent jets directed at an angle to a surface so that the fluids impinge on it, are used because of the high coefficients which are generated in the vicinity of the impingement region.

4. THE PROCESS OF DRYING—CONSTANT-RATE PERIOD

4.1. Wet-bulb Theory

During the period of initial adjustment (Fig. 1), the material is brought into a state of dynamic equilibrium with its external environment. Once this equilibrium state has been established then the steady rate at which heat is transferred to the surface of the material, is just sufficient to supply the energy to evaporate the moisture. At equilibrium, the surface temperature is equal to the wet bulb temperature. Equations (3.5) and (3.8) can be used to express this energy balance

$$\alpha A(T_b - T_{wb}) = \beta A(\rho_{wb} - \rho_b)\Delta h_v \tag{4.1}$$

The subscript wb refers to the wet-bulb state at the surface. Equation (4.1) can be rearranged to yield the temperature difference across the boundary-layer, the 'wet-bulb depression'

$$T_b - T_{wb} = \frac{(\rho_{wb} - \rho_b)\Delta h_v}{(\alpha/\beta)} \tag{4.2}$$

4.1.1. Surface Conditions
The vapour concentration at the surface can be calculated by noting that
the vapour exerts the saturated pressure p_{sat} corresponding to the surface
temperature T_{wb}. Saturated data for a pure substance are normally
tabulated in *Standard Tables of Thermodynamic Data* (Perry and Chilton[6]).
When the vapour pressure is sufficiently low, the saturated vapour
concentration at the surface may be calculated from the ideal gas law

$$\frac{P_{sat}}{\tilde{\rho}_{wb}} = \tilde{R}T_{wb} \tag{4.3}$$

$\tilde{R}$ = Universal gas constant (kJ/kg-mol K)
$\tilde{\rho}$ = Molar mass density (kg-mol/m³)

4.2. Psychrometry
In drying and air conditioning, the quantity of vapour in a vapour/gas
mixture is frequently expressed in terms of the humidity Y. This is the mass
of vapour m_v associated with a mass of gas m_a

$$Y = \frac{m_v}{m_a} \tag{4.4}$$

Using the perfect gas law

$$Y = \frac{p_v}{P_b - P_v} \frac{M_v}{M_a} \tag{4.5}$$

where p_b = total pressure of mixture
p_v = partial pressure of vapour
M_v = molecular mass of vapour
M_a = molecular mass of gas

For the water vapour/air system, (M_v/M_a) has a value of 0·622. The relative
humidity is defined as

$$\psi = \frac{p_v}{p_{sat}} \tag{4.6}$$

p_{sat} = saturated vapour pressure at the temperature of the mixture.
   The thermodynamic properties of gas/vapour mixtures are conveniently
set out in the form of a psychrometric, or humidity, chart (Fig. 3). The
humid (specific) heat, C_s, is the energy required to raise the temperature of
1 kg of gas and its associated vapour by 1°C at constant pressure

$$C_s = C_{pa} + YC_{pv} \tag{4.7}$$

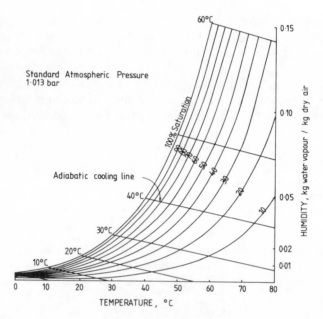

FIG. 3. Psychrometric chart.

4.2.1. Adiabatic Cooling

When a gas/vapour mixture, initially unsaturated at humidity Y, is brought into contact with cooler liquid at temperature T_{as} and isolated, the humidity of the air will increase, eventually becoming saturated. Because the process is adiabatic, energy for evaporation is provided by a cooling of the gas.

This process may be represented on the psychrometric chart as an adiabatic saturation line, which has the equation

$$C_s(T_1 - T_{as}) = (Y_1 - Y_{as})\Delta h_v \tag{4.8}$$

T_{as} = adiabatic saturation temperature.

4.2.2. The Psychrometric Ratio

Equation (4.2) for the wet-bulb depression could have been derived using a mass transfer coefficient based on humidity (eqn. (3.9))

$$T_b - T_{wb} = \frac{(Y_{wb} - Y_b)\Delta h_v}{(\alpha/k_Y)} \tag{4.9}$$

The ratio (α/β) in eqn. (4.2), or the ratio (α/k_Y) above, are sometimes referred to as the psychrometric ratio (Treybal[9]). Semi-analytical expressions for the ratio have been presented by a number of researchers, e.g. Wilke[24] and Neal.[25] For present purposes it will be assumed that the Colburn analogy (eqn. (3.18)), will be sufficiently accurate.

$$\frac{\alpha}{\beta} = \rho C_P \, Le^{2/3} \qquad (3.18)$$

Le = Lewis number

For the case of flow of a gas over a wetted cylinder similar to a wet-bulb thermometer, it has been found (Treybal[9]) that

$$\frac{\alpha}{k_Y} = C_s Le^{0.56} \qquad (4.10)$$

For the air/water system, the Lewis number is approximately unity

$$\frac{\alpha}{k_Y} = C_s \qquad (4.11)$$

which is known as the Lewis relation.

A comparison of eqns. (4.2) and (4.9) shows that for the air/water system the wet-bulb and the adiabatic saturation temperatures are approximately equal.

4.2.3. Constant-rate Drying

In the wet-bulb theory set out above, it was assumed that heat transfer by conduction and radiation were absent. Additional heat from these sources will cause the surface to rise above the wet-bulb temperature, and if sufficient will cause the moisture to boil.

It is frequently assumed that constant-rate drying is an equilibrium condition in which the body takes up the wet-bulb temperature. For a discussion of the difficulties inherent in simple theories of constant-rate drying, see van Brakel.[26]

4.2.4. Falling-rate Period

Analysis of drying in this period presents fundamental difficulties. Drying rate is controlled by moisture movement within the solid. However, in a range of materials moisture may be transferred by mechanisms, acting singly or in combination, which may differ fundamentally in their characteristics. According to van Brakel[26] theoretical models of real solids fall into three classifications:

(i)   capillary-porous media, e.g. porous solids such as beds of sand, nonhygroscopic crystals;
(ii)   hygroscopic-porous media, e.g. wood, textiles;
(iii) colloidal (non-porous) media, e.g. continuous, homogeneous materials such as soap, glue, gels and some polymers.

In a theoretical analysis the moisture transfer mechanism is expressed as a differential equation, and the dryer or environment by appropriate boundary conditions. The difficulty with such mathematical models is that the phenomenological coefficients are not simple constants. In practice the equations are highly non-linear and can usually only be solved by numerical methods on a computer. For a review of the historical development of drying theory see the articles by Keey[1] and reference 13.

4.2.5. Diffusion Theory

Liquid is transferred in a homogeneous solid by the mechanism of molecular diffusion. The mathematical model of this process expresses conservation of matter for a control volume of differential extent. In a cartesian coordinate system, conservation of component A in a binary mixture of A and B may be written as a partial differential equation

$$\frac{\partial}{\partial X}\left(D\frac{\partial C}{\partial X}\right) + \frac{\partial}{\partial Y}\left(D\frac{\partial C}{\partial Y}\right) + \frac{\partial}{\partial Z}\left(D\frac{\partial C}{\partial Z}\right) = \frac{\partial C}{\partial t} \tag{4.12}$$

where C = concentration of component A in A–B
      D = binary diffusion coefficient, A through B.

Analytical solutions of eqn. (4.12) are available only for a number of special cases (Crank[27]). For the one-dimensional case eqn. (4.12) reduces to

$$\frac{\partial}{\partial X}\left(D\frac{\partial C}{\partial X}\right) = \frac{\partial C}{\partial t} \tag{4.13}$$

Equation (4.13) is difficult to solve analytically when D is itself a function of concentration. However, when D may be assumed constant

$$D\frac{\partial^2 C}{\partial X^2} = \frac{\partial C}{\partial t} \tag{4.14}$$

This equation is sometimes referred to as Fick's second law, and the authoritative monograph by Crank[27] constitutes an invaluable compendium of its solutions. For evaporation at the surface the following boundary condition holds

$$D\left(\frac{\partial C}{\partial X}\right)_s = \alpha(C_s - C_1) \qquad (4.15)$$

subscripts s and l denoting surface and free stream respectively.

4.3. Capillary Theory

Moisture transfer in porous solids, or through beds of granular material (class i, above), may be explained on the basis of capillary theory. At the free ends of the capillary-like pores of the body, liquid is subjected to surface tension forces which cause movement of the moisture through the pores to the surface. When all capillaries are full the liquid is said to be in the funicular state. When the liquid is not present as a continuum, and capillary action is broken, the moisture distribution is termed pendular. During constant-rate drying moisture concentration profiles are set up within the body, their levels progressively falling as the average moisture content diminishes.

In the analysis by Peck et al.[28] capillary action is sufficient to maintain a uniform wetted surface up to the critical point. The first-falling rate period is characterised by the partial breakdown of capillarity, air entering the solid, and the appearance of dry spots on the surface. When the surface is completely dried, the liquid surface recedes into the solid, marking the beginning of the receding-front period of drying. The basic partial differential equation to be solved is

$$\frac{\partial W}{\partial t} = \frac{\partial}{\partial X}\left(B\frac{\partial W}{\partial X}\right) \qquad (4.16)$$

where W is a dimensionless water concentration
B is the permeability of the material.

Other versions of capillary theory are possible. For example vapour movement from liquid front to free surface might be by some form of evaporation/condensation cycle.

4.4. The Characteristic Drying Curve

Keey[5] has drawn attention to the usefulness of the concept of the characteristic drying curve. In this approach the drying-rate at the critical point N_c is used to normalise the drying rate at any other time t. The dimensionless coordinates of the characteristic drying curve are:

$$f = \frac{N}{N_c} \quad \text{and} \quad \phi = \frac{X}{X_c} \qquad (4.17)$$

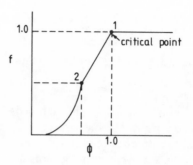

FIG. 4. Characteristic drying curve.

If for a given material f is a unique function of ϕ, independent of external conditions (Fig. 4), then modelling of falling-rate drying is simplified.
Assume that the curve of Fig. 4 can be represented by the following empirical equations

(i)   zone 1 $\phi_2 \leqslant \phi \leqslant 1\cdot 0$ $f = a + b\phi$
(ii) zone 2 $0 \leqslant \phi \leqslant \phi_2$ $f = c\phi^n$

Integration of eqn. (2.3) gives drying times

$$t = \frac{LX_c}{AN_c} \int \frac{d\phi}{\phi} \tag{4.18}$$

(i)   zone 1 $t = \dfrac{LX_c}{AN_c} \ln\left(\dfrac{a+b}{a+b\phi}\right)$ (4.19)

(ii) zone 2 $t = \dfrac{LX_c}{AN_c}\left\{\ln\left(\dfrac{a+b}{a+b\phi_2}\right)\right\} + \dfrac{1}{C}\left(\dfrac{\phi_2^{1-n} - \phi^{1-n}}{1-n}\right)$ (4.20)

The theoretical foundations of the concept of the characteristic drying curve have been analysed by Suzuki et al.[29] and by Keey.[5]

5. DRYER DESIGN AND DRYER SELECTION

5.1. Introduction

For an understanding of the continuous operation of dryers the basic principles of heat and mass transfer introduced in the previous sections must be extended, see Keey.[30]

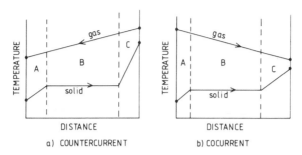

FIG. 5. Temperature profiles in a dryer.

As the drying gas passes through the dryer its temperature falls and its humidity increases; consequently the drying rate changes from point-to-point along the path. Typical temperature profiles in a dryer are shown in Fig. 5.

Figure 5 shows that in zone B the temperature of the material remains substantially constant during evaporation at approximately constant rate. During the falling-rate period, zone C, the material dries out, its temperature continuously rising to approach that of the drying gas. In practice the lines which make up the profiles in Fig. 5 are not straight, but have a variable slope due to changes in mass and specific heat during drying. The psychrometric chart can be used to estimate gas and solid temperatures in zone B.

If the heat loss from the dryer is small then the temperature of the gas (1–2, Fig. 6) will follow a line of adiabatic cooling (eqn. (4.8)). This line may be plotted on the psychrometric chart (1–2, Fig. 6) to give the humidity and

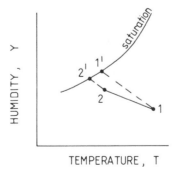

FIG. 6. Temperature humidity conditions in a dryer.

temperature of the gas. The solid will take up the corresponding wet-bulb temperature (points 1' and 2', Fig. 6) which may be estimated using eqn. (4.2). For the air/water–vapour system ($Le = 1$) the wet-bulb and the adiabatic-saturation temperature are the same, and lines 1–2 and 1–1' are coincident. With heat losses the gas cooling line will lie below 1–2, and with heat addition above it.

The high temperatures generated in combustion yield effective drying and high thermal efficiency, but in a direct-dryer there may be a risk of damage to heat sensitive materials. This damage can be mitigated by the use of cocurrent gas flow. In this arrangement the temperature of material in contact with the hottest gas is held down by its burden of moisture. Cocurrent flow also offers the possibility of using the outlet gas temperature to control the temperature of the final product, the two temperatures approaching each other.

Dryer design is based on the solution of two independent, but complementary, sets of equations as follows.

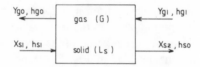

FIG. 7. Energy and material balances.

5.1.1. Energy and Material Balances (Fig. 7)
Moisture balance

$$L_s(X_{s1} - X_{s2}) = G(Y_{g0} - Y_{g1}) \tag{5.1}$$

Energy balance

$$G(h_{g1} - h_{g0}) = L_s(h_{s0} - h_{s1}) + q_L \tag{5.2}$$

where L_s = mass flow rate of dry solid (kg/m²s)
G = mass flow rate of dry gas (kg/m² s)
h_s = enthalpy solid (J/kg dry solid)
h_g = enthalpy gas (J/kg dry air)
q_L = energy loss rate (W/m²)

5.1.2. Heat and Mass Transfer Rate Equations

$$qA = \alpha A \Delta T_m \tag{5.3}$$

$$NA = \beta A \Delta \rho_m \tag{5.4}$$

$\bar{\alpha}$ = average value of heat transfer coefficient (W/m² K)
$\bar{\beta}$ = average value of mass transfer coefficient (m/s)
ΔT_m = mean temperature difference (K)
$\Delta \rho_m$ = mean concentration difference (kg/m³)

It may be convenient to solve these equations for a particular zone of the dryer. For further details and a description of the transfer unit method, see reference 31. Alternatively, the equations could be solved on a computer, at a series of discrete steps along the drying path.

5.2. Dryer Design

A rational design method, avoiding empiricism where possible, should be based on a realistic, validated model of the material being dried and the environment of the dryer. Unfortunately real materials have an extremely complex structure. It has proved extremely difficult to evolve a general model of this structure, which can be widely used for drying design, and which does not contain an unacceptably large number of adjustable coefficients. The reader should be aware of the discrepancy between the simple models used for research and the complexity of real materials. In addition in spray and pneumatic dryers conditions are so complex and drying times so short that investigations are hampered.

In general then, dryer design is not based entirely on theory. This is not to say that the steps leading to the selection of a dryer cannot be codified, see Nonhebel and Moss.[2] Indeed parts of the design procedure, e.g. humidity calculations, are based on well established theory. What must be appreciated is that most branches of drying technology rely quite heavily on past experience. Design methods must be based on laboratory tests and pilot-plant trials, using the actual material to be dried. In some instances, trials should be carried out on a dryer as near the full size as possible.

To improve the relation between theory and design, Reay[10] has proposed a rational design method, mentioned briefly in Section 1. At its simplest Reay's proposal sub-divides the total drying process into a drying kinetics model, and a particle transport model. In this way the drying characteristics of the material can be studied separately from that of its environment. When possible the concept of the characteristic drying curve is used. In this way theory provides a useful framework for codifying previous experience. The main steps in the proposed 'scientific' approach to dryer design may be paraphrased as follows:

(1) Specification of material to be dried.
    Moisture–solid equilibrium data.

(2) Drying kinetics model:
    (a) Measurement of batch drying curves, under conditions which simulate the full-scale dryer as closely as possible. Determine particle residence time.
    (b) Transformation of batch drying curves to different operating conditions. Based on characteristic drying curve if possible.
(3) Particle transport (equipment) model.
    Relate particle residence time to equipment size.
(4) Heat and mass balances.

Some difficulties remain. Drying curves obtained under test conditions which realistically simulate conditions in the real dryer are difficult to measure. Realistic particle transport models for some types of dryer (spray, pneumatic) are at present unsatisfactory. Scale-up is not an exact science (Purcell[35]).

5.3. The Choice of Dryer

When considering the subject of dryer selection the focus of attention is shifted from the designer or manufacturer, to the user. This important subject is complicated by the fact that the same product may be dried in a variety of dryer types. The range of dryer types is quite large (some important types are discussed in the following sections) and even for a user with experience dryer selection is not straightforward.

The background to the difficulties of choosing a dryer are described in two stimulating papers by van Brakel.[26,32] Among other points, van Brakel claims that textbooks on drying contain only limited guidance on dryer selection, and that a dryer manufacturer sells only one or a few related types.

There are other important points to be considered. For example, local legislation regarding atmospheric pollution has become more stringent. Consequently the cost of plant for solvent recovery, or incineration, may form a significant proportion of the total capital cost. Of course, when relevant costs are available, the choice should be based on a realistic economic assessment. Capital and running costs require continual re-appraisal, as costs rise and interest rates change. It will be apparent that dryer selection will require close liaison between the user who knows the material to be dried, and the manufacturer who must design the plant to meet this requirement.

6. DRYER TYPES

6.1. Tray Dryers

This type of dryer represents a relatively straightforward application of the principles of forced convection described in Section 2. Trays containing the moist material are stacked and loaded as a batch into a drying oven, which usually consists of an insulated box-like compartment (Fig. 8). Alternatively solid objects, such as pottery, are placed on shelves within the oven. When the drying cycle is complete, operation is stopped and the batch is discharged.

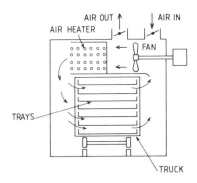

FIG. 8. Tray dryer.

Air delivered by a fan is first heated by passing it over the coils of a heater bank, and then flows between the trays across the surface of the material to be dried. The fan, which may be of the propeller type, produces large volume flows of air at modest velocities (0–10 m/s). When the coils are heated by steam, hot water or electricity, air outlet temperatures of the order of 100–200°C are produced. At each pass across the trays, some moisture is removed, but the drying rate falls as the humidity of the drying air increases. To keep up the drying rate, some fraction of the air should be vented to the atmosphere and replaced with fresh. Energy conservation may indicate that the hot vented air be dehumidified and recycled as make-up.

Many possible variations on this basic arrangement are possible. The rate of heat transfer to material can be increased by using metal trays which allow heat to be conducted from the lower surface. Provided that the solid is suitably permeable, trays with perforations can be used so that air flows through the bed. This tends to increase the drying rate, because of the increase in heat transfer coefficient (reduction in boundary-layer build-up) and in surface area, and because of the reduced distance the moisture must travel through the bed.

More complex dryers, with multiple stacks of trays, allow combinations of series and parallel air-flow paths. Careful design of the air distribution system is required if the final product is to be evenly dried. The objective is to make the air velocity across all trays as uniform as possible, and in particular to avoid dead-spots. In practice, material loaded unevenly into trays causes blockages. Increasing the speed and temperature of the air will increase the drying rate, but will of course also increase both fan power and energy costs.

Standard heat and mass transfer correlations can be used to predict tray dryer performance in the constant-rate period (Nonhebel and Moss[2]). For air flow parallel to the surface of the bed they suggest the use of the following relation for the heat transfer coefficient (Perry[6])

$$\alpha = 0.057\, G^{0.8} \qquad (6.1)$$

G = mass velocity of gas (g/s m^2)

In the falling-rate period it appears that the prediction of dryer performance entirely from theory is unreliable and is not recommended.[2] Drying data should be obtained either from experiment or from tests on a full-scale dryer.

Although tray dryers are used extensively in some industries (e.g. for ceramics) they have a number of disadvantages. The labour costs associated with loading and unloading batch pallettes is high, which tends to limit their application to low throughputs. The heat transfer coefficients are relatively low; when the layer of material in the tray is thick, the residence time will be long.

The turbo-tray dryer approaches more closely to the principle of continuous drying. Layers of circular trays continuously rotate about the vertical axis of a cylindrical drying enclosure, whose central section contains heaters and fans. Material on a rotating tray encounters a dam and cascades to the next lower tray. Wet feed is introduced at the top and emerges continuously at the bottom. For a more detailed description of the turbo-tray dryer, and of tray dryers generally, see Williams-Gardner.[3]

6.2. Continuous Dryers

Batch drying suffers from the disadvantage that the oven must be repeatedly heated up and cooled down. This can be avoided if batches are placed on trucks which are mechanically transported through a drying tunnel. The process is semi-continuous, each batch in turn passing through a drying cycle. For more truly continuous drying, the wet material must be suitable for feeding on to a moving belt or band which conveys it through the drying tunnel. The air flow may be arranged in a variety of ways including cocurrent, countercurrent and combinations of these; cross-flow arrangements are also quite common. In cross flow the tunnel may be divided along its length into zones, the air flow through each of which may be individually adjusted either by fan or damper. In this way the drying profile of the material may be controlled in its passage through the dryer. Heat for drying may be provided either directly from a burner or indirectly from a heat exchanger.

Continuous tunnel dryers tend to be used when the quantity of material to be dried is greater than can be economically dealt with by the intermittent operation of a batch-oven. However, because of the relatively low air speeds, and the depth of material on the conveyor, drying rates are low. The consequent long residence time entails that tunnels are long. Adequate insulation must be provided to reduce heat loss. Thus, in some instances, tunnel dryers are large items of equipment occupying a large floor area. Care is required when circulating large quantities of gas that fan noise does not become a problem.

Drying rates can be increased if the conveyor is constructed of an open mesh, and the hot gas is blown through the bed. This greatly increases the area for contact between air and wet material, and also reduces the distance moisture must travel within the bed. Through-drying requires that the wet material be divided and particulate in form, so that it is permeable to air flow. However, it must not be so unduly fine that it cannot be supported by the mesh. Impinging jets are sometimes used to increase the heat transfer coefficients.

Heat transfer correlations can be used to predict drying rates in the constant-rate period. Correlations for through circulation are given by Perry.[6] Laboratory tests on the material to be dried can be used to construct a characteristic drying curve, which can be used for scale-up. In this case, the particle transport model is relatively straightforward.

6.3. Rotary Dryers
This type of dryer consists in essence of a cylindrical shell rotating about its axis which is usually inclined at a small angle to the horizontal (Fig. 9).

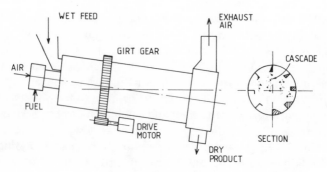

FIG. 9. Rotary dryer.

Heated gas flowing through the cylinder acts as the drying medium.

Wet feed stock enters the dryer at its raised end. The action of the 'flights' on the inside surface of the cylinder is intermittently to pick-up and drop the solid material as it is conveyed under the action of gravity to the outlet end of the cylinder. The flow of hot gas through the cascade of falling material promotes effective heat transfer. In a direct-heat dryer, fuel is burnt, and the products of combustion are used as the drying gas. The gas flow may be either cocurrent or counter current, largely dependent upon the heat sensitivity of the material to be dried.

Rotary dryers are widely used in industry and are well suited to handling a variety of granular free-flowing solids (Nonhebel and Moss[2]). Feed rates of up to several hundred metric tons/h may be processed (Baker[34]). They are versatile, in that drying remains effective even when the feed stock is subjected to the quite large changes in moisture content and particle size which can occur in practice. However, when this is practical, excessive moisture in the feed stock should be removed prior to drying. The problem of excessive dust at the delivery point, arising from drying finely divided particles, may be solved by fitting cyclone dust collectors.

During operation, there is some holdup of solid material within the dryer. Solids reside for a time either in the flights or on the lower half of the cylinder. The relation between the average residence time τ of a particle in the dryer and the holdup H, is given by the relation

$$\tau = \frac{H}{F} \tag{6.2}$$

where F is the solids feed rate.

When a dryer is overloaded, more material is fed in than can be picked up by the flights. Some material passes along the lower half of the dryer without effective contact with the heated air stream, and is not satisfactorily dried.

Friedman and Marshall[33] recognised that a rotary dryer performed two distinct functions, it operated both as a conveyor and as a heat transfer device. These aspects were treated separately in their research on an experimental dryer. The effect of different materials, feed rate, air rate, speed of rotation, etc., on the performance of the dryer as a conveyor was investigated. Satisfactory operation was obtained when holdup was in the range 3–7%. Because the total surface area of the solid material is difficult to determine, Friedman and Marshall used a heat transfer coefficient (Ur) related to the volume of the dryer. This volumetric coefficient is defined by the equation

$$Q = (Ur)V'\Delta T_m \tag{6.3}$$

where Q = heat transfer rate (W)
   U = heat transfer coefficient (W/m^2 K)
   r = ratio (surface area solid/dryer volume)
   V' = dryer volume (m^3)
   ΔT_m = mean temperature difference (°C)

Different investigators have presented correlations for the volumetric heat transfer coefficient, usually in terms of G, the mass flow rate of gas per unit area of dryer cross-section.

The current state of knowledge of cascading rotary dryers is reviewed by Baker.[34] Once again the two aspects of dryer performance, conveying and heat transfer, are discussed separately. The factors affecting hold-up are examined. Particle transport models, together with corresponding predictions of residence time, are compared. Data from heat transfer investigations have been presented either in terms of the overall volumetric heat transfer coefficient (Ur) or in terms of the more commonly used heat transfer coefficient α. This latter method has the advantage of allowing a separate heat transfer investigation based on standard methods.

Baker concludes his review with the observation that in spite of a great deal of research, a satisfactory understanding of many aspects of rotary-dryer peformance had not been achieved. Methods for calculating particle residence time, and heat transfer rates remained unsatisfactory. The paper by Purcell[35] gives valuable insight into the design of rotary dryers.

6.4. Drying in the Packaging and Coating Industries

In the printing, packaging and allied industries, large high speed rotary presses are used to deposit a thin coating of 'ink' onto a moving web or substrate. The basic components of an ink are a finely ground pigment and a polymer resin, mixed in a blend of solvents to a viscosity suitable for printing. The solvents are normally organic in nature, but recently water has been increasingly used. Printing inks may dry by a variety of physical and chemical processes, such as penetration into the substrate, oxidation, thermal setting, etc. However, inks which dry by evaporation are widely used and this is the only type of drying to be considered here. In the packaging industry the ink may be coated into thin films of plastic which are largely impervious to solvent penetration.

In tracing the evolution of the modern rotary press, Harrison[36] describes the period from the year 1945 as one of progressive and rapid increase in both printing speed and web width. The three articles by Graf[37] constitute a useful review of drying problems in rotogravure printing. The drying process may be accelerated by passing the moving web through a drying hood which contains nozzles so arranged that air jets impinge normally on the moving web (Fig. 10). The nozzles which emit the jets may be of any

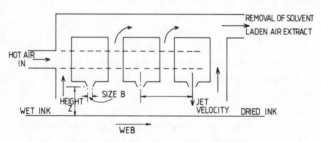

FIG. 10. Dryer for colour printing.

shape, but most commonly are either long (one-dimensional) slots, or circular (axi-symmetric) holes. In practice a bank of nozzles may be supplied with high pressure air from a common plenum chamber. After interaction with the ink, the air together with its burden of solvent vapour must be removed from the vicinity of the web by a suitable extraction system. In practice plenum chamber, nozzles and extraction ducts are often combined into a unit dryer box.

The difficulties of measuring accurate drying curves from thin (2–15 μm) paint films, under realistic drying conditions, illustrate the general problem of obtaining accurate drying data. Hardisty[38] used a beam of infra-red (IR) radiation of precise frequency to measure the quantity of solvent ('wetness') in the ink layer. Solvent in the ink absorbs the IR radiation and reduces the intensity of radiation returning to a detector in the optical sensing head. The signal from the detector was electronically processed to give an instrument output proportional to the amount of solvent in the IR beam. This technique was successfully used to record drying curves from thin films of a research ink printed by a small gravure press.

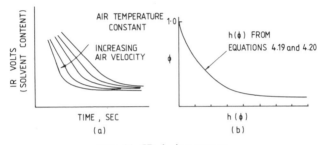

FIG. 11. IR drying curves.

Figure 11(a), adapted from Hardisty,[38] shows a series of IR drying curves from stationary ink films drying in the wall jet adjacent to a slot nozzle. The IR drying curves show that the early period of drying occurs at approximately constant rate. In the later falling-rate period, it appears that drying is limited by the rate at which solvent can diffuse through the non-volatile ink residue to the free surface.

A comprehensive series of tests was carried out to demonstrate the effect of varying air temperature and air velocity on drying time in the constant-rate period. Figure 11(a) shows that at constant temperature, increasing the velocity of the drying air produced a corresponding decrease in drying time. At constant velocity, increasing the air temperature decreased the drying time in a generally similar manner. Drying calculations require the availability of data on solvent vapour pressure, and on heat transfer coefficients. Heat transfer under impinging jets has been investigated experimentally by Gardon and Akfirat.[39] The effect of nozzle shape has been investigated by Hardisty and Can.[40] Predictions of constant-rate drying times, based on wet-bulb theory, gave good agreement with results from IR drying curves (Hardisty[38]).

The falling-rate region of the experimental IR curves has also been investigated (Hardisty[41]). Results were consistent with the hypothesis that drying rate is controlled by the rate of solvent diffusion through the ink layer. The solvent-in-polymer diffusion coefficient appears to be concentration dependent. The concept of the characteristic drying curve was successfully used to correlate the effects of changes in the drying rate brought about by changes in air velocity, air temperature and ink thickness, Fig. 11(b). Characteristic drying curves were found to have the characteristic shape illustrated in Fig. 4; they could be represented by the simple two-zone empirical model expressed by eqns. (4.19) and (4.20).

These research results are encouraging in that they demonstrate that the process of rapid drying of thin films is amenable to experimental investigation and theoretical modelling. However, further work is required to extend the research on a single solvent ink, to the solvent blends used in industry. To complement this, instruments should be developed capable of measuring ink solvent content (dryness) on operational presses.

This particular application can be used to illustrate some of the more general difficulties encountered by the designer. To design an airjet system, the designer must specify the number of nozzles, together with their size, shape, pitch and distance from the web (Fig. 10). Air temperature, air velocity (Reynolds number) and the amount of gas recirculation must also be specified. All these parameters affect the space average value of the heat transfer coefficient. The heat transfer distribution is particularly uneven under impinging jets, having a pronounced peak directly under the nozzle opening and falling off steeply on either side. On a modern multi-colour printing press each colour must be palpably dry before the succeeding colour can be printed on top of it. Inter-colour drying presents the designer with a particularly difficult problem because of space limitations between colour units. In addition the specification of a low value of 'retained solvents' in the final product will entail that final drying before reeling requires critical attention. The designer's task is to solve a multi-variable problem. It is imperative that the speed of a large modern printing press is not limited by the capacity of the dryer to evaporate the solvents from the inks.

6.5. Spray Dryers

Spray dryers belong to the class of suspended-particle processing systems in which the particles are dried while suspended in air. In this type of dryer, feed stock in some pumpable form is sprayed into heated air in a drying chamber. The small droplets produced by the spray have an enormous surface area, and the effect is to produce extremely rapid, 'instantaneous', drying. Dried particles, the solid residue which remains after droplet evaporation, are continuously produced; the final product being in the form of granules, fine powder, etc. Spray drying is particularly suitable for food products, such as dried milk, instant coffee, etc., but is also widely used in a range of industries including pharmaceutical, detergent, bulk chemicals, etc. (Masters[42]).

Spray drying has a number of advantages. The quality and properties of the final product can be controlled, which is of particular importance in the food industry. Because the temperature of the droplet is held down close to the wet bulb temperature during evaporation, heat sensitive products can be satisfactorily dried. The process is suitable for large throughputs, and this taken together with continuous operation and automatic control, leads to relatively low costs. The dried product is produced without contact with drier surfaces, thus eliminating contamination problems. Spray drying also suffers from some disadvantages. The final product may not be in the desired form; also because the feedstock must be in liquid form, the energy required for evaporation is large.

The monograph by Marshall[43] is a valuable source of reference. According to Marshall the virtually instantaneous operation of spray drying can be split up into the following three distinct stages:

(i)   atomisation of the liquid into a spray;
(ii) mixing of droplets in the spray with hot gases;
(iii) evaporation of moisture from the drops.

Of course these must be followed by a fourth stage in which the dry product is separated and collected.

6.5.1. Atomisation[43]

Atomisers break up the fluid stream into a finely divided spray. This process requires energy, which is usually supplied by one of the following methods:

(a) Pressure nozzle.
    The forces acting on a jet of liquid emerging at high speed from a small diameter nozzle lead to instability and jet break-up.
(b) Spinning disc (rotor).
    Liquid breaks up when thrown at high speed from the periphery of a rotating disc.
(c) Two fluid (pneumatic) nozzle.
    Liquid break-up is brought about by the action of a high velocity gas stream. This type of atomiser is restricted to special applications, and is less widely used than types (a) and (b).

The subject of spray drying is comprehensively covered in the handbook by

Masters.[42] The particle size distribution in the final product depends on the type of atomiser selected and its specification. The ideal is an atomiser which produces droplets of identical size. This avoids overdrying and dust problems with undersized particles, and impingement on chamber walls with oversized particles. In practice particles and drops are produced with sizes distributed over a range. When selecting an atomiser a number of factors must be considered, such as feed capacity range, particle-size distribution, chamber design, etc.[42] The most frequently used mechanical and pneumatic atomising devices are reviewed by Filkova and Cedik.[44]

6.5.2. Drying Chamber

The type of spray atomiser which is selected has a considerable influence on the dimensions of the drying chamber (Lang[45]). Spinning disc atomisers produce droplets whose trajectory lie in the horizontal plane of the wheel, and consequently require a chamber of relatively large diameter and small height. On the other hand pressure atomisers produce conical sprays, and require relatively tall, small diameter chambers.

The airflow/spray contact in the drying chamber is discussed by Masters.[46] Flow may be cocurrent, counter current or mixed flow (Fig. 12). The cocurrent arrangement which is the most common is suitable for heat sensitive materials.

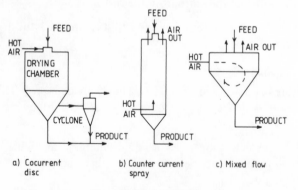

FIG. 12. Spray dryers.

In an open-cycle system, air drawn from the atmosphere and heated by direct combustion flows through the drying chamber, then through a collector where fine particles are removed, and is finally discharged to the atmosphere. A closed-cycle arrangement is used when the product to be dried contains solvents which cannot be discharged to the atmosphere, and/or an explosion risk exists. In this case an inert gas, heated in a secondary heat exchanger, forms the drying medium. The undesirable vapours are removed and the gas cooled, before it is recirculated to complete the cycle.

The need for improved product quality and greater dryer thermal efficiency, has led to the development of two-stage systems.[42] In such systems the product passes to a fluid bed which allows further drying to low moisture contents; after-treatment of the final product may also be carried out.

6.5.3. Droplet Evaporation
The first stage of droplet evaporation takes place at constant rate, the droplet remaining essentially at the wet-bulb temperature. When first ejected from the atomiser the droplet has a high velocity relative to the air. However, fluid friction (drag) acting on the surface of the drop causes a rapid deceleration. Eventually, when the initial kinetic energy has been dissipated the drop falls freely under gravity, and Stokes's Law applies.

For steady evaporation of drops of pure liquid in moving air, the heat and mass transfer coefficients have been correlated by Ranz and Marshall.[47] For such a model rate equations can be integrated to express the time to evaporate a fraction of the mass of the drop.[42] Unfortunately, in the real drying chamber air flow distribution is extremely complex and in general cannot be represented by a simple analytical model. Flow conditions are complex, and droplets break up. Atomiser selection and chamber design are based on experience and pilot-plant tests. Design procedures are reviewed by Masters[42] and the views of Lang[45] are valuable. For comments regarding food processing see Judson King et al.[48]

6.6. Flash or Pneumatic Dryers
Components of a typical flash dryer are an air heater, and a fan to produce flow of heated air upwards through a long vertical drying duct (Fig. 13). The material to be dried, in suitable particulate form, is introduced into the airstream by the feeder, the hot air conveying the particles through the duct on cocurrent flow. The particles emerge from the duct in various stages of dryness, depending upon their size distribution at inlet. In the final stage a classifier separates dried product from air, in some cases recycling a proportion of the material for further processing.

In dryers of this type residence (drying) times are short, of the order of a few seconds, which is the origin of the name 'flash'. Small particles will dry more rapidly because of their relatively large surface area for heat transfer,

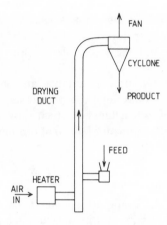

FIG. 13. Flash dryer.

and the shorter path for moisture transfer in the falling-rate region. Air velocities usually lie within the range 20–25 m/s, duct lengths in the range 5–40 m. Although in principle, the drying duct is a relatively simple item of equipment, the feed system may present handling problems depending on the properties of the wet solid, and its state when delivered to the feeder (Lang[49]). Wet feed material may be too sticky for adequate dispersion and rapid drying; this wetness can be reduced by mixing with the feed dry product recycled from the dryer outlet. Recycling can also be used to increase the residence time of large particles which tend to be underdried. Pneumatic dryers may have more than one stage; a range of dryers is described in reference 2.

6.6.1. Dryer Design

Psychrometric calculations, heat and mass balances can be used to estimate the air-flow rate, but this must be sufficient to convey the air. For a given air velocity the duct length determines the residence. In the constant-rate region, the particle will be approximately at the wet-bulb temperature. For a known and constant particle size, the particle velocity and drying-rate can be estimated, see Williams-Gardner.[3] The difficulty is that in many practical applications the particle size is not known precisely, and in addition particles fracture as they move up the tube. It appears that particle behaviour in the duct is not fully understood, and at present dryers cannot be designed entirely from theory. 'Nearly all flash dryer designs are based on pilot plant testing.... The testing should, where possible, be performed on equipment of similar geometry to that intended for the full scale plant' (Lang[49]).

6.7. Fluid Bed Dryer

The layout of a typical open-cycle, continuous operation fluid bed dryer is shown diagrammatically in Fig. 14. A fan discharges air through a heater and into a plenum chamber below a perforated grid or plate, upon which rests a bed of particulate solid material. The grid distributes the air evenly

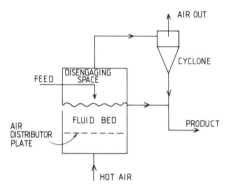

FIG. 14. Fluid bed dryer.

over the lower surface of the bed. In passing through the bed the air pressure falls to overcome viscous friction. Increasing the air velocity through the bed causes the pressure drop across the bed to increase, until, at some velocity v_0, the pressure drop is sufficient to lift the weight of the particles in the bed.

$$\Delta p = \frac{mg}{A} = H \rho g$$

where H = height of bed (m)
A = area of bed (m^2)
ρ = density (kg/m^3)

The bed begins to lose its properties of solidity, particles move and mix, and the bed behaves as a fluid. The velocity v_0 is termed the velocity for incipient fluidisation. As the air velocity is further increased, air bubbles are formed, movement in the bed becomes extremely agitated, and mixing is intense. The volume of the bed expands, and its behaviour resembles that of a boiling liquid. Lighter particles are ejected from the surface into the space above the bed, some falling back and others being carried off with the airstream. At very high air velocities all particles are entrained, in a manner similar to a pneumatic conveyor.

Because of the intimate mixing between particles and air, and the huge surface area for contact, heat and mass are transferred extremely effectively in a fluid bed. Drying in the constant-rate period is rapid. A consequence of particle mixing is that the bed temperature is relatively uniform. Air flow through the bed is essentially cocurrent, and because of the high heat transfer rates the air temperature leaving the bed approaches the temperature of the bed itself.

The height of the bed is determined by the vertical position of an overflow weir or discharge opening. Wet material fed into the bed at a steady rate by the feeder should be well dispersed through the bed; dried product flows from the discharge. The relatively low velocity in the large space above the bed allows all but the lightest particles to separate from the airstream; this disengagement space acts as a classifier. The air passes finally through a cyclone dust separator before discharge to the atmosphere.

The fluid bed dryer is suitable for a wide range of particulate solid material, in the size range $10\,\mu m$ to a few cm (Perry[6]). There are no mechanical moving parts, and the floor space required is relatively small. Continuous operation with automatic control allows large-scale operation, with bulk handling of feed and product. The uniform bed temperature can be controlled so as to protect heat sensitive materials. To be suitable for effective drying in a fluid bed, particles should be of regular shape and fairly uniform in size. Undersized particles will be ejected from the bed, while oversize particles (unless they break up during mixing) are not properly fluidised. Particles in the bed must not be sticky, or agglomeration will occur, with consequent loss of fluidity.

The grid which supports the bed may be manufactured from ceramic for high temperature operation. Variations of detail design are possible, but the plate must prevent backflow of solids during shut-down, and ensure even air-flow distribution during normal operation. To achieve this even distribution the pressure drop over the distributor plate itself should be a significant percentage of the drop over the bed (Perry[6]). Pilot-plant tests are required to establish the suitability of the wet material for fluidisation, the air velocity, the bed temperature to avoid damage of material, etc. The particle residence time is a function of bed height, but variations will occur because of backmixing.

Arrangements other than the continuous operation open-cycle plant described above are possible. If batch operation is used it should be noted that after the critical point has been reached the temperature of the material will rise and approach the temperature of the drying gas. Air temperature control may be required. In a multi-stage continuous dryer, fluidised material flows in series between stages, in a manner approximating counter flow. Where toxic vapours cannot be discharged to the atmosphere, or an explosion risk is present, a closed-cycle using an inert gas with indirect heating may be used.

Recent developments in fluid-bed design have been reviewed by Gupta and Mujumdar.[50] The total mixed bed described above may not be suitable for prolonged drying in the falling-rate period. Plug-flow operation can be achieved if the material is introduced centrally, and then constrained by a baffle to follow a long spiral path, before being discharged at the periphery of the bed. It has been found that particles which are sticky, or have a wide size distribution, are difficult to fluidise in a stationary fluid bed. Such problems can be overcome if the bed is vibrated to assist fluidisation. In this way lower air velocities can be used, and the entrainment of fine particles reduced. The vibration of a relatively long bed can be used to convey the material lengthwise through the dryer. Another way of achieving greater flexibility in design is to transfer some of the heat required for drying by means of coils or tubes immersed in the bed. Heat transfer from immersed surfaces in a vibro-fluidised bed is discussed by Ringer and Mujumdar.[51]

7. OTHER DRYER TYPES

There are more types of dryer, and many more variants of these types, than could be covered in the restricted space of this review. However, enquiries into the broader fields of drying can be pursued through the references provided. To provide a focus for this review, attention was principally directed to convective drying. Explicit reference has not been made to dryers whose mode of operation is largely dependent either on conduction (e.g. drum dryers) or on radiation. Some brief comments on these two branches of drying will serve to bring this review to a close.

The paper and board making industry is large, and was historically one of the earliest branches of drying technology to develop. After mechanical removal of water, the wet web is dried as it passes over a series of large steam heated cylinders. Heat is conducted through the cylinder and into the web. Paper making machines are large, costly and technologically complex.

Over its long history, and because of its economic importance, paper making has been extensively investigated. However, the process of paper drying has proved difficult to analyse; the various attempts to formulate a theoretical model have been reviewed by Kirk.[52] Such an important and specialised branch of the drying industry merits study in its own right.

Radiant heat has been used for drying in stoves and furnaces, and also for paint films. Thermal radiation of this type is emitted by a high temperature source and has a wavelength which lies principally in the infra-red region of the electromagnetic spectrum. It can be provided by incandescent bulbs, or more recently by quartz tubes. IR must be used with care, it is absorbed largely in the surface of the material, and preferentially by darker areas of high absorptivity. On the other hand, radiation of radio waves and microwaves can be used to heat a body composed of suitable molecules, uniformly throughout its extent. Energy is generated when polar molecules are subjected to a rapidly alternating electric field (dielectric drying). Not all molecules have a suitable structure for this type of heating to be effective. However mains water heats much more readily than many common fibres. This property can be used to good effect in dielectric drying, the wet areas being selectively heated. It will be apparent that design and selection of dielectric dryers requires specialist knowledge. For a unified treatment of electromagnetic heating see Metaxas.[53]

REFERENCES

1. KEEY, R. B. Theoretical foundations of drying technology, Ch. 1, *Advances in Drying–Vol. 1*, ed., A. S. Mujumdar, 1980, Hemisphere, McGraw-Hill, New York.
2. NONHEBEL, G. and MOSS, A. A. H. *Drying of Solids in the Chemical Industry*, 1971, Butterworths, London.
3. WILLIAMS-GARDNER, A. *Industrial Drying*, 1976, George Godwin, London.
4. KRISCHER, O. *Die Wissenschaftlichen Grundlagen der Trocknungtechnik*, 1962, Springer, Berlin.
5. KEEY, R. B. *Introduction to Industrial Drying Operations*, 1978, Pergamon Press, Oxford.
6. PERRY, R. H. and CHILTON, C. H. (eds.) *Chemical Engineers Handbook*, 5th edn., Section 20, 1973, McGraw-Hill, New York.
7. KIRK, L. A. and OTHMER, D. E. (eds.) *Encyclopedia of Chemical Technology*, Vol. 8, 3rd edn., 1979, Interscience, New York.
8. CHAPMAN, A. J. *Heat Transfer*, 4th edn., Collier Macmillan, New York.
9. TREYBAL, R. E. *Mass Transfer Operations*, 2nd edn., 1968, MacGraw-Hill, New York.

10. REAY, D. Theory in the design of dryers, *Chem. Engng*, July 1979, No. 343, 501.
11. MUJUMDAR, A. S. (ed.) *Proceedings of First International Symposium on Drying*, 1978, Science Press, Princeton, N. J.
12. MUJUMDAR, A. S. (ed.) *Proceedings of Second International Symposium on Drying*, See Vol. 2 *Drying '80*, 1980, Hemisphere, McGraw-Hill, New York.
13. *Proceedings of Third International Drying Symposium*, 2 Vols. J. C. Ashworth (ed.), 1982, Drying Research Ltd, Wolverhampton, UK.
14. MUJUMDAR, A. S. (ed.) *Drying '80*, 2 Vols., 1980, Hemisphere, McGraw-Hill, New York.
15. MUJUMDAR, A. S. (ed.) *Drying '82*, 1982, Hemisphere, McGraw-Hill, New York.
16. MUJUMDAR, A. S. (ed.) *Drying '84*, 1984, Hemisphere, McGraw-Hill, New York.
17. MUJUMDAR, A. S. (ed.) *Advances in Drying–Vol. 1*, 1980, Hemisphere, McGraw-Hill, New York.
18. MUJUMDAR, A. S. (ed.) *Advances in Drying–Vol. 2*, 1983, Hemisphere, McGraw-Hill, New York.
19. MUJUMDAR, A. S. (ed.) *Advances in Drying–Vol. 3*, 1984, Hemisphere, McGraw-Hill, New York.
20. SCHLICHTING, H. *Boundary Layer Theory*, 1960, McGraw-Hill, New York.
21. BIRD, R. B., STEWART, W. E. and LIGHTFOOT, E. N. *Transport Phenomena*, 1960, John Wiley, New York.
22. ROHSENOW, W. and CHOI, H. *Heat, Mass and Momentum Transfer*, 1961, Prentice Hall, New Jersey.
23. SHERWOOD, T. K. *Mass, Heat and Momentum Transfer between Phases*, 1959, C.E.P. Symposium Series, No. 25, 55, American Inst. Chem. Engrs.
24. WILKE, C. R. A new correlation for the psychrometric ratio, *AIChE–IChemE*, Symposium Series No. 6, 1965.
25. NEAL, S. B. H. C. The development of the thin-film naphthalene mass-transfer analogue technique for the direct measurement of heat-transfer coefficients, *Int. J. Heat Mass Transfer*, 1975, **18**, 559.
26. VAN BRAKEL, J. Mass transfer in convective drying, *Drying '84*, ed., A. S. Mujumdar, 1984, Hemisphere, McGraw-Hill, New York, 217.
27. CRANK, J. *The Mathematics of Diffusion*, 1st edn., 1956, Oxford University Press, Oxford.
28. PECK, R. E., VYAS K. C. and TOEI R. Capillary theory applied to drying, AIChE Symposium Series No. 163, 63, Vol. 73, 1977.
29. SUZUKI, M., KEEY, R. B. and MAEDA, S. On the characteristic drying curve, AIChE Symposium series, No. 163, Vol. 73, 1977.
30. KEEY, R. B. Process design of continuous drying equipment, AIChE Symposium series, No. 163, Vol. 73, 1977.
31. SLOAN, C. E., WEELOCK, T. D. and TSAO, G. T. Drying, *Chem. Engng*, June 19, 1967, 167–214.
32. VAN BRAKEL, J. The choice and design of dryers, *Chem. Engng*, July 1979, 493.
33. FRIEDMAN, S. J. and MARSHALL, W. R. Studies in rotary drying, *Chem. Eng. Progress*, 1949, No. 8, 482, No. 9 573, Vol. 45.
34. BAKER, C. G. J. Cascading rotary dryers, Ch. 1 *Advances in Drying–Vol. 2*, 1983, Hemisphere, McGraw-Hill, New York.

35 PURCELL, J. G. Practical rotary cascading dryer design, *Chem. Engng*, July 1979, No. 343, 496.
36. HARRISON, R. T. H. Advances in printing technology, *Proc.I.Mech.E.*, 1978, **192**, 16.
37. GRAF, E. Drying problems in rotogravure, *Gravure*, Nov., Dec., 1969, Jan 1970.
38. HARDISTY, H. The analysis of the drying process in thin films of ink, *Proceedings of First International Symposium on Drying*, edn., A. S. Mujumdar, 1978, Science Press, Princeton, N.J., 208.
39. GARDON, R. and AKFIRAT, J. C. Heat transfer characteristics of impinging two-dimensional air jets, *Trans. ASME J. Heat Transfer*, Feb. 1966, 101.
40. HARDISTY, H. and CAN, M. An experimental investigation into the effect of changes in the geometry of a slot nozzle, *Proc.Inst.Mech.Engrs*, March 1983, **197C**.
41. HARDISTY, H. An investigation into the falling-rate period of ink drying using IR dryness measurement, *J. Separ. Proc. Technol.*, 1981, 2(3), 24–36.
42. MASTERS, K. *Spray Drying Handbook*, 3rd edn, 1979, George Godwin, London.
43. MARSHALL, W. R. Atomisation and Spray Drying, *Chem.Eng.Prog.*, Monograph Series, 1954, No. 2, 50, American Inst. Chem. Engrs.
44. FILKOVA, I. and CEDIK, P. Nozzle atomisation in spray drying, Ch. 5, *Advances in Drying–Vol. 3*, ed., A. S. Mujumdar, 1984, Hemisphere, McGraw-Hill, New York.
45. LANG, R. W. Spray drying, a personal view, *J.Separ.Proc.Technol.*, 1980, 1(2), 19–22.
46. MASTERS, K. Spray drying, Ch. 8, *Advances in Drying–Vol. 2*, ed., A. S. Mujumdar, 1983, Hemisphere, McGraw-Hill, New York.
47. RANZ, W. E. and MARSHALL, W. R. *Chem.Eng.Prog.*, 1952, **48**, 141, 173.
48. JUDSON KING, C., KIECKBUSH, T. G. and GREENWALD, T. G. Food quality factors in spray drying, Ch. 3, *Advances in Drying–Vol. 3*, ed., A. S. Mujumdar, 1984, Hemisphere, McGraw-Hill, New York.
49. LANG, R. W. *Spray Drying. Short Course on Drying*, 1978, McGill University, Montreal, Canada.
50. GUPTA, R. and MUJUMDAR, A. S. Recent developments in fluidized-bed drying, Ch. 5, *Advances in Drying–Vol. 2*, ed., A. S. Mujumdar, 1983, Hemisphere, McGraw-Hill, New York.
51. RINGER, D. and MUJUMDAR, A. S. Flow and immersed surface heat transfer in vibro-fluidized bed, *Drying '82*, 1982, Hemisphere, McGraw-Hill, New York.
52. KIRK, L. A. A literature review of computer simulation of paper drying, Ch. 1, *Advances in Drying–Vol. 3*, ed., A. S. Mujumdar, 1984, Hemisphere, McGraw-Hill, New York.
53. METAXAS, A. C. A unified approach to the teaching of electromagnetic heating of industrial materials, *Int.J.Elec.Educ.*, 1985, **22**, 101.

Chapter 6

HEAT TRANSFER IN AGITATED VESSELS

G. Breber

Heat Transfer Research, Inc., Alhambra, California, USA

SUMMARY

The most commonly used agitated vessel heat transfer surfaces and impellers are covered and preliminary selection criteria are given in this chapter. Equations for the determination of the time for heating or cooling of a batch of liquid for the most typical agitated vessel systems are given in some detail. The main intent of this chapter is to provide heat transfer correlations to enable the design engineer to predict the amount of heat to be transferred with reasonable accuracy. The recommended heat transfer correlations are tabulated separately for jacketed vessels, helical coils, and baffle-type coils. The chapter finishes with a brief discussion on the jacket side and helical coil side coefficient predictions for most typical cooling and heating media.

NOTATION

A	Heat transfer surface area
a	Exponent of Reynolds number
b	Exponent of Prandtl number
C_p	Specific heat
c	Exponent of the viscosity ratio
D	Diameter
G_c	Geometric correction factor
H	Height
h	Heat transfer coefficient
K	Constant in eqn. (41)

k	Thermal conductivity
L	Blade height parallel to axis of rotation
LMTD	Logarithmic mean temperature difference
l	Characteristic length of system
m	Mass flow rate
N	Number (general)
Nu	Nusselt number, $= hl/k$
n	Impeller rotational speed
P	Pitch of propeller or helical ribbon impeller
Pr	Prandtl number, $= C_p\mu/k$
Q	Heat transfer rate
Re_a	Reynolds number defined for agitation, $= nD_i^2\rho/\mu$
S	Width
T	Temperature
t	Time
U	Overall heat transfer coefficient
V	Volume
Vi	Viscosity ratio
W	Liquid mass
WELH	Water equivalent liquid height
x	Ratio between the jacket and coil flow rates

Greek

Δ	Difference
Θ	Angle between a pitched blade on an impeller and a plane normal to the axis of rotation
μ	Dynamic viscosity
ρ	Density of liquid
ϕ	Parameter used in solving differential equations in Section 2

Subscripts

a	Blade arm of anchor or helical ribbons
b	Batch liquid
ba	Baffle
bl	Blade
c	Coil
cl	Clearance
co	Cooling medium
f	Fin
g	Gap (space) between tubes
h	Heating medium

i   Impeller
j   Jacket
l   Liquid level
m   Mean
pc   Plate coil
s   Space between the fins
t   Tube
v   Vessel
w   Wall

1. INTRODUCTION

1.1. Agitation as Process Operation

The objective of agitation is homogenization, manifesting itself as a reduction of concentration or temperature gradients, or both simultaneously, within the agitated system. Agitation operations differ, depending upon the various properties of the mixture under consideration. The systems to be stirred are either fluids or particulate solids. Fluids are divided into gases and liquids, according to their state. Liquids are sub-divided into Newtonian and nonNewtonian liquids.

The system may be homogeneous or heterogeneous. Only liquid homogeneous and a few heterogeneous systems, e.g. gas dispersed in liquids, immiscible liquids, solids suspended in a liquid, are typical for agitated vessels.

Agitated vessels, which besides homogenization also provide heat transfer, belong to the category of mechanically aided heat transfer exchangers from the point of view of heat transfer engineering. This category can cover a very wide range of equipment, including thin film wiped evaporators, scraped surface exchangers, rotary kilns and driers, vibrating conveyor coolers, etc.

Agitated vessels can be sub-divided into vessels with mechanical agitators, gas sparging, and liquid jets.

Only vessels with mechanical agitators and systems of Newtonian liquids are discussed in this chapter. The basic requirements regarding shape and arrangement of the vessel, type and arrangement of the impeller, and the like are essentially the same for the dispersion of liquids and, finally divided solids in Newtonian liquids. This type of agitation utilizes one or more rotating impellers immersed in the liquid to accomplish the mixing or dispersion. There are literally hundreds of devices using this principle, the major variations being found in cases where chemical or biochemical reactions are carried out. And yet, mechanical agitation, this ancient and omnipresent operation is very poorly understood, according to Ulbrecht and Patterson.[1] The design of mixers relies heavily on experience and engineering intuition based on common sense and a library of case histories. One of the difficulties in solving a mixing, and with it the connected heat transfer problem stems from the fact that, apart from the impossibly complex boundary conditions, the process is neither entirely random nor entirely deterministic. Thus, neither a purely analytical nor an integral 'black box' approach is likely to provide a complete answer.

Agitated vessels are useful for liquids of any viscosity up to 750 000 cP, although in contacting two liquids for reaction or extraction purposes, viscosities in excess of 100 cP are only rarely encountered. In many cases, the contents of agitated vessels are to be heated or cooled, and often heating and cooling are required at different portions of the production cycle. Heat transfer is then an important factor influencing the design of agitated vessels and for determining the operating cycle. The impeller speed and the agitator selection determine the heat transfer in the particular system. But other requirements such as the flow characteristics of the fluid and processing conditions determine the power requirements and the agitator selection primarily in most cases. Therefore, the comments will be confined to the heat transfer equations used once the agitator has been specified rather than to the selection of the most suitable agitator and vessel geometry. The main types of impellers and the basic vessel features will be covered in this chapter only for completeness, and only preliminary selection criteria will be given.

1.2. Most Commonly Used Impellers

Uhl and Gray[2] and also Penney[3] categorize the types of impeller as *proximity* when the blades sweep close to the vessel wall and as *nonproximity* when the impeller blades rotate some distance from the wall. Sterbacek and Tausk[4] distinguish impellers according to the type of flow pattern in the vessel. The flow can be predominantly tangential, radial, axial, and compound flow. Tangential flow is produced, for example, by paddle impellers with straight blades or by anchors. The group of impellers with pronounced radial flow comprises, for example, turbines with stator (disc). Propellers produce purely axial flow. Compound flow occurs, for example, with paddle mixers having pitched blades.

1.2.1. Proximity Impellers
The role of these slowly rotating, large area agitators is to circulate high-

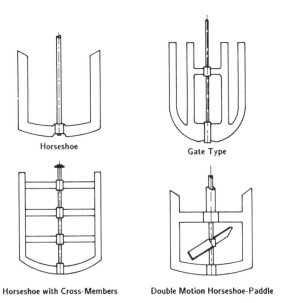

Horseshoe

Gate Type

Horseshoe with Cross-Members

Double Motion Horseshoe-Paddle

FIG. 1. Anchor impellers (according to reference 5).

consistency material to all sections of a vessel by the only practical action, positive displacement, according to Uhl and Gray.[2] For heat transfer operation it is desirable that this displacement be most marked adjacent to the heat transfer surfaces. The impeller must also incorporate blade elements which circulate the bulk of the material to and from the wall.

Anchors. Anchor impellers, see Fig. 1, have been successfully used in the batch operations having viscosities approaching 100 000 cP.[5] For liquids of low viscosity, 100–1000 cP, the plain horseshoe type anchor is recommended by Uhl and Gray.[2] Penney[3] recommends the application of anchor impellers for $Re_a > 50$ and $2000 < \mu < 100\,000$ cP. For liquids of higher viscosity, cross-members or auxiliary paddles are required to overcome viscous drag forces and maintain motion in the bulk. For very viscous liquids double motion anchor–paddle combinations are useful. For pseudoplastic types of nonNewtonian fluid, and for the situation where material accumulates on or tenaciously adheres to the wall surface, wall scrapers are utilized, especially for heat transfer applications.

Helical ribbons. Helical ribbon impellers, see Fig. 2, are considered to be a most efficient device for mixing viscous fluids. Penney[3] recommends their applicability for $Re_a < 50$ and $100\,000 < \mu < 1\,000\,000$ cP. Double helical ribbon impellers also exist. They produce the same flow pattern at the wall

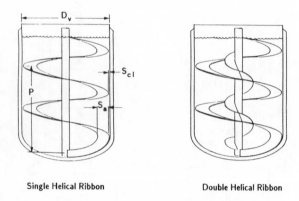

Single Helical Ribbon   Double Helical Ribbon

FIG. 2. Helical ribbon impellers.

as the single helix, but, in addition, provide positive displacement in the bulk.

1.2.2. Nonproximity Impellers

The nonproximity impellers are the propeller, the various turbines, and the paddles. All these agitators provide a high circulation rate and allow a minimum of energy to be dissipated initially by shear forces in the vicinity of the impeller.

Paddle impellers. These impellers, see Fig. 3, usually have flat rectangular blades perpendicular or oblique to the axis. A blade-to-vessel diameter ratio

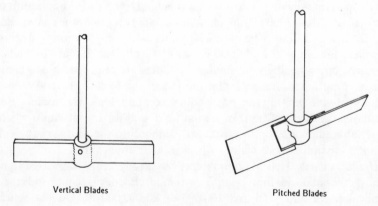

Vertical Blades   Pitched Blades

FIG. 3. Paddle impellers.

FIG. 4. Three-bladed marine-type propeller.

is in the range of $\frac{1}{3}-\frac{2}{3}$, according to Mueller[6] and $\frac{2}{3}-\frac{9}{10}$ according to Sterbacek and Tausk.[4] The main advantage is simplicity and low cost. A disadvantage is their small pumping capacity. The main disadvantage of these mixers is that they can be used only for liquids with a viscosity of up to 1000 cP[4] and that the axial flow of liquid is small. The axial flow can be increased by tilting the paddle blades by 30°–45° to the axis of the shaft.

Propellers. A three-bladed modified marine-type propeller, see Fig. 4, is often used. The propeller is fixed to a rotating vertical, horizontal or inclined shaft. The main advantage of propeller mixers is the axial flow and great pumping effect which permits a short mixing time. A disadvantage is the weight of large propellers and their cost. This kind of impeller is not recommended for gas dispersion. A propeller diameter to vessel diameter ratio usually is $\frac{1}{3}$. The applicability, recommended by Penney[3], is $Re_a > 300$, $\mu < 2000$ cP, $V < 6·0$ m^3. Also, Sterbacek and Tausk[4] recommend the maximum viscosity at which propeller mixers can still be used to be 2000 cP.

Turbines. There are two basic forms of turbines, see Fig. 5, the flat blade radial discharging type, and the pitched blade axial thrust type. All others are modifications of these basic styles. Suction, as in centrifugal pumps, occurs in the center and delivery on the circumference of the blades. Upon discharge from the impeller the liquid impinges on the wall where it splits up into two streams.

Flat-blade turbine. This is the most widely used type of mechanical agitator. The number of blades is usually 4–12. The shaft of the agitator is vertical; an eccentric position is rather unusual. The rotational speed of these mixers is, as a rule, 120–200 rpm, and the peripheral velocity or tip

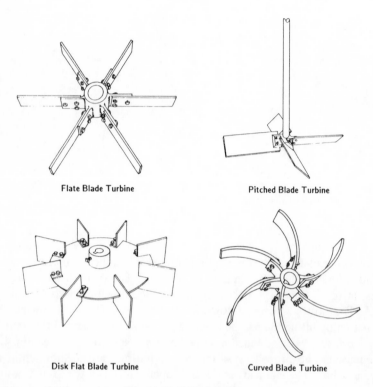

Flate Blade Turbine   Pitched Blade Turbine

Disk Flat Blade Turbine   Curved Blade Turbine

FIG. 5. Turbine impellers.

speed is usually between 200 and 500 m/min.[4] This turbine is primarily used for liquid–liquid dispersion. The ranges of applicability are $Re_a > 50$ and $\mu < 20\,000$ cP.[3] Turbines with curved blades are used for higher viscous liquids. Maximum recommended viscosity is 700 000 cP.

Pitched-blade turbine. The purpose of pitching the blades is to increase axial flow. The blade slope can be anywhere from 0° to 90°, but 45° is the commercial standard. This turbine is recommended for all single-phase and solid–liquid operations where $Re_a > 100$ and $\mu < 10\,000$ cP.

Disk flat blade turbine. This turbine is widely used industrially and has been employed in many investigations, but in recent literature it is recommended for gas dispersion only.[3] The recommended ranges of applicability are $Re_a > 50$ and $\mu < 20\,000$ cP. The turbine versus vessel diameter ratio is usually $\frac{1}{3}$.

1.3. Heat Transfer Surfaces in Agitated Vessels

Heat transfer in agitated vessels is predominantly brought about by means of a jacket, an internal helical pipe coil, tube baffles, and plate coil baffles.

1.3.1. Jackets

The jacket (Fig. 6), may be plain, with a spiral baffle, a coil welded to the shell, a half-pipe welded to the shell, or dimpled.

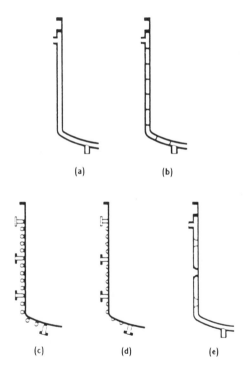

(a)   (b)

(c)   (d)   (e)

FIG. 6. Types of jacket construction (according to reference 2): (a) Plain jacket. (b) Jacket with spiral baffle. (c) Pipe coil welded to shell. (d) Half-pipe welded to shell. (e) Dimpled jacket.

The plain jacket design is used for steam or for coolant. Liquid flow velocities in the plain jackets are very low and flow is poorly distributed; hence, natural convection equations are suitable for calculating heat transfer. Cooling film coefficients have low values ($220 \ \text{W/m}^2/\text{K}$ or less[2]).

High velocity tangential nozzles can be inserted into the jacket to increase fluid velocity and eliminate 'hot spots'. The number and location of the nozzles in the jackets influence the heat transfer. Mueller[6] stated that Pfaudler Permutit, Inc. makes a nozzle that screws into a radial coupling and turns the flow into a tangential path in the jacket.

High flow velocities in the jacket can be reached by using baffled jackets, one form of which is obtained by welding a spiral of angle iron to the jacket shell or to the vessel wall. Some clearance needs to be provided so that the jacket can be assembled after fabrication. Although the clearance between the helical baffle and the wall may be small the total leakage area per baffle turn around the vessel may be substantial compared to the cross-sectional flow area of the baffle passage and, hence, the velocity will be only a fraction of the expected value.[6] A sure seal can be secured by use of a rubber insert.

Coils and half pipes need to be used where very high pressure must be handled. The coils and half pipe jackets will give a predictable velocity and heat transfer, but they are expensive. Heat transfer cements of high thermal conductivity are sometimes used in the space between the coil and the outside of a vessel.

The dimpled construction is a design for pressure service which permits thinner shells. The dimpled jackets are used for steam or condensing vapors of heat transfer fluids, e.g. Dowtherm.

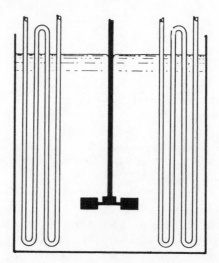

FIG. 7. Agitated vessel with tube baffles (from reference 5).

1.3.2. Helical Pipe Coils

The helical pipe coils are often used because of lower cost and the ability to accommodate higher pressures in a coil or circulate fluids at higher velocities and hence attain higher heat transfer coefficients. The helical pipe coils can augment the available jacketed surface and offer the only practical heat transfer surface for ceramic-lined vessels in corrosive conditions. The helical pipe coils are concentric with the tank axes. Sometimes two or more coils are used concentrically with a recommended clearance of two pipe diameters between the coils. In this case the heat transfer coefficients decrease with additional coil in the radial direction. The tube side coefficients for the coils is calculated by a Dittus–Boelter type equation modified for the coil curvature. The other recommendations are as follows: (a) Ratio between the pipe and vessel diameters should be 30. (b) The gap between pipes in a helix need not be greater than the pipe diameter. (c) The coil pitch should be two pipe diameters.

1.3.3. Tube Baffles and Plate Coil Baffles

An agitated vessel equipped with rows of vertical tubes (Fig. 7), uses the baffle effect of such tubes to generate axial mixing in addition to heat transfer. The tubes become areas of high turbulence and generally good heat transfer coefficients can be achieved.

A variation of the vertical tube heat transfer system is that using vertical plate coils instead of tubes. Plate coils are simpler to install and maintain than vertical tubes. Their baffling effect is significantly greater, but the fluid flow around the heat transfer surface is restricted due to the nature of their construction.

The tube baffles and plate coil baffles can be angled at 45° with the vessel radius for maximum heat transfer area. Four or five tubes are recommended per baffle. Four or six baffles are recommended per vessel.

In polymerization and biotechnology, particularly where vessels tend to have large height-to-diameter ratios (2:1 or 3:1), these devices allow far more heat transfer area for precise control of heat transfer.

1.4. Vessel Construction

1.4.1. Standard Tank Configuration

There was an attempt, described by Holland and Chapman,[5] to establish 'Standard Tank Configuration' that would provide adequate mixing for most processing requirements found in industry. It was a rather arbitrary standard which in many applications did not bring satisfying results.

The Standard Tank Configuration has, for example, the following recommendations: (a) The impeller is a 6 flat blade turbine. (b) The turbine diameter is $\frac{1}{3}$ of the vessel diameter. (c) The turbine height from the tank bottom is also $\frac{1}{3}$ of the vessel diameter. (d) The turbine blade width is $\frac{1}{5}$ of impeller diameter. (e) The liquid height is equal to the vessel diameter. (f) There are four baffles, vertically mounted at the tank wall and extending from the tank bottom to above the liquid surface. (g) The width of the baffles is $\frac{1}{10}$ of the vessel diameter.

The Standard Tank Configuration can best satisfy processes with low viscosity liquids. This configuration may be impractical for high viscosity, for mixing of liquids with a high solid content, for many polymerization and biochemical processes.

If the liquid height in a vessel is greater than 1·25 tank diameter, multiple impellers are recommended. Vessels which have the liquid height to the vessel diameter ratio from 2:1 to 3:1 are commonly used in extraction, polymerization, and gas–liquid contacting processes (aeration). The disk flat blade turbine was often used in these processes. The number of turbines to be used on an agitator shaft is determined with the formula[4]

$$\text{Number of turbines} = \text{WELH/Vessel diameter} \qquad (1)$$

where WELH is the water equivalent liquid height. The next highest whole number is used if the eqn. (1) result is not a whole number.

The cylindrical tank may have a flat or dished bottom.

1.4.2. Baffles
If any nonproximity impeller is used in an unbaffled vessel contaning low viscosity liquid, vortexing develops. The vortexing increases with impeller speed and eventually the vortex passes through the agitator. In some processes the vortexing is required, for example, during the mixing of powders with liquids or for some gas–liquid contacting processes (aeration from the surface). The mixing efficiency of vortexing systems is usually lower than for geometrically similar nonvortexing systems.

Baffles are often used near the walls to prevent swirling and reduce vortexing. These baffles are approximately $\frac{1}{12}$ the vessel diameter and located $\frac{1}{75}$ the vessel diameter from the wall, according to Mueller.[6] As liquid viscosity increases, the need for baffles to reduce vortexing decreases and the baffle width may be reduced to $\frac{1}{20}$ vessel diameter.[4]

Since baffled vessels are capable of obtaining much higher Reynolds numbers, they are ultimately capable of higher heat transfer coefficients.

The industrial use of unbaffled tanks is quite limited because unbaffled systems give poor bulk mixing throughout the medium.

2. TIME ESTIMATE FOR HEATING OR COOLING OF A BATCH OF LIQUID IN AN AGITATED VESSEL

Agitated vessels are used for either batch or continuous service. Most of the agitated vessels are operating in a batch mode, and hence, the mean temperature difference between the batch liquid and heating or cooling medium is a function of time. When the overall heat transfer coefficient U is known or determined from the appropriate correlations, such correlations are presented and discussed in Sections 3 and 4, the time to heat or cool a batch of liquid in an agitated vessel can be estimated. The equations for the determination of such a time can be found in Kern's[7] or Holland and Chapman's[5] books for many common cases. The calculation methods for the most typical systems, and systems where cooling or heating is provided simultaneously by both the helical pipe coil and the jacket are described in this section.

With continuous operation the vessel may be sized to provide any holding time desired.

2.1. Constant Temperature Heating Medium. Heating Surface: Helical Pipe Coil or Jacket

The heat transfer rate can be calculated from the equation

$$Q = WC_p \frac{dT_b}{dt} = UA(T_h - T_b) \tag{2}$$

where T_h is the temperature of the heating medium, e.g. steam, T_b is the temperature of the batch liquid, W is the batch liquid mass, and C_p is the specific heat capacity of the batch liquid. Equation (2) can be rearranged in the form

$$\frac{dT_b}{T_h - T_b} = \frac{UA}{WC_p} dt \tag{3}$$

and integrated over the time interval Δt required to heat the agitated liquid from a temperature T_{b1} to T_{b2} to give

$$\int_{T_{b1}}^{T_{b2}} \frac{dT}{T_h - T_b} = \frac{UA}{WC_p} \int_0^{\Delta t} dt \tag{4}$$

which provides

$$\ln\left(\frac{T_h - T_{b1}}{T_h - T_{b2}}\right) = \frac{UA}{WC_p}\Delta t \tag{5}$$

From eqn. (5) the heating time, Δt, can be calculated.

2.2. Constant Temperature Cooling Medium. Cooling Surface: Helical Pipe Coil or Jacket

The cooling medium is, for example, a refrigerant at its isothermal boiling temperature. The analogous equation to eqn. (2) is

$$Q = -WC_p\frac{dT_b}{dt} = UA(T_b - T_{co}) \tag{6}$$

where T_{co} is the temperature of the cooling medium. The term dT_b/dt is negative because the temperature gradient is the opposite for cooling than for heating. The resulting equation after integration is

$$\ln\left(\frac{T_{b1} - T_{co}}{T_{b2} - T_{co}}\right) = \frac{UA}{WC_p}\Delta t \tag{7}$$

where Δt is the time taken to cool the agitated liquid mass of W from a temperature T_{b1} to T_{b2}.

2.3. Constant Temperature Heating Medium. Heating Surfaces: Helical Pipe Coil and Jacket

For this case, the total heat transfer rate is a sum of the heat transfer rate from the helical coil and from the jacket. It is given, at a particular point in time, by the equation

$$Q = WC_p\frac{dT_b}{dt} = (U_cA_c + U_jA_j)(T_h - T_b) \tag{8}$$

where U_c is the helical coil average heat transfer coefficient and A_c is the coil heat transfer area. U_j and A_j are the analogous terms for the jacket. Equation (8) after integration is analogous to eqn. (4)

$$\ln\left(\frac{T_h - T_{b1}}{T_h - T_{b2}}\right) = \frac{U_cA_c + U_jA_j}{WC_p}\Delta t \tag{9}$$

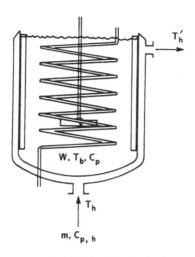

FIG. 8. Sensible heating by jacket.

2.4. Constant Temperature Cooling Medium. Cooling Surfaces: Helical Pipe Coil and Jacket

The resulting equation is similar to eqns. (7) and (9).

$$\ln\left(\frac{T_{b1} - T_{co}}{T_{b2} - T_{co}}\right) = \frac{U_c A_c + U_j A_j}{W C_p} \Delta t \tag{10}$$

2.5. Sensible Heating Medium. Heating Surface: Helical Pipe Coil or Jacket

The heating medium has a constant flow rate, m, and inlet temperature, T_h, but a variable outlet temperature, T'_h (see Fig. 8). For this case, the heat transfer rate at a particular point in time is given by the equation

$$Q = W C_p \frac{dT_b}{dt} = m C_{p,h}(T_h - T'_h) = U A \Delta T_m \tag{11}$$

$$\Delta T_m = \text{LMTD} = \frac{T_h - T'_h}{\ln\left(\dfrac{T_h - T_b}{T'_h - T_b}\right)} \tag{12}$$

Equation (11) can be rearranged in the form

$$\frac{U A}{m C_{p,h}} = \ln\left(\frac{T_h - T_b}{T'_h - T_b}\right) \tag{13}$$

Let

$$\phi_h = \frac{T_h - T_b}{T'_h - T_b} = \exp\left(\frac{UA}{mC_{p,h}}\right) \tag{14}$$

then

$$T'_h = T_b + \frac{T_h - T_b}{\phi_h} \tag{15}$$

Equation (11) can be rearranged in the form

$$\frac{dT_b}{T_h - T'_h} = \left(\frac{mC_{p,h}}{WC_p}\right) dt \tag{16}$$

and after substitution of T'_h from eqn. (15) and the rearrangement, can be written

$$\frac{dT_b}{T_h - T_b} = \left(\frac{\phi_h - 1}{\phi_h}\right)\left(\frac{mC_{p,h}}{WC_p}\right) dt \tag{17}$$

Equation (17) can be integrated over the time interval Δt required to heat an agitated batch from a temperature T_{b1} to T_{b2}

$$\int_{T_{b1}}^{T_{b2}} \frac{dT_b}{T_h - T_b} = \left(\frac{\phi_h - 1}{\phi_h}\right)\left(\frac{mC_{p,h}}{WC_p}\right)\int_0^{\Delta t} dt \tag{18}$$

which becomes

$$\ln\left(\frac{T_h - T_{b1}}{T_h - T_{b2}}\right) = \left(\frac{\phi_h - 1}{\phi_h}\right)\left(\frac{mC_{p,h}}{WC_p}\right)\Delta t \tag{19}$$

2.6. Sensible Cooling Medium. Cooling Surface: Helical Pipe Coil or Jacket
The nonisothermal cooling medium, e.g. cooling tower water, is flowing at rate m through a pipe coil or vessel jacket. The time, Δt, required to cool an agitated liquid mass, W, from a temperature of T_{b1} to T_{b2} is given by the equation

$$\ln\left(\frac{T_{b1} - T_{co}}{T_{b2} - T_{co}}\right) = \left(\frac{\phi_{co} - 1}{\phi_{co}}\right)\left(\frac{mC_{p,co}}{WC_p}\right)\Delta t \tag{20}$$

where $\phi_{co} = \exp\left(\frac{UA}{mC_{p,co}}\right)$ and T_{co} is the coolant inlet temperature, $C_{p,co}$ is the specific heat capacity of the coolant.

2.7. Sensible Heating Medium. Heating Surfaces: Helical Pipe Coil and Jacket

See Fig. (9) and Table 1 for nomenclature. Similarly as in the case described in Section 2.3, the total heat rate, Q, is the sum of the heat transfer rates from the helical pipe coil and from the jacket,

$$Q = U_c A_c \Delta T_{m,c} + U_j A_j \Delta T_{m,j} \tag{21}$$

$$\Delta T_{m,c} = \frac{T_h - T'_{h,c}}{\ln\left(\dfrac{T_h - T_b}{T_{h,c} - T_b}\right)} \tag{22}$$

$$\Delta T_{m,j} = \frac{T_h - T'_{h,j}}{\ln\left(\dfrac{T_h - T_b}{T_h - T_b}\right)} \tag{23}$$

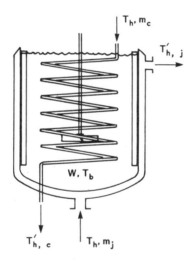

FIG. 9. Sensible heating by helical pipe coil and jacket.

TABLE 1

NOTATION TO SECTION 2.7

	Mass flow rate	Temp. inlet	Temp. outlet	Heat trans. area	Heat trans. coefficient
Coil	m_c	T_h	$T_{h,c}$	A_c	U_c
Jacket	m_j	T_h	$T_{h,j}$	A_j	U_j

The heat transfer rate is also given by the equation

$$Q = WC_p \frac{dT_b}{dt} = m_c C_{p,c}(T_h - T'_{h,c}) + m_j C_{p,j}(T_h - T'_{h,j}) \tag{24}$$

If the ratio between the jacket and coil heating medium flow rate is x and the same heating medium is used in the coil and the jacket, then it can be written that

$$m_j = xm_c \tag{25}$$

$$C_{p,c} = C_{p,j} = C_{p,h} \tag{26}$$

Substituting in eqn. (24),

$$Q = m_c C_{p,h}[(T_h - T'_{h,c}) + x(T_h - T'_{h,j})] \tag{27}$$

Rearranging,

$$Q = m_c C_{p,h}[(x+1)T_h - T'_{h,c} - xT'_{h,j}] \tag{28}$$

Let

$$\phi_{c,h} = \exp\left(\frac{U_c A_c}{m_c C_{p,h}}\right) = \frac{T_h - T_b}{T'_{h,c} - T_b} \tag{29}$$

and

$$\phi_{j,h} = \exp\left(\frac{U_j A_j}{xm_c C_{p,h}}\right) = \frac{T_h - T_b}{T'_{h,j} - T_b} \tag{30}$$

then

$$T'_{h,c} = T_b - \frac{T_h - T_b}{\phi_{c,h}} \tag{31}$$

$$T'_{h,j} = T_b + \frac{T_h - T_b}{\phi_{j,h}} \tag{32}$$

Combining eqn. (24) with eqn. (28) and rearranging

$$\frac{dT_b}{(x+1)T_h - T'_{h,c} - xT'_{h,j}} = \frac{m_c C_{p,h}}{WC_p} dt \tag{33}$$

Substituting in eqn. (33) for $T'_{h,c}$ and $T'_{h,j}$ from eqns. (31) and (32), and integrating from T_{b1} to T_{b2} while the time passes from 0 to Δt,

$$\int_{T_{b1}}^{T_{b2}} \frac{dT_b}{T_h - T_b} = \left[(x+1) - \left(\frac{1}{\phi_{c,h}} + \frac{x}{\phi_{j,h}}\right)\right] \frac{m_c C_{p,h}}{WC_p} \int_0^{\Delta t} dt \qquad (34)$$

The resulting equation is

$$\ln\left(\frac{T_h - T_{b1}}{T_h - T_{b2}}\right) = \frac{m_c C_{p,h}}{WC_p}\left[(x+1) - \left(\frac{1}{\phi_{c,h}} + \frac{x}{\phi_{j,h}}\right)\right]\Delta t \qquad (35)$$

2.8. Sensible Cooling Medium. Cooling Surfaces: Helical Pipe Coil and Jacket

The analogous equation to eqn. (35) can be derived

$$\ln\left(\frac{T_{b1} - T_{co}}{T_{b2} - T_{co}}\right) = \frac{m_c C_{p,co}}{WC_p}\left[(x+1) - \left(\frac{1}{\phi_{c,co}} + \frac{x}{\phi_{j,co}}\right)\right]\Delta t \qquad (36)$$

where Δt is the time taken to cool the agitated liquid of mass W from a temperature of T_{b1} to T_{b2} by the coolant where the inlet temperature is T_{co}. The ratio between the jacket and coil cooling medium flow rate is x. The coil coolant flow rate is m_c. ϕ_c and ϕ_j are defined as follows

$$\phi_{c,co} = \exp\left(\frac{U_c A_c}{m_c C_{p,co}}\right) \qquad (37)$$

$$\phi_{j,co} = \exp\left(\frac{U_j A_j}{x m_c C_{p,co}}\right) \qquad (38)$$

2.9. Constant Temperature Heating Medium. Heating Surface: External Heat Exchanger

The arrangement is illustrated in Fig. 10. The liquid in the agitated vessel is heated by the external heat exchanger. The total liquid mass is W and the liquid flow rate through the exchanger is m. The similar differential heat transfer balance as in the previous cases was used for the determination of the resulting equation

$$\ln\left(\frac{T_h - T_{b1}}{T_h - T_{b2}}\right) = \frac{m}{W}\left(\frac{\phi - 1}{\phi}\right)\Delta t \qquad (39)$$

where Δt is the time interval required to heat the liquid from a temperature

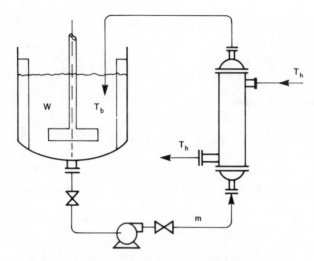

FIG. 10. Agitated vessel with external heat exchanger.

of T_{b1} to T_{b2}

$$\phi = \exp\left(\frac{UA}{WC_p}\right) \tag{40}$$

The other systems using an external heat exchanger can be found in Kern's book.[7]

3. HEAT TRANSFER COEFFICIENTS ON THE AGITATED FLUID SIDE

Heat transfer correlations for the agitated fluid are mainly based on experiments performed on small model tanks that are geometrically scaled down versions of plant equipment. In all the calculations the bulk average temperature of the batch is assumed to be uniform at any instant. This is far from reality, especially at low Reynolds numbers where the mixing may not be uniform and large temperature gradients can exist.

There are different equations for heat transfer to the jacket wall and to the helical pipe coil. The jacket overall heat transfer coefficients are often lower than the helical coil coefficients. The jacket wall is much thicker than the walls of the pipe coils and this thermal resistance can be significant, especially if a ceramic coating vessel is used. In addition the heat transfer coefficient of the jacket fluid is often low; hence, coils are more effective in removing heat.[6]

The wide variety of impeller types, sizes, and relative locations within the vessel which can be equipped by jacket, helical pipe coils, tube baffles, or plate coil baffles plus additional factors of vessel shape, baffles, etc., results in a number of empirical correlations which are often in or can be converted to the form

$$Nu = K Re_a{}^a Pr^b Vi^c G_c \qquad (41)$$

where

$$Vi = \mu_b/\mu_w \qquad (42)$$

and G_c is a geometric correction factor as recommended in Tables 3–5.

Values of the constant and powers are listed in Tables 2–5 for various heat transfer surfaces and impeller configurations. In unbaffled vessels, even small changes, such as the eccentric location of the agitator impeller, may lead to different exponents of the Reynolds number term in the heat transfer coefficient correlation.

Note that the characteristic length in the Nusselt number for the jacket is the vessel inside diameter, D_v; for the helical pipe coil it is always the pipe (tube) outside diameter, D_t; and for plate coils the width of the plate coil, S_{pc} divided by the number of internal passes.

TABLE 2

HEAT TRANSFER CORRELATIONS FOR JACKETED VESSELS WITH PROXIMITY IMPELLERS (eqn. (43))

Impeller	P/D_v	Range of Re_a	K	Exponent of Re_a
Anchor	n/a	$Re_a < 12$	1·05	1/3
		$12 < Re_a < 100$	0·69	1/2
		$Re_a > 100$	0·32	2/3
Helical ribbon	1/4	$Re_a < 9$	0·98	1/3
		$9 < Re_a < 135$	0·68	1/2
		$Re_a > 135$	0·3	2/3
	1/2	$Re_a < 13$	0·94	1/3
		$13 < Re_a < 210$	0·61	1/2
		$Re_a > 210$	0·25	2/3

3.1. Heat Transfer Correlations for Jacketed Vessels with Proximity Impeller

The most recommended correlations for both main kinds of proximity impellers, the anchors and the single helical ribbons, are those developed by Harry and Uhl.[8] The main geometric parameters for their tests, both for the anchor and for the helical ribbons, were $D_i/D_v = 0.96$, $S_a/D_v = 0.082$, and $S_{cl}/D_v = 0.02$. D_i is the impeller diameter, D_v is the vessel inside diameter, S_a is the width of the blade, S_{cl} is the clearance between the impeller blade tip and the vessel wall. The pitch of the helical ribbon, P, versus the vessel inside diameter, D_v, was 1/2 and 1/4 for two; otherwise the same geometries of the tested helical ribbons.

For these geometries the experimental data have been correlated satisfactorily by

$$Nu = K \, Re_a^a \, Pr^{1/3} \, Vi^{0.14} \tag{43}$$

The values of the parameters K and a varied with Re_a. They are given in Table 2.

The clearance between the impeller tip and the vessel wall, S_{cl}, is an apparently significant geometric variable, but none of the recommended correlations includes a factor for the wall clearance. Uhl and Gray[2] found that the film coefficients for the common range of S_{cl}/D_v in practice, namely between the values 0.01 and 0.03, are 20–30% less than at smaller or larger clearances. The data of Brown et al.[9] show a 20% better rate of heat transfer for S_{cl}/D_v equal to 0.08 than for 0.017. This phenomenon was studied in more detail by Uhl and Voznick.[10] Their results, illustrated also by Mueller,[6] indicate the minimum heat transfer coefficient in the range of S_{cl}/D_v equal to 0.02–0.03 and the maximum at 0.08–0.09. Penney[3] described disagreement among the data of other authors and presented a graphical correlation which indicates the highest heat transfer coefficient for zero clearance (scrapers) and gradual decrease of the coefficient with the increase of the S_{cl}/D_v ratio.

3.2. Heat Transfer Correlations for Jacketed Vessel with Nonproximity Impellers

Correlation constants from the results of selected tests are given in Table 3. The exponent of the viscosity ratio, c, eqn. (41), was taken as 0.14 by many authors to be in agreement with the classic work of Sieder and Tate for forced convection in pipes, although the data indicate an absolute value of the exponent c close to 0.25, as was discussed by Uhl and Gray.[2] Oldshue[20] stated that unless the temperature differential is very large, the viscosity

TABLE 3
HEAT TRANSFER CORRELATION FOR JACKETED VESSEL WITH NONPROXIMITY IMPELLERS (eqn. (41))

Impeller	N_{bl}	Baffles	K	Exponents of Re_a	Pr	Vi	Recommended geometric corrections[3,12] (G_c)	Ref.
Paddle	2	Yes[a]	0·415	2/3	1/3	0·24		11[b]
		No	0·112	3/4	0·44	0·25	$\left(\dfrac{D_v}{D_i}\right)^{0\cdot40}\left(\dfrac{L_i}{D_i}\right)^{0\cdot13}$	12
Various turbines: disk, flat, and pitched blades	6	No	0·54	2/3	1/3	0·14	$\left(\dfrac{L_i/D_i}{1/5}\right)^{0\cdot15}\left(\dfrac{N_{bl}}{6}\right)^{0\cdot15}[\sin(\theta)]^{0\cdot5}$	13, 14
		Yes	0·74	2/3	1/3	0·14	$\left(\dfrac{S_{bl}/D_i}{1/5}\right)^{0\cdot2}\left(\dfrac{N_{bl}}{6}\right)^{0\cdot2}[\sin(\theta)]^{0\cdot5}$	14, 15, 16
		No	0·37	2/3	1/3	0·14	$\left(\dfrac{D_v/D_i}{3}\right)^{0\cdot25}\left(\dfrac{H_i}{H_l}\right)^{0\cdot15}$	17, 18
Propeller	3	Yes	0·5	2/3	1/3	0·14	$\left(\dfrac{1\cdot29\,P/D_i}{0\cdot29+P/D_i}\right)$	19

[a] Baffled and unbaffled.
[b] Relatively low range of Reynolds numbers, 20–4000. The other correlations presented in this table were developed for ranges of Re_a reaching 10^5 and more.

ratio is likely to be close to 1. In this case, whether the exponent is 0·14 or 0·25, the effect on the value of the heat transfer coefficient will be minimum.

The principal contributions to this area, when paddle impellers are used, are the works of Gordon,[21] Chilton et al.,[22] Kraussold,[23] Uhl[11] and Pursell.[12] The correlations of the last two authors are recommended. Penney's[3] selection of correlations for various turbines and propellers is recommended also in this chapter. Oldshue[20] also recommends the work of Brooks and Su[14] for its excellent agreement with works of Strek[15] and Chapman et al.[16]

3.3. Heat Transfer Correlations for Helical Coil with Nonproximity Impellers

Correlation constants from the results of selected tests are given in Table 4. Uhl and Gray[2] discussed an analogy between the liquid regime in the agitated vessels with immersed helical coils and the shellside of baffled shell and tube heat exchangers. In both cases the liquid velocity varies over a wide range with position in the shell or vessel and the velocity direction ranges from normal to parallel with the tubes. A variation in the tube outside diameter, D_t, and the space between individual tubes (turns of the coil), S_g, affect the flow distribution through and around the coil or the degree of by-passing quite significantly. Similar variation in D_t and S_g in a shell and tube heat exchanger does not have such a large effect, according to Uhl and Gray.[2] Oldshue and Gretton[24] experimentally investigated the influence of the tube diameter and spacing in the practical ranges of parameters in the system with a turbine. Their work showed that the tube spacing between two and four diameters provided consistent results. Skelland et al.[26] also investigated the influence of these and other geometric parameters but in the system with a propeller. From their resulting correlation

$$Nu = 0.0573 \, Re_a^{0.67} \, Pr^{0.41} \, Vi^{0.034}(H_i/D_v)^{-0.254}(P/D_i)^{2.33}$$

$$(N_{ba})^{-0.077} \, (S_{ba}/D_v)^{-0.058} \, (D_t/D_v)^{0.572} \, (S_g/D_t)^{-0.018} \qquad (44)$$

where H_i is height of propeller above the vessel floor; P is the propeller pitch; N_{ba} is the number of baffles; and S_{ba} is the baffle width. It appears that the group $(S_g/D_t)^{-0.018}$ practically has no effect on the heat transfer coefficient.

Note that Skelland et al.[26] found a relatively low exponent on Vi. They quoted a Malina and Sparrow[27] statement that '....the Seider–Tate correction $(\mu_b/\mu_w)^{0.14}$ overpredicts the variable property effects ... it would

TABLE 4

HEAT TRANSFER CORRELATIONS FOR HELICAL COIL WITH NONPROXIMITY IMPELLERS (eqn. (41))

Impeller	N_{bl}	Baffle	K	Exponents of			Recommended geometric correction by Penney[3] G_c	Ref.
				Re_a	Pr	Vi		
Paddle	2	No	0·87	0·62	1/3	0·14	$\left(\dfrac{L_i/D_i}{1/5}\right)^{0\cdot15}\left(\dfrac{D_t/D_v}{0\cdot064}\right)^{0\cdot5}$	22
Various turbines: disk, flat, and pitched blades	6	No	0·08	0·56	1/3	0·14	$\left(\dfrac{L_i/D_i}{1/5}\right)^{0\cdot2}\left(\dfrac{D_t/D_v}{0\cdot04}\right)^{0\cdot5}$	18, 24
		Yes	0·03	0·67	1/3	0·14	$\left(\dfrac{N_{bl}}{6}\right)^{0\cdot2}\left(\dfrac{D_v}{H_1}\right)^{0\cdot5}[\sin(\theta)]^{0\cdot5}$	
Propeller	3	No	0·078[a]	0·62	1/3	0·14	$\left(\dfrac{D_t/D_v}{0\cdot03}\right)^{0\cdot5}\left(\dfrac{D_v/D_i}{3}\right)^{0\cdot2}$	17, 18
		Yes	0·016	0·67	0·37	0·14	$\left(\dfrac{D_i/D_v}{1/3}\right)^{0\cdot1}\left(\dfrac{D_t/D_v}{0\cdot04}\right)^{0\cdot5}$	25, 26

[a]This value appears too high. The value of 0·05 is recommended by Penney.[3]

appear that $(\mu_b/\mu_w)^{0.05}$ serves as an adequate correction factor' to support their experimental result. Oldshue[20] and Oldshue and Gretton[24] found the exponent on Vi to vary widely and in a complex manner with fluid properties such as viscosity, thermal capacity, thermal conductivity, and with a type of tube for a coil with turbine agitation. They developed an empirical correlation for the exponent c which results in values ranging from 0·1 to 1·0.

Also note the effects of the number of baffles, N_{ba}, and the width of the baffles, S_{ba}, in eqn. (44). They are consistent with the expected result of decreasing the fluid velocity past the heat transfer surface as these variables increase, but the effect is relatively small. Oldshue and Gretton[24] report that standard baffles ($S_{ba} = D_v/12$) can be located either inside or outside the helical coil to provide similar heat transfer coefficients.

More than one helical pipe coil may be used for added heat transfer area. Due to the interference of flow pattern between the coils, the heat transfer coefficients decrease with additional coils. Although published data are not available, the thermal effectiveness of the second coil is estimated[20] to be between 70 and 90% of the effectiveness of the first coil, assuming the same heat transfer area per coil.

Pratt[28] found no variation in the heat transfer coefficient with variation of the vertical location of a paddle impeller between the top and bottom level of the helical coil. However, Rushton et al.[29] demonstrated for a disk-type flat-blade turbine with vertical baffle pipes that the optimum rate of heat transfer occurs when the impeller is located in the center of the baffle coil. This is generally applied also for helical coils and the intermediate position of an impeller is recommended.[2]

3.4. Heat Transfer Correlations for Vertical Tube Baffles and Plate Coil Baffles with Nonproximity Impellers

In Table 5 are presented constants of the recommended correlations. Results of Gentry and Small's[30] work are tabulated for vertical tube baffles, and constants from Petree and Small's[31] work are presented for plate coil baffles.

3.4.1. Vertical Tube Baffles

Very favorable heat transfer-power expenditure characteristics of vertical pipe baffles were reported by Oldshue and Gretton[24] as early as 1954. The authors have shown that the vertical tube baffles will have a value of the heat transfer coefficient 13% higher than for a helical coil in a baffled tank at conditions of comparable power input. Rushton et al.[29] obtained heat

TABLE 5
HEAT TRANSFER CORRELATIONS FOR VERTICAL TUBE[a] AND PLATE COIL BAFFLES WITH NON-
PROXIMITY IMPELLER (eqn. (41))

Impeller	N_{ba}	Heat transfer surface	Range of Re_a	K	Exponents of			S_s/S_f
					Re_a	Pr	Vi	
Two six-		Bare tubes		0·020 5	2/3	0·4	0·27	n/a
bladed,		Low fins		0·005 0	0·765	0·4	0·287	0
flat	4	Medium fins	55–200 000	0·004 6	0·788	0·4	0·284	0
blade		Fins (general		0·003 8	0·778	0·4	0·288	0·145
turbines		equation						
		Plate coil	$Re_a < 1·4(10)^3$	0·178 8	0·448	0·33	0·5	n/a
			$Re_a > 1·4(10)^3$	0·031 7	0·658	0·33	0·5	n/a

[a] Four vertical tubes at 45° to radius.

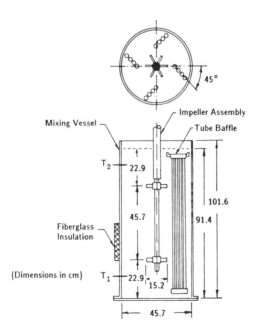

FIG. 11. Agitated vessel arrangement (from reference 30).

transfer results for water. Dunlap and Rushton[32] developed a heat transfer correlation for vertical tube baffles from data obtained from two different sized mixing vessels, filled with three test fluids. Appleton and Brennan[33] published experimental results for bare and low finned tubes, with separate correlating curves for each surface geometry and test fluid.

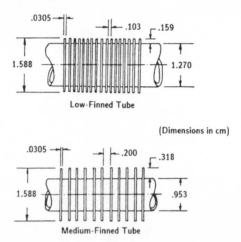

FIG. 12. Finned tube dimensions. (From Ref. 30; reproduced by permission of C. C. Gentry.)

Gentry and Small's[30] correlations were based on both heating and cooling data using four test fluids. They tested three heat transfer surfaces: bare tubes, low finned tubes, and medium finned tubes. The geometry of their vessel is shown in Fig. 11 and the geometric parameters of the finned tubes in Fig. 12. The vessel contained four vertical tube baffles, and agitation was provided by a dual, six-flat-blade turbine. Agreement between results of their study and previous works was found satisfactory.

3.4.2. Plate Coil Baffles
A variation of vertical tube baffles heat transfer system is that of using vertical plate coils. Only one paper providing heat transfer correlations, the work of Petree and Small,[31] was found in the open literature. Note the viscosity ratio exponent which was found equal to 0·5. The authors also noted that the angle at which the plate coil intersects the vessel radius has no significant effect on the heat transfer coefficient.

4. HEAT TRANSFER COEFFICIENTS ON THE HEATING AND COOLING MEDIUM SIDE

4.1. Jacket Side Coefficient

Data for this case are limited. The half pipe spiral jacket is the only jacket construction in which fluid velocities and heat transfer coefficients can be estimated within acceptable error.[6] For fluid flowing in plain jackets the heat transfer coefficient can be calculated from the Colburn and Hougen[34] equation developed for free convection, reduced by 20%. This is recommended[2] for liquid velocities up to 0·03 m/s or Re up to 2000. In calculating the Reynolds number, the equivalent diameter was taken as twice the inside width of the jacket space. The reduction of 20% takes into account the fact that the Colburn and Hougen correlation was developed for a vertical cylinder, and the considerable area in the bottom of the vessel is almost horizontal.

For jackets with agitating nozzles Lehrer[35] developed special correlations for nozzles with radial entry and for nozzles with tangential entry to the jacket. The heat transfer coefficient depends on the vessel size, number of nozzles, flow rates, and nozzle pressure drop. The coefficient ranges[6] from 1700 to 6000 $W/m^2 K$ for water.

The flow path and velocity distribution in the dimpled jacket is unknown. The jacket with a spiral baffle can be the subject of considerable leakage across the baffle. A Dittus–Boelter equation can be used, but only 60% of the total mass flow is recommended as an effective flow in the spiral passage by Bondy and Lippa.[36]

Condensing steam in jackets provides relatively high film coefficients compared with the overall resistance to heat transfer. They are of the order 5000–7000 $W/m^2 K$. The actual value is affected by proper venting of noncondensables and descending condensate, especially in high vessels.

4.2. Helical Pipe Coil Side Coefficients

Values of helical coil heat transfer coefficients for sensible heat transfer can be determined from the well established relations for flow inside conduits by Dittus–Boelter. Because of turbulence induced by the coil, coefficients are higher than those for a straight tube. It has been suggested by Jeschke[37] that the coil side coefficient be obtained by multiplying the straight tube coefficient by a factor of $(1 + 3·5 D_i/D_c)$, where D_i/D_c is the ratio of the tube inside diameter to the diameter of the coil.

For condensing steam the film coefficient is high, reaching 6000–

8000 W/m^2 K. For more accurate prediction, the Traviss *et al.*[38] correlation for high velocities and Kern's modification of the Nusselt equation[39] for low steam velocities are recommended.

5. CONCLUSION

This chapter deals with the heat transfer in vessels with mechanical agitators and Newtonian liquids only. The most commonly used heat transfer surfaces in agitated vessels were described, and correlations for the determination of the heat transfer coefficients for their particular surfaces were recommended. Vessel jackets are usually adequate to provide the required heat transfer surface for low or moderate heat duties. Helical pipe coils, vertical tube baffles, or other kinds of internal heat transfer surface are suitable for higher heat duties. For very high heat duties, adequate heat transfer capability is not possible with internal heat transfer surfaces and when external heat exchangers are used.

Proximity impellers, such as anchor and helical ribbons, are used with highly viscous liquids where homogeneous mixing is important for the control of the heat of reaction. Nonproximity impellers, such as paddles, axial-flow turbines, and propellers are not suitable for highly viscous liquids in heat transfer applications.

All recommended agitated vessel side heat transfer correlations are applicable for forced convection only. Several empirical relationships to determine the minimum agitator speed to ensure forced convection was developed and described in the literature.[32]

Scale-up is inherent in the application of the recommended heat transfer correlations which were developed mostly from small scale tests to industrial process equipment design. Equations (41), (42) or (43) provide the bases for scale-up for most design situations. General scale-up considerations are discussed, for example, by Uhl and Gray[2] or by Oldshue.[20] However, the literature does not provide sufficient means to scale-up from pilot plant *heat transfer* studies to large size systems. In many flow-controlled applications, for equal process results, the impeller power input is scaled-up by the batch volume directly (i.e. same power input per unit volume) assuming geometric similarity. This means calculating the constant power input per unit volume to achieve *approximately* the same heat transfer coefficient for the same impeller type. The effect of the impeller power input on the heat transfer coefficient is relatively small, as was shown by Oldshue.[20] Thus, even a moderate error in the impeller scale-up will have only a small effect on the agitated liquid heat transfer coefficient. Note, that in a jacketed vessel, the heat transfer area per unit volume decreases on scale-up. To maintain the same proportionate heat transfer per unit volume, additional heat transfer surface such as helical coils may be necessary. Despite the relatively large number of papers and studies on heat transfer in agitated vessels, a relatively small amount of published information exists on the temperature distribution in the batch of various systems and on its effect on the mean temperature difference. There is also a lack of data on scale-up and heat transfer in less common arrangements.

REFERENCES

1. ULBRECHT, J. J. and PATTERSON, G. K. *Mixing of Liquid by Mechanical Agitation*, 1985, Gordon and Breach, New York.
2. UHL, V. W. and GRAY, J. B. *Mixing–Theory and Practice*, Vol. 1, 1966, Academic Press, New York.
3. PENNEY, W. R. Agitated vessels. In: *Heat Exchanger Design Handbook*, 1983, Hemisphere, Washington.
4. STERBACEK, Z. and TAUSK, P. *Mixing in Chemical Industry*, 1965, Pergamon Press, Oxford.
5. HOLLAND, F. A. and CHAPMAN, F. S. *Liquid Mixing and Processing in Stirred Tanks*. 1966, Reinhold, London.
6. MUELLER, A. C. Mechanically-aided heat exchangers, *Proc. Advanced Study Institute on Heat Transfer Equipment*, 1986, Nat. Chem. Laboratory, Puna, India.
7. KERN, D. Q. *Process Heat Transfer*, 1950, McGraw-Hill, New York.
8. HARRY, F. P. and UHL, V. W. Heat transfer for highly viscous materials in a vessel with a helical ribbon impeller, Paper presented at the 74th Nat. AIChE Meeting, 1973, New Orleans.
9. BROWN, R. W., SCOTT, R., and TOYNE, C. An investigation of heat transfer in agitated jacketed cast iron vessels, *Trans. Inst. Chem. Engrs.*, 1947, **25**, 181–9.
10. UHL, V. W. and VOZNICK, H. P. The anchor agitator, *Chem. Engng. Progr.*, 1960, **56**, 3, 72–7.
11. UHL, V. W. Heat transfer to viscous materials in jacketed agitated kettles, *Chem. Engng. Prog. Sym. Ser.*, 1955, **51**, 17, 93–108.
12. PURSELL, H. P. M. S. Thesis, 1954, Newark College of Engineering, Newark, New Jersey.
13. NAGATA, S. *et al.* Turbulent heat transfer from the wall of a jacketed tank, *Heat Transfer Jpn. Res.*, 1972, **1**, 1, 66–74.
14. BROOKS, G. and SU, G. J. Heat transfer in agitated vessels, *Chem. Engng. Prog.*, 1959, **55**, 10, 54–7.
15. STREK, F. Heat transfer in liquid mixer—study of a turbine agitator with six flat blades, *Int. Chem. Engng.*, 1963, **3**, 4, 533–56.
16. CHAPMAN, F. S., DALLENBACH, H. and HOLLAND, F. A. Heat transfer in baffled, jacketed agitated vessels, *Trans. Inst. Chem. Engng.*, 1964, **42**, T398–T406.

17. ACKLEY, E. J. Film coefficients of heat transfer process vessels, *Chem. Engng.*, 1960, August 22, 133–40.
18. NAGATA, S. *et al.* Turbulent heat transfer from helical cooling coils in agitated vessels, *Heat Transfer Jpn. Res.*, 1972, **1**, 2, 44–56.
19. STREK, F. *et al.* Heat transfer in mixers of liquids (studies of propeller agitators), *Int. Chem. Engng.*, 1965, **5**, 4, 695–710.
20. OLDSHUE, J. Y. Heat transfer in agitated vessels. In: *Fluid Mixing Technology*, 1983, McGraw-Hill, New York.
21. GORDON, M. Ph. D. Thesis, 1941, University of Minnesota, Minneapolis.
22. CHILTON, T. H., DREW, T. B. and JEBENS, R. H. Heat transfer coefficient in agitated vessels, *Ind. Engng. Chem.*, 1944, **36**, 510–16.
23. KRAUSSOLD, H. Heat transfer in stirred containers, *Chem. Ing. Tech.*, 1951, **23**, 8, 177–83.
24. OLDSHUE, J. Y. and GRETTON, A. T. Helical coil heat transfer in mixing vessels, *Chem. Engng. Prog.*, 1954, **50**, 615–21.
25. OLDSHUE, J. Y. Fluid mixing, heat transfer and scale-up, *Chem. Process Engng.*, 1966, 183–88.
26. SKELLAND, A. H. P., ULRICH, J. A. and MACH, T. F. Effects of baffles on heat transfer to coils in a propeller agitated vessel, 1963, AIChE preprint 1, 6th Nat. Heat Transfer Conf., also SKELLAND, A. H. P., BLAKE, W. K. *et al.*, *AIChE J.*, 1965, **11**, 5, 951–4.
27. MALINA, J. A. and SPARROW, E. M. *Chem. Engng. Sci.*, 1964, **19**, 957–8.
28. PRATT, N. H. Heat transfer in reaction tank cooler by means of a coil, *Trans. Inst. Chem. Engrs.*, 1947, **25**, 163–80.
29. RUSHTON, J., LICHTMAN, R. S. and MAHONEY, L. H., *Ind. Engng. Chem.*, 1948, **40**, 1082.
30. GENTRY, C. C. and SMALL, W. M. Heat transfer and power consumption for agitated vessels having bare and finned vertical tube baffles, *Proc. 6th Int. Heat Transfer Conf.*, 1978, **4**, 13–18, Toronto.
31. PETREE, D. K. and SMALL, W. M. Heat transfer and power consumption for agitated vessels with vertical plate coils, AIChE Sym. Ser., 1978, **74**, 174, 53–59.
32. DUNLAP, I. R. and RUSHTON, J. H. *Chem. Engng. Prog.*, 1953, **49**, 5, 137–51.
33. APPLETON, W. T. and BRENNAN, W. C. Some observations on heat transfer to agitated liquids, *Can. J. Chem. Engng.*, October 1966, 276–80.
34. COLBURN, A. P. and HOUGEN, O. A. *Ind. Engng. Chem.*, 1930, **22**, 522, summarized in MCADAMS.[40]
35. LEHRER, I. H. Jacket side Nusselt numbers, *Ind. Engng. Chem. Proc. Des. Dev.*, 1970, **9**, 553–8.
36. BONDY, F. and LIPPA, F. Heat transfer in agitated vessels, *Chem. Engng.*, April 1983, 62–71.
37. JESCHKE, D., *Z. Ver. Deut. Ing.*, 1925, **69**, 1525, summarized in MCADAMS.[40]
38. TRAVISS, D. P., BARON, A. B. and ROHSENOW, W. M. Forced-convection condensation inside tubes, 1971, Report No. DSR 72591-74. MIT, Cambridge, Massachusetts.
39. PERRY, R. H. (ed.) *Chemical Engineering Handbook*, 5th edn., 1973, McGraw-Hill, New York, 10–19.
40. MCADAMS, W. H. *Heat Transmission*, 2nd edn., 1942, McGraw-Hill, New York.

Chapter 7

FALLING FILM EVAPORATION IN VERTICAL TUBES

J. W. PALEN

Heat Transfer Research, Inc. Alhambra, California, USA

SUMMARY

A brief survey is made of the state of the art of thermal design for vertical intube falling film evaporators. Much information is now available on heat transfer and hydrodynamics for a water film. Some correlations are general and can be applied to other pure fluids. Mass transfer effects for mixtures have received little attention so far, except for absorption, but some articles are now emerging on this subject.

In addition to briefly summarizing the available literature, it was intended to bring together design equations which will permit a realistic estimate of the tube-side heat transfer rates and pressure drops for a falling film evaporator. Many of the methods presented, however, need additional data for confirmation, and should be considered as a first estimate rather than final design calculations.

Even with approximate methods, it can be shown that the falling film evaporator has great advantages over other types of vapor generators in cases of low temperature difference, low operating pressure, and for viscous or heat sensitive fluids. With the increasing energy shortage forcing more low ΔT operation, it is expected that more use will be made of falling film evaporators in the process industries. However, more reliable design methods will require additional research.

NOTATION

B_c Empirical constant, mixture correction
BR   Boiling range, dew point–bubble point (K)

B_f	Film breakdown criterion for evaporation
C	Empirical constant
C_p	Liquid heat capacity (J/kg K)
C_{pv}	Vapor heat capacity (J/kg K)
D_i	Tube inside diameter (m)
F_c	Mixture correction factor
F_p	Nucleate boiling pressure function
f_v	Friction factor for vapor if flowing alone
G_t	Total flow mass velocity (kg/m^2 s)
G_v	Vapor phase mass velocity (kg/m^2 s)
g	Acceleration due to gravity (m/s^2)
h^*	Dimensionless heat transfer coefficient for the film
h_b	Nucleate boiling heat transfer coefficient (W/m^2 K)
h_c	Convective film heat transfer coefficient (W/m^2 K)
h_d	Developing region heat transfer coefficient (W/m^2 K)
h_e	Evaporation heat transfer coefficient (W/m^2 K)
h_{ef}	Evaporating film heat transfer coefficient (W/m^2 K)
h_f	Film heat transfer coefficient, developed region (W/m^2 K)
h_l	Liquid phase heat transfer coefficient (W/m^2 K)
h_{sv}	Sensible vapor heat transfer coefficient (W/m^2 K)
h_v	Vapor phase heat transfer coefficient (W/m^2 K)
j_g^*	Wallis dimensionless gas velocity
k	Liquid thermal conductivity (W/m K)
k_v	Vapor thermal conductivity (W/m K)
L	Tube length (m)
L_d	Length for developed flow (m)
n	Empirical constant
P	Operating pressure (kPa)
P_c	Critical pressure (kPa)
Pr	Liquid Prandtl number
Pr_v	Vapor Prandtl number
q	Heat flux (W/m^2)
q_b	Heat flux due to nucleate boiling (W/m^2)
q_{sv}	Sensible vapor heat flux (W/m^2)
R_v	Vapor volume fraction
Re	Liquid Reynolds number
Re_t	Effective transition Reynolds number
Re_v	Vapor Reynolds number
W_v	Flow rate of vapor (kg/s)
y	Mass fraction vapor

y_{in} Mass fraction vapor in
y_{out} Mass fraction vapor out

Greek

ΔP_l Liquid-Phase pressure drop (Pa)
ΔP_{tp} Two-phase pressure drop (Pa)
ΔP_{tpf} Two-phase pressure drop, friction (Pa)
ΔP_{tpm} Two-phase pressure drop, momentum (Pa)
ΔP_{tps} Two-phase pressure drop, static head (Pa)
ΔP_v Vapor-phase pressure drop (Pa)
ΔT_b Temperature difference between tubewall and liquid film (K)
ΔT_{fb} Maximum temperature difference for nucleate boiling (K)
ΔT_v Temperature change of vapor in axial direction (K)
Γ Liquid flowrate per unit circumference (kg/ms s)
λ Latent heat (J/kg)
μ Liquid viscosity (N s/m^2)
μ_w Liquid viscosity at tube wall (N s/m^2)
ρ Liquid density (kg/m^3)
ρ_v Vapor density (kg/m^3)

1. INTRODUCTION

Falling film evaporators have been used for many years for such applications as concentration of inorganic salts in fertilizer production, concentration of kraft liquor in the pulp and paper industry, and desalination.

1.1. Areas of Increasing Application

In recent years the advantages of the falling film evaporation process in additional process applications have been recognized, prompting a revival of interest and new research in this area. This increased interest is seen to be growing mainly out of the three following trends in the process industries.

(a) Vaporization at very low temperature differences. As requirements for energy conservation become even more stringent, the plant entropy gains will be minimized and this ultimately results in lower temperature differences which can be afforded for vaporization. For other types of process vaporizers there can be an exponential decrease in the heat transfer rate at low temperature differences due to the effect of the static head

necessary for circulation on the boiling temperature difference. The effect is especially severe for vacuum operation.

(b) *Vaporization of solvent from viscous fluids.* A question arising more frequently in the process industries, as the use of plastics continues to increase, is how best to vaporize fluid systems which include a volatile solvent and a nonvolatile solute, which may be viscous and which may require vacuum operation. Experience has shown that vertical thermosiphon reboilers give very poor performance for this type of system. One route taken by some companies is to use a tube-side forced flow vaporizer with suppressed vaporizaton. This ensures circulation but requires a high operating cost, which is contrary to goals of minimized energy consumption. Also, for suppressed vaporization all energy input must be taken as sensible heat, and this may cause an unacceptably high fluid temperature before flashing.

(c) *Heat sensitive fluids.* Biological solutions, explosive fluids, and fluids which decompose all require a limitation on wall temperature and a minimum residence time in the vaporizer. These fluids may also require vacuum operation in order to minimize bulk temperature and, as with vacuum operation in general, require a minimum of boiling point rise due to static head.

In each of the above situations a falling film evaporator is potentially a good solution, minimizing both static head and residence time, and at the same time achieving very high heat transfer coefficients at low temperature differences. Although these units have been used for many years for evaporation of aqueous solutions of soluble salts, they have not been used extensively in the process industries for situations as described above.

1.2. Important General Design Considerations

Some of the areas which need to be investigated for an adequate design are as follows:

(a) *Matching heat transfer rates to tube dimensions.* It is important that the fluid be evaporated to the specified vapor fraction and heavy component concentration in the specified tube length. Too much evaporation can cause dryout and possible component deterioration, while too little evaporation causes incorrect bottom liquid composition and need for excessive recycling. Therefore, the tube length and flow rate must be matched carefully with the heat transfer rate, and this requires an accurate prediction of the heat transfer coefficient.

(b) *Effect of nucleate boiling.* Under pure component conditions the heat transfer coefficient for the liquid film, in the absence of nucleate boiling, is usually predicted by relationships similar to those used for vertical tube-side condensation of a pure component. However, under conditions of interest there is always a possibility of some nucleate boiling, which may greatly increase the local heat transfer rate but may also cause dryout at the bottom of the tube. Very little information is available on determination of the onset and effect of nucleate boiling, especially for fluids other than water.

(c) *Effect of mixtures.* Fluids evaporated are seldom pure components. However, for some aqueous solutions of soluble salts, the deviation from pure component behavior is not great, and nearly all methods in the literature treat this case only. In studies of nucleate and convective boiling it has been confirmed that there is a severe effect of the mixture boiling range on the heat transfer coefficient. Most of the mixtures which would be vaporized in the process industries in falling film evaporators have very large boiling ranges. Nearly all research on mass transfer effects in falling films has dealt with absorption of soluble vapors into a pure liquid film, although some more recent work is being done with evaporation of binaries, as discussed in following sections.

(d) *Pressure drop.* Pressure drop is generally low in falling film evaporators, which is one of the big advantages. However, since these units may be used under very high vacuum, the pressure drop available is close to zero; so any pressure drop generated cannot be ignored. The largest component of pressure drop is expected to be due to acceleration of the vapor. Unfortunately, the acceleration component is strongly related to the slip between the vapor and liquid phases, which is an empirically determined relationship and not generally available for the applicable conditions.

(e) *Tube entrance flow distribution.* In order for a falling film evaporator to work properly, liquid must be supplied uniformly to all tubes. This has long been recognized to be a necessary component of the design, and various devices have been proposed for the tube entrances to improve distribution.

(f) *Film breakdown.* It is recognized that above a certain heat flux and below a certain liquid film flowrate, the film begins to break down, forming dry patches on the surface. This is, of course, an undesirable condition causing low average heat transfer coefficients and possibility for product overheating and decomposition. A general method to predict the onset of film breakdown presently does not exist.

Other important design unknowns, such as the film boiling maximum allowable heat flux and the optimum recycle rate, have received very little attention in the literature.

2. LITERATURE

Over 90 pertinent references on this subject are listed. Most are these were published since 1970. However, a few earlier references were included if particularly useful.

2.1. Reviews and General Design Data

Recent reviews of the state of the art are presented by Ganic,[1] and by Seban.[2] Ganic[1] references fifteen sources of data for heat transfer to falling films, eight for vertical tubes or surfaces and seven for horizontal tubes. The majority of the data are for water, although three sources are for ammonia on horizontal tubes, two are for aqueous solutions,[3,4] and one early data set from Bays and McAdams,[5] is for oil. Data from a full scale apparatus for desalination of sea water was reported in an early paper by Sinek and Young.[6] Much additional work has been done in this area. A recent thesis by Lampert[7] gives extensive data for double fluted tubes. An earlier symposium[8] also emphasizes enhanced tubes for desalination.[9] Hasson and Perl[10] discuss scale deposition in desalination.

2.2. Mechanical Features and Economics

General descriptions of applications and mechanical features of falling film evaporators are given by Sack,[11] Smith[12] and more recently by Mehra.[13] Economic benefits are discussed by Fosberg and Claussen,[14] and by Murray.[15]

2.3. Heat and Mass Transfer

Methods for correlation of the heat transfer coefficient for a falling film are given in the review references 1 and 2, as summarized below. Heat transfer is also discussed in references 16–26. Nucleate boiling effects are treated in references 27–30. Mass transfer during absorption is discussed in references 31–36. References 37–41 cover evaporation mass transfer, and theoretical aspects are discussed in references 42 and 43.

2.4. Film Dynamics and Stability

A relatively large number of references[44–62] were concerned with the dynamics, stability and breakdown of liquid films. Ganic and Mastanaiah[57] present an extensive review in which they reference and categorize 26 experimental studies of the hydrodynamics of this liquid films. This reference also updates the review of heat transfer given by Ganic[1] and references seven additional heat transfer investigations.

2.5. Pressure Drop and Miscellaneous

Pressure drop considerations are discussed in references 63–67. Additional references involving enhanced surfaces are 68–71.

Critical heat fluxes, as such, are discussed only in references 72 and 73, although references listed above on film breakdown also treat a type of heat flux limitation.

In the following sections some practical design guides based on material from the above references are summarized.

3. CONSTRUCTION FEATURES

3.1. General Configuration

Figure 1 is a schematic illustration of a typical falling film evaporator arrangement. This type can be either a concentrator or a vaporizer, depending on whether the product is considered to be the vapor or the liquid. The liquid feed enters the top chamber, is distributed to the tubes, and falls by gravity in a thin film down the inside of each tube. For the most common type of operation, the vapor generated by the hot tube wall flows downward also and is discharged along with the liquid at the bottom of the unit. The tubes are heated usually by introducing steam or other condensable vapor at the top of the unit outside the tubes (shell-side). A hot liquid or gas may also be used, and in this case might be introduced at the bottom rather than the top to obtain counter current flow. The shell-side should have baffles to increase velocity for single phase heating media and to provide tube rigidity, to prevent vibration, for condensing media.

In Fig. 1, the vapor and liquid streams are partially separated in the bottom chamber of the evaporator and the liquid is drawn off the bottom of the unit. The vapor with entrained liquid flows into a centrifugal separator from which the remaining liquid is removed. The vapor continues upward through a mesh-type entrainment eliminator and out.

For the unit shown in Fig. 1, it is assumed that the vapor being produced is steam, and a direct contact condenser is used to produce water which flows out to a hotwell. Noncondensable gases are vented from the direct contact condenser to vacuum jets, in case of vacuum operation. This type of arrangement could be used either to concentrate a solute, as in the fertilizer and pulp-paper industries, or to produce pure water from salt water as in the desalination industry.

In other cases, the vapors may be used to supply a distillation column for low pressure, low temperature difference separation processes. Figure

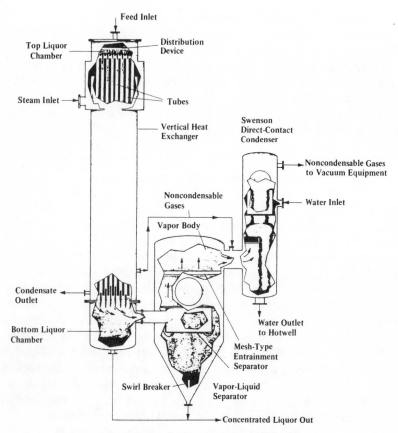

FIG. 1. Falling film evaporator (courtesy Swenson Inc.).

2 illustrates a possible arrangement for a falling film vaporizer used as a distillation column reboiler. In this case the vapor and liquid flow together through a mitered exit nozzle, to minimize pressure drop, into the bottoms reservoir of the distillation columm, where the liquid separates and the vapor flows upward to the first tray.

Liquid from the bottom reservoir is recycled to the top of the evaporator, as illustrated in Fig. 2. Since both economics and performance are affected by the amount of recycle, it is important to be able to determine the minimum recycle rate. This value is dependent both upon the minimum wetting rate and upon the effect of the fraction vaporized on the available temperature difference for heat transfer.

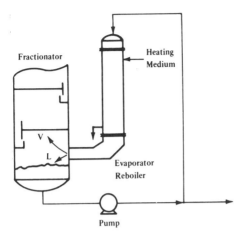

FIG. 2. Falling film evaporator as distillation column reboiler.

3.2. Liquid Distribution

One of the best known design rules for falling film evaporators is that it is important to obtain uniform distribution of the liquid to the tubes. As liquid flows into the top chamber, distribution must take place in two steps, distribution to the tube-sheet, and distribution to the tubes. Two possible methods of distribution to the tube-sheet are illustrated in Fig. 3. In (a) the side nozzle feed is shown, while in (b) a top feed nozzle is shown. In the latter case, a hat-type distributor protects tubes from direct impingement of inlet

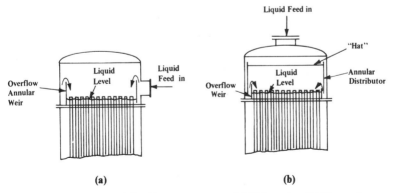

FIG. 3. Two types of liquid entry systems. (a) Side entry. (b) Top entry.

liquid. The liquid flows down though an annular space to the outside of the tube-sheet and over a weir to establish a level on the tube-sheet. The tube ends, or tube inserts, extend up above the tubesheet.

In Fig. 4, tube distribution devices are illustrated. The simple weir

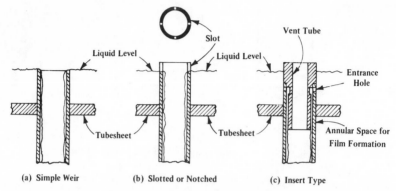

(a) Simple Weir   (b) Slotted or Notched   (c) Insert Type

FIG. 4. Tube side liquid distributors.

configuration (Fig. 4 (a)) is not recommended since it does nothing to minimize maldistribution caused by the liquid gradient established by the flow inward across the tubesheet. The slot type distributor (Fig. 4 (b)) is commonly used, with either rectangular slots or V notches cut in the tube to provide pressure drop to overcome the flow gradient. At high flow rates it is possible for the liquid to shoot through the slots into the center of the tube rather than falling down the wall. This effect can be mostly eliminated by cutting the slots on a angle so that the liquid enters the tube tangentially. For this option, round holes, which are easier to produce tangentially, may be used rather than slots. A more elaborate distribution scheme is also shown (Fig. 4 (c)) in which an annular film is assured by use of an insert which mechanically forces annular flow. Presently there is some indication from industry that the slotted distributor can give adequate performance, especially if tangentially cut slots are used. These are, of course, made in inserts which fit into the tops of the tubes, rather than in the tubes themselves.

3.3. Vapor Discharge
Design of the vapor discharge system is important, especially for vacuum conditions, where pressure drop must be minimized. There are three basic

configurations for vapor discharge. For downward flow of vapor, the phases may be separated as in Fig. 1 or flow out together as in Fig. 2. In this latter case care should be taken that the exit pipe size is large enough to prevent excessive pressure drop.

In some cases, especially when dealing with inert gases in the vapor it may be preferable to have the vapor flowing upward counter current to the liquid and discharging from the top of the unit. Such an arrangement is shown in Fig. 5. This counter current flow arrangement provides maximum

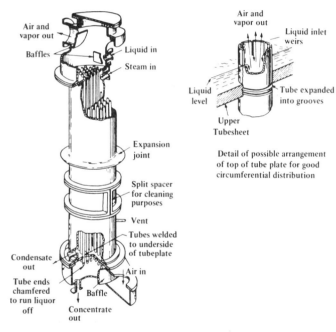

FIG. 5. Falling film evaporator with upflow of vapor.

stripping of volatile components from the liquid, but complicates the film distribution problem. As shown in Fig. 5, the highest gas velocity at the exit of the tube is working against the establishment of a uniform film. The gas velocity must be limited so as not to produce carryover of liquid, flooding, or to cause dry spots by holdup of the film. A more elaborate tube distribution device, such as the one in Fig. 4(c), may be required.

4. TUBE-SIDE HEAT TRANSFER COEFFICIENTS

Most work on heat transfer coefficients for a falling film in a vertical tube has been done with water and apply only to pure fluids in the absence of both vapor shear and nucleate boiling. However, it is the intent of this section to cover as much as possible all realistic conditions which would be found in a commercial evaporator.

4.1. Convection in a Falling Film

The greatest advantages of falling film evaporators are seen when the temperature difference for vaporization is low. Therefore, for many practical applications, the effects of vapor shear and of nucleate boiling can be neglected.

4.1.1. Negligible Vapor Shear Effect

For the case of laminar flow, Chun and Seban[18] have obtained a complete solution of the differential equations for the developing thermal boundary layer by numerical integration. Seban[2] presents a plot of local heat transfer coefficients from this solution, and shows that measured heat transfer coefficients for water fall about 20–50% higher than the calculated theoretical curve. For fully developed flow the local heat transfer coefficients become independent of length at a given Reynolds number. Chun and Seban present a design correlation for the developed laminar regime, as follows:

$$h^* = 0.821 Re^{-0.22} \qquad (1)$$

The term, h^*, which will be used throughout, is the dimensionless heat transfer coefficient, as defined by Ganic,[1] where

$$h^* = h_f(\mu^2/\rho^2 k^3 g)^{1/3} \qquad (2)$$

Equation (1) was found to fall about 10% lower than the data of Fujita and Ueda,[46] which is considered to be good agreement.

For turbulent flow, the data of Chun and Seban are correlated by the following equation:

$$h^* = 0.0038 Re^{0.4} Pr^{0.65} \qquad (3)$$

Fujita and Ueda,[46] for water evaporating at atmospheric pressure, recommend,

$$h^* = 0.006 Re^{0.4} \qquad (4)$$

Equations (3) and (4) are equivalent at a Prandtl number of about 2·0. The actual Prandtl number for water at 100°C is about 1·8. The exponent on the Prandtl number in eqn. (3) seems rather high when compared to the Prandtl number dependency usually observed in turbulent convective heat transfer. The range of Prandtl numbers covered by Chun and Seban, using water as the test fluid, was 1·8–5·7. The data of Wilke,[3] for heat transfer to a subcooled turbulent film of ethylene glycol/water cover a Prandtl number range of 5·4–210 and can be represented by the following equation:

$$h^* = 0.008\ 71\ Re^{0.4}\ Pr^{0.334} \qquad (5)$$

Likewise, Gimbutis[80] obtained an exponent of 0·34 on the Prandtl number for heat transfer to a turbulent falling film of subcooled water over a Prandtl number range of 4·3–8·4. Based upon these observations, it is recommended that care be used in extrapolation of eqn. (3) to high Prandtl numbers. A suggested approach is to calculate by both eqn. (3) and eqn. (5) and use the lower value.

Prior to the experimentally backed analytical work of Chun and Seban, falling film heat transfer coefficients for evaporation, as well as for condensation were often estimated by the theoretically derived curves of Dukler.[81] These were calculated numerically, and based on a combination of the Deissler and Von Karman equations for eddy diffusivities. It is presently considered that these solutions give reasonably good results at low Prandtl numbers, but tend to become optimistic at high Prandtl numbers. A more recent theoretical analysis by Sandall et al.[16] uses an empirical function obtained from the Chun–Seban data.

Figure 6 shows a comparison of the Chun–Seban empirical correlations given above with the Dukler curves for $Re > 100$. For $Pr > 1$, it is more conservative to use the Chun–Seban equations, especially in the transition Reynolds number regions.

It is seen in Fig. 6 that the transition between laminar and turbulent Chun–Seban correlations, if taken as the intersection, varies with respect to Prandtl number. The transition Reynolds number obtained from eqns. (1) and (3) (does not necessarily infer the hydrodynamic transition) is the following,

$$Re_t = 5800/Pr^{1.06} \qquad (6)$$

For completeness, the classical Nusselt equation for condensation heat transfer with a smooth laminar falling film is also shown in Fig. 6. The Chun–Seban correlation for laminar flow is seen to intersect the Nusselt

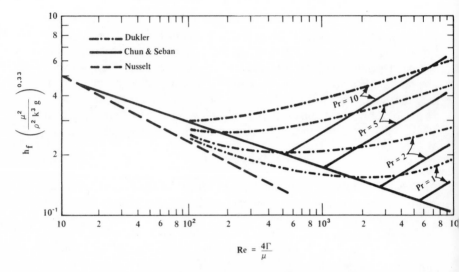

FIG. 6. Falling film heat transfer coefficient, zero shear.

curve at a Reynolds number of about 20, below which the Nusselt values should be used.

The above equations apply to the case of fully developed flow. In the entrance region, the local heat transfer coefficients will be larger. Lorenz and Yung,[82] give an equation for the average heat transfer coefficient in the developing region.

$$h_d = 0.375 C_p (\Gamma/L_d) \tag{7}$$

where

$$L_d = [\Gamma^{1.33} C_p / 4\pi k][3\mu/g\rho^2]^{0.33} \tag{8}$$

The average heat transfer coefficient for the film over a length, L, according to Lorenz and Yung is then calculated as

$$h_c = h_d(L_d/L) + h_f(1 - L_d/L) \tag{9}$$

According to eqn. (8), the development length, L_d, is negligible for fluids with low viscosity and high thermal conductivity, such as water, but can be significant, especially at high Reynolds number for fluids such as ethylene glycol or heavy oils. For practical use, eqn. (9) should be limited so that h_c is always greater than or equal to h_f.

4.1.2. Vapor Shear Effects

Normally, falling film evaporators are designed for conditions such that the vapor velocity is low and shear effects of the film can be neglected. This is usually the case if the vapor Reynolds number is less than about 20 000. For vacuum operations at high heat flux, shear forces can begin to dominate, and for shear controlled flow, the heat transfer correlations shown above no longer apply. A criterion which has been used successfully in condensation to distinguish between shear controlled and gravity controlled flow is the Wallis[83] dimensionless gas velocity, j_g^*.

$$j_g^* = G_v/[D_i g \rho_v (\rho_l - \rho_v)]^{0.5}$$ (10)

If it is assumed that the same regime boundaries used for condensation are at least roughly applicable to evaporation, eqn. (9) is applicable only for $j_g^* \leqslant 0.5$.

For $j_g^* \geqslant 1.5$, it is assumed that forced convection annular flow exists for which a Chen-type two-phase convection correlation is applicable.

$$h_c = h_l(\Delta P_{tpf}/\Delta P_l)^{0.44}$$ (11)

where the liquid phase heat transfer coefficient, h_l, can be estimated by a Dittus–Boelter-type correlation.

$$h_l = 0.023(k_l/D_i)Re^{0.8}Pr_l^{0.4}(\mu/\mu_w)^{0.14}$$ (12)

The ratio of two-phase to liquid phase pressure drop shown in eqn. (11) is further discussed in a later section. For $0.5 < j_g^* < 1.5$ it is recommended to calculate h_c by both eqn. (9) and eqn. (11) and linearly interpolate with respect to j_g^*.

4.1.3. Nucleate Boiling Effects

Much is still not known about bubble nucleation in falling films. In recent experimental and theoretical work, Cerza and Sernas[28] concluded that the Clapeyron criteria was a necessary but not sufficient condition for nucleation. It was determined that not only nucleation site dimensions but also contact angle and viscous controlled capillary penetration must be taken into account if accurate prediction is to be made of the temperature difference at which nucleate boiling takes place.

For design it is usually conservative to neglect nucleate boiling, unless the boiling is so vigorous as to disrupt the film and cause dry patches, see below. One reasonable approach, if the effect of nucleate boiling is to be included, is to calculate the heat flux according to the falling film equations and also according to the nucleate boiling correlations and use the method which gives the highest heat flux. This is the method of parallel mechanisms, which has been used successfully in other similar situations, and which usually gives a somewhat conservative result. Another less conservative approach suggested by Lorenz and Yung[82] is to sum the heat transfer coefficients for boiling and convection as was done by Chen[84] for upflow convective boiling.

$$h_{ef} = F_c h_b + F_c^n h_c \qquad (13)$$

The term, F_c, in eqn. (13) is a mixture correction, which is 1·0 for pure components and is explained for mixtures in Section 4.1.4 below.

The nucleate boiling heat transfer correlation can be obtained from several sources. Chen uses the Forster–Zuber correlation.[85] A more recent correlation developed from a very large data base by Stephan and Abdelsalam[86] was found to give good results for pool boiling. For quick estimations, a reasonable short cut equation is the following by Mostinski.[87]

$$h_b = 0·004\ 17 P_c^{0·69} q_b^{0·7} F_p \qquad (14)$$

where

$$F_p = 1·8(P/P_c) + 4·0(P/P_c)^{1·2} + 10·0(P/P_c)^{10} \qquad (15)$$

Since eqn. (14) is dimensional, units of q must be W/m^2 and units of P and P_c must be kPa.

Equation (13) does not contain an empirical suppression factor for the nucleate boiling heat transfer coefficient, as in the Chen correlation. Although Lorenz and Yung assumed this factor to be 1·0, it is suggested that some suppression be accounted for by evaluating at the nucleate boiling heat flux, q_b, rather than the total heat flux, q.

$$\Delta T_b = q/h_{ef} \qquad (16)$$

and

$$q_b = h_b \Delta T_b \qquad (17)$$

This approach requires a trial and error procedure in which q_b is first assumed equal 0·5 q, h_b is calculated from eqn. (14), and h_{ef} is calculated from eqn. (13). Finally, q_b is checked by eqns (16) and (17), adjusted and steps are repeated until q_b is converged upon.

4.1.4. *Liquid Phase Mass Transfer Effects*

Although most fluids evaporated are not pure components, very little attention has been given to the effect of mixture composition on heat transfer in falling films. In nucleate pool boiling, it is known both from data, e.g. reference 88 and from theory, e.g. reference 30, that the effective boiling heat transfer coefficient decreases severely as the boiling range (dew point minus bubble point = BR) increases.

Empirical design methods are available to roughly account for this effect in process reboilers.[89] Recent work by Gropp and Schluender[90] discusses application of theoretical approaches for pool boiling to falling films. In reference 90 it is shown that for mixtures of R-11 and R-113 (boiling range = about 4·4 K) there is very little effect of mass transfer resistance at a heat flux of 6000 W/m², for which there was no nucleate boiling. However, as heat flux was increased to 16 000 W/m², nucleate boiling was observed and the heat transfer coefficient became slightly less than the average value for the pure components, indicating mass transfer resistance. This effect became stronger as heat flux was further increased. For this narrow boiling range, mass transfer resistance effects would be expected to be less severe than for wide boiling ranges. There are no data known at this time for film evaporation of wide boiling range mixtures. Since some mass transfer resistance effect is inevitable, to ignore the effect would be to err on the unsafe side, so it is recommended that a correction be applied for mixtures. Although methods used for pool boiling may be somewhat conservative for falling film evaporation, due to nonequilibrium effects, there is presently no better practical approach for design.

The Schluender method[30] for nucleate pool boiling is recommended when data are available for its application. An alternative short-cut empirical equation is proposed in reference 91.

$$F_c = 1/[1 + B_c q^{0.15} BR^{0.75}] \qquad (18)$$

where

$B_c = 0.0235$ for q in W/m² and BR in K
$B_c = 0.018$ for q in Btu/h ft² and BR in F.

Based on the data of Gropp and Schluender it is apparent that the mixture correction should mostly be applied to the nucleate boiling mechanism. However, for higher boiling range mixtures it is theoretically possible to have a significant diffusion resistance in the absence of nucleate boiling. It is proposed that the mixture correction factor raised to some power less than 1·0 also be applied to the convective term, as is shown in eqn. (13). Presently there are no wide boiling range data to permit evaluation of the exponent n in eqn. (13). For the Gropp and Schluender data (BR = 4·4 K) good agreement is obtained with $n = 0$. However, to be on the safe side for wide boiling mixtures it is proposed that for design an n of at least 0·33 be used in eqn. (13). Additional data are badly needed.

4.2. Vapor Phase Heat Transfer
For cases with large amounts of noncondensable gas or with a very large temperature change from inlet of the tube, it is necessary to account for sensible heat transfer to the gas phase. For typical designs this is not a large effect and it is sufficiently accurate to use an approximation. In reference 92 it is shown that the heat transfer resistance for the vapor phase in boiling can be approximated by the Silver–Bell resistance proration method normally used for condensation.

$$h_e = [1/h_{ef} + 1/h_v]^{-1} \tag{19}$$

The vapor phase heat transfer coefficient is approximated as,

$$h_v = h_{sv}(q/q_{sv}) \tag{20}$$

The sensible vapor heat flux is obtained as,

$$q_{sv} = W_v C_{pv} \Delta T_v \tag{21}$$

The sensible vapor convective heat transfer coefficient is obtained from the Dittus–Boelter-type correlation,

$$h_{sv} = 0·023(k_v/D_i) Re_v^{0·8} Pr_v^{0·4} \tag{22}$$

5. FILM BREAKDOWN

In all vaporizers, it is necessary to keep a liquid film on the tube wall for effective operation. Vapor contact with the tube wall, which causes a much lower heat transfer coefficient, can be produced by several different mechanisms.

(a) Dry spots can appear on the surface due simply to insufficient liquid flow for wetting. This phenomenon is a function of surface tension and contact angle. A number of models have been proposed, as described by Ganic.[1,57]

(b) Rivulets can be formed by Marangoni effects in case of surface tension gradients caused by local concentration and temperature gradients. This is a variation of the nonwetting effect which occurs especially with mixtures.

(c) During nucleate boiling liquid droplets from bursting vapor bubbles are entrained in the vapor core and cause a reduction in the film flow rate which can result in the appearance of dry patches in the lower end of the tube.

(d) The wall temperature must be below a certain critical value to prevent blanketing of the surface by vapor due to the Leidenfrost effect. Normally however, for falling film vaporizers the design temperature difference is too low for Leidenfrost type film boiling.

An excellent experimental and theoretical treatment of the first three mechanisms, water data only, is given by Fujita and Ueda.[45,46]

Mechanisms (a) and (b) occur chiefly in sub-cooled films or mixtures. Since the nonwetting phenomenon is highly dependent on contact angle and on local surface tension gradients, neither of which are easy to measure, these mechanisms are extremely difficult to generalize. Fundamental work in evaporation at solid–liquid–vapor contact points is being performed by Wayner and Parks.[93] Figure 7 illustrates data of references 25 and 45 for

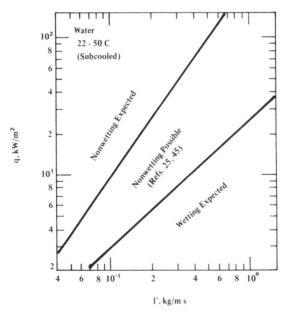

FIG. 7. Film breakdown due to sub-cooled films and aqueous mixtures.

film breakdown (nonwetting) for sub-cooled water films. It is doubtful whether the same effects would be observed for other fluids with lower values of surface tension, but effects may be similar for aqueous mixtures. Fortunately, saturated films tend to wet the heating surface much better, at least for pure components. According to Fujita and Ueda, the process of film breakdown in evaporating films is expected to be much different from that in highly sub-cooled films, and occurs as a result of evaporation and droplet entrainment, mechanism (c) above. One reasonable approach to a criterion for the minimum allowable liquid rate for evaporating films is to evaluate the ratio of liquid supplied to liquid evaporated per unit tube circumference. This criterion, termed B_f, is formulated as follows.

$$B_f = (\Gamma \lambda)/(qL) \tag{23}$$

Figure 8 illustrates the data of reference 46 for evaporation of water at 95·5°C outside a 46 mm tube 1000 mm long with downflow of water and upflow of steam. As function of heat flux and outlet Γ, there were observed regions of (1) no dry patches, (2) intermittent dry patches and (3) permanent dry patches. Permanent dry patches were seen to occur at the bottom of the

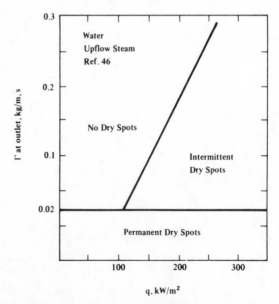

FIG. 8. Film breakdown due to evaporation of pure component films.

tube for an outlet Γ less than 0.01–0.02 kg/m s. For saturated water at atmospheric pressure this limiting Γ corresponds to a Re of about 140–280. For the case shown in Fig. 8, a value of B_f based on the inlet value of Γ corresponding to an exit value of 0.02 at a heat flux of $150\,000$ W/m^2 is calculated to be roughly 1.0. This is equal to the minimum logical value of B_f. Allowing for some safety factor, it is proposed that the limiting value of B_f for design be taken as,

$$B_f > 1.5 \tag{24}$$

Equation (23) can be used to estimate either the maximum value of Γ for a given length or the maximum tube length for a given liquid loading at a certain average design heat flux. However, it should be recognized that eqn. (24) is only an estimated rule of thumb, and should be improved with data whenever possible. It is probably unsafe for aqueous mixtures (use Fig. 7.).

The final mechanism listed above, (d), is not expected to occur in normal designs because the most economical application of falling film evaporators is at low temperature differences, and also at low pressures where the critical temperature difference is highest. Nevertheless, if the Leidenfrost temperature should be exceeded, the effect on performance would be catastrophic, so to be on the safe side the critical temperature difference should be checked. A simplified equation for estimating the critical temperature difference above which film boiling will begin to occur is taken from the Cichelli and Bonilla pool boiling data.[91,94]

$$\Delta T_{fb} = 0.555[52(1 - P/P_c) + 0.04/(P/P_c)^2] \tag{25}$$

Since the critical temperature difference may be somewhat less for a vaporizing falling film than for pool boiling it is recommended that the design temperature difference between the tube wall and the saturation temperature of the film not exceed 0.6 of ΔT_{fb} from eqn. (25).

6. PRESSURE DROP

Pressure drop in falling film evaporator tubes is very low under normal design conditions. However, typical falling film evaporators may operate at very low absolute pressures, and under these conditions the pressure drop should be calculated. The three components of pressure drop, friction, acceleration, and static head are shown in the following equation:

$$\Delta P_{tp} = \Delta P_{tpf} + \Delta P_{tpm} + \Delta P_{tps} \tag{26}$$

6.1. Gravity Controlled Flow

Gravity controlled falling film flow should take place if $j_g^* < 0.5$, as calculated from eqn. (10). Under this condition, the two-phase static head, ΔP_{tps}, is just equal to the weight of the vapor, $(\rho_v g L)$, and normally is negligible, especially in vacuum.

The friction loss, ΔP_{tpf}, should be somewhat higher than that for vapor flow alone due to waves on the liquid interface and the slightly reduced cross-section for flow. To account for these effects, it is suggested that a multiplier of 1·3 be used with the vapor phase pressure drop.

$$\Delta P_{tpf} = 4f_v(L/D_i)[G_v^2/(2\rho_v)](1·3) \tag{27}$$

Especially for vacuum operation, the majority of the pressure drop should be obtained from the momentum change due to vaporization. Under these conditions, the acceleration of the liquid film can be ignored with respect to the acceleration of the vapor, and the momentum change pressure drop may be calculated as follows.

$$\Delta P_{tpm} = G_t^2\{\Delta[y^2/(\rho_v R_v)]\} \tag{28}$$

The vapor volume fraction, R_v, can be approximated as 1·0 under these conditions. The vapor density is essentially constant so momentum pressure drop for vaporization in a tube in gravity controlled flow at low absolute pressure may be approximated as follows.

$$\Delta P_{tpm} = (G_t^2/\rho_v)(y_{out}^2 - y_{in}^2) \tag{29}$$

6.2. Shear Controlled Flow

If the factor, j_g^*, from eqn. (10) is greater than 1·5, it may be assumed that shear forces are significantly greater than gravity forces and therefore upflow or downflow orientation gives essentially the same pressure drop. Under these conditions there is significant entrainment of the liquid film into the vapor and normal Martinelli–Chisholm-type methods[95] may be used. A convenient form for the friction loss arising from the Chisholm C type curve fit[95] is,

$$\Delta P_{tpf} = \Delta P_l + C(\Delta P_v \Delta P_l)^{1/2} + \Delta P_v \tag{30}$$

where the factor, C, can be taken as 20 for a first approximation.

For shear controlled flow the momentum change must consider both phases due to entrainment. Since empirical correlations for slip in downflow boiling are scarce and not generally reliable, it is recommended to use the homogeneous approximation for the momentum change.

$$\Delta P_{tpm} = G_t^2\{\Delta[y/\rho_v + (1-y)/\rho_l]\} \tag{28}$$

Most of the pressure drop in falling film vaporizers will probably be consumed in the exit header and piping. Calculations depend upon the exact piping configuration, but should not be ignored in the final design. Useful relationships for two-phase flow pressure drop in piping configurations are given in reference 95.

7. FLOODING

One very good reason for having downflow of vapor is that flooding does not occur. However, there are some situations, such as in stripping components out of the liquid stream in which upflow of vapor is preferred. In this case it is important to limit the vapor velocity so that there is not a large upflow of liquid, flooding. The critical region is at the top of the tube where the flow rates of both the liquid and the vapor are greatest.

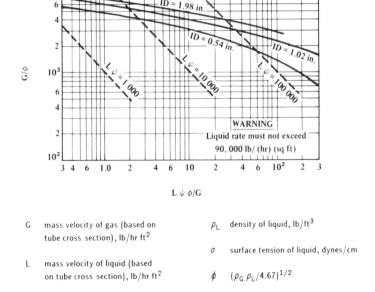

L ψ φ/G

| G | mass velocity of gas (based on tube cross section), lb/hr ft² | ρ_L | density of liquid, lb/ft³ |

G   mass velocity of gas (based on tube cross section), lb/hr ft²

L   mass velocity of liquid (based on tube cross section), lb/hr ft²

μ_L viscosity of liquid, cP

ρ_G density of gas, lb/ft³

ρ_L density of liquid, lb/ft³

σ   surface tension of liquid, dynes/cm

φ $(\rho_G \rho_L/4.67)^{1/2}$

ψ $(73/\sigma)[\mu_L (62.3/\rho_L)^2]^{1/3}$

FIG. 9. Holmes curves for flooding velocities.

It is logical to assume that flooding cannot occur in gravity controlled flow. Therefore, consistent with the above discussion, one limiting criterion should be $j_g^* < 0.5$ at the top of the tube. This criterion may not be sufficient at high liquid rates. Alternatively, estimate of the maximum allowable vapor velocity can be obtained from the curves of Holmes,[79] (Fig. 9).

8. CONCLUSIONS AND RECOMMENDATIONS

Falling film evaporators can have great advantages in case of low available temperature difference, low operating pressure, and for viscous or heat sensitive fluids. Reasonably good correlations are available for calculation of the heat transfer coefficient for pure components in the absence of vapor shear and nucleate boiling. Fortunately many practical applications fall within these constraints. However, for a general industrial design procedure it is necessary to have the ability to account for mixture, vapor shear, and nucleate boiling effects. In addition it is very important to be able to estimate the minimum amount of liquid recirculation to assure good operation. Most of these latter effects have not been resolved; certainly not for typical process fluids.

The correlations and rules of thumb given in the preceding sections are intended to guide the engineer to a reasonable first estimate of a workable design. However, for a final design prior industrial experience should be consulted. Companies which manufacture falling film evaporators usually have proprietary knowledge in specific applications, especially with respect to detailed mechanical design.

Ultimately it is likely that falling film evaporators, like other types of reboilers, will be designed primarily by computer programs. Before such programs can be considered reliable, however, it will be necessary to obtain a significant amount of additional data over a wide range of process conditions.

REFERENCES

1. GANIC, E. N. On the heat transfer and fluid flow in falling film shell-and-tube evaporators, *Heat Exchangers, Thermal-Hydraulic Fundamentals and Design*, S. Kakac, A. E. Bergles and F. Mayinger, (eds.), 1981, Hemisphere, New York, 705–19.
2. SEBAN, R. A. Transport to Falling Films, Keynote Address, *6th Int. Heat Trans. Conf.*, 1978, Hemisphere, Washington DC, 417–28.
3. WILKE, W. Waermeuebergang und Rieselfilme, *ForshHft. Ver. Dt. Ing.*, **490**, B.

4. PONTER, A. B. and DAVIES, G. A. Heat transfer to falling films, *Chem. Engng. Sci.*, 1968, **23**, 664–5.
5. BAYS, G. S. and MCADAMS, W. H. *Ind. Engng. Chem.*, 1937, **29**, 1240.
6. SINEK, J. R. and YOUNG, E. H. Heat transfer in falling-film long tube evaporators, *Chem. Engng. Prog.*, Dec. 1962, **58**(12), 74–80.
7. LAMPERT, W. Falling film heat transfer on vertical double fluted tubes, Ph.D. thesis, University of Michigan, 1985.
8. SCHROEDER, J. J., SANDER-BEUERMANN, W. and FAST, P. Optimization of heat transfer on vertically finned falling film evaporator surfaces, *Proc. Int. Symp. Fresh Water Sea 7th*, Vol. 1, 229th Event of the Eur. Fed. of Chem. Eng., Amsterdam, Neth., Sept. 23–26, 1980. Available from Work Party on Fresh Water from the Sea, Athens, Greece, 253–62.
9. Symposium on Enhanced Tubes for Desalination Plants, US Dept. of Interior, Office of Saline Water, US Government Printing Office, July 1970.
10. HASSON, D. and PERL, I. Scale deposition in a laminar falling-film system, *Desalination*, June 1981, **37**(3), 279–92.
11. SACK, M. Falling film shell-and-tube heat exchangers, *Chem. Engng. Prog.*, July 1967, **63**(7), 55–61.
12. SMITH, R. A. *Evaporators, Heat Exchanger Design Handbook*, Section 3.5, 1982, Hemisphere, Washington, D.C.
13. MEHRA, D. K. Selecting evaporators, *Chem. Engng.*, February 3, 1986, 56–72.
14. FOSBERG, T. M. and CLAUSSEN, H. L. Falling film evaporators recover chemicals efficiently, *Tappi*, Aug. 1982, **65**(8), 63–6.
15. MURRAY, A. J. Practical and economic benefits of falling film evaporation, *Plant Operations Progress*, 1986, **5**(1), 31–4.
16. SANDALL, O. C., HANNA, O. T. and WILSON, C. L. III, Heat transfer across turbulent falling films, *AIChE Symp. Ser.*, Heat Transfer Niagara Falls, AIChE, NY, 1984.
17. CHUN, K. R. and SEBAN, R. A. Heat transfer to evaporating films, *J. Heat Transfer*, 1971, **93**, 391–6.
18. CHUN, K. R. and SEBAN, R. A. Performance prediction of falling film evaporators, *J. Heat Transfer*, 1972, **94**, 432–6.
19. MILLS, A. F. and CHUNG, D. K. Heat transfer across turbulent falling films, *Int. J. Heat Mass Transfer*, 1973, **16**, 694–6.
20. HUBBARD, G. L., MILLS, A. F. and CHUNG, D. K. Heat transfer across a turbulent falling film, with cocurrent vapor, *J. Heat Transfer*, May 1976, **98**, 319–20.
21. YIH, SIU MING and LIU JUNG-LIANG, Prediction of heat transfer in turbulent falling films with or without interfacial shear, *AIChE J.*, Nov. 1983, **29**(6), 903–9.
22. WASSNER, L. Heat transmission measurements for condensation and evaporation on a vertical falling film evaporator, *Brennst.-Waerme-Kraft (FRG)*, June 1984, **36**(6), 258–66.
23. CONDER, J. R., GUNN, D. J. and SHAIKH, M. A. Heat and mass transfer in two-phase flow—a mathematical model for laminar film flow and its experimental validation, *Int. J. Heat Mass Transfer*, 1982, **25**(8), 1113–26.
24. PEREZ-BLANCO, H. and LINKOUS, R. L. Overall heat transfer coefficients for a vertical tube evaporative cooler, *Proc. ASME-JSME Therm. Eng. Jt. Conf.*, 1983, Vol. 1, 511–16, ASME, New York.

25. GANIC, E. N. and ROPPO, M. N. A note on heat transfer to falling liquid films on vertical tubes, *Lett. Heat Mass Transfer*, 1980, **7**(2), 145–54.
26. ROTHFUS, R. R. and LAVI, G. H. Vertical falling film heat transfer: a literature survey, *Proc. Ocean Therm. Energy Convers. Conf., 5th*, A. Lavi, and T. N. Veziroglu (eds), Vol. 3, 1978, Conf.-780236, VI/90–VT/110.
27. CERZA, M. and SERNAS, V. Boiling nucleation criteria for a falling water film, multiphase flow and heat transfer, HTD-Vol. 47, 111–116, ASME Publication, 23rd National Heat Transfer Conference Denver, Colorado, 1985.
28. CERZA, M. and SERNAS, V. Boiling nucleation in developing laminar falling films, *ASME-JSME Thermal Engineering Joint Conference Proceedings*, Honolulu, Hawaii, March, 20–24 1983, Vol. 1, ASME, New York, 111–18.
29. BENNETT, D. L., DAVIS, M. W. and HERTZLER, B. L. The suppression of saturated nucleate boiling by forced convective flow, *AIChE Symp. Ser.*, 1980, Vol. 76, No. 199, 91–103, Heat Transfer-Orlando.
30. SCHLUENDER, E. U. Heat transfer in nucleate boiling of mixtures, *Int. Chem. Engng*, 1983, **23**(4), 589–99.
31. CHUNG, D. K. and MILLS, A. F. Experimental study of gas absorption into turbulent falling films and ethylene glycol–water mixtures, *Int. J. Heat Mass Transfer*, Jan. 1986, **19**(1), 51–9.
32. WON, Y. S. and MILLS, A. F. Correlation of the effects of viscosity and surface tension on gas absorption rates into freely falling turbulent films, *Int. J. Heat Mass Transfer*, 1982, **25**(2), 223–9.
33. YIH, S. M. and HUANG, P. G. Gas absorption with and without chemical reaction in laminar non-Newtonian falling liquid films, *Chem. Engng. Sci.*, 1981, **36**(2), 387–97.
34. VYROL, L. and MIKA, V. Film absorption in liquids of different viscosities, *Collect. Czech. Chem. Commun.*, 1981, **46**(1), 161–72.
35. HUGHMARK, G. A. Mass transfer and flooding in wetted-wall and packed columns, *Ind. Engng. Chem. Fundam.*, 1980, **19**(4), 385–9.
36. YIH, S.-M. and SEAGRAVE, R. C. Mass transfer in falling laminar films with accompanying heat transfer and vapor shear, *Int. J. Heat Mass Transfer*, 1980, **23**(6), 749–58.
37. GROPP, U., SCHNABEL, G. and SCHLUENDER, E. U. The effect of liquid-side mass transfer resistance on selectivity during partial evaporation of binary mixtures in a falling film, *Int. Chem. Engng.*, 1983, **23**(1), 1–17.
38. GROPP, U. Waerme- und Stoffuebergang bei der Oberflaechenverdampfing und Blasensieden eines Binaeren Kaeltemittelgemisches am Rieselfilm, Dr.-Ing. Thesis, University of Karlsruhe, 1985.
39. KOLAR, V. and CERVENKA, J. Simultaneous heat and mass transfer during evaporation from a film of liquid into the turbulent gas, *Collect. Czech. Chem. Commun.*, 1982, **47**(3), 766–75.
40. ITO, R., TOMURA, K., YAMAMOTO, M., OKADA, Y., TSUBOI, N., NAKAJIMA, T. and KAWAI, M. Simultaneous measurements of thickness and local mass transfer rate on falling liquid films, *J. Chem. Engng. Jpn.*, 1979, **12**(6), 483–5.
41. KALTENBACHER, E. and SCHLUENDER, E. U. Batch stripping process of a mixture of isopropanol and water in a falling film column, *Verfahrens Technik*, March 1979, **13**(3), 161–3.

42. KRISHNA, R. Comparison of models for ternary mass transfer, *Letters in Heat and Mass Transfer*, Jan.–Feb. 1979, **6**(1), 73–6.
43. BESHKOV, V., ELENKOV, D., BOYADZHIEV, Kh. and PAPADOPOV, L. On the theory of mass transfer in falling liquid films, *Izv. Khim.* (English), 1978, **11**(2), 204–8.
44. IHNATOWICZ, E., GUMKOWSKI, S. and MIKELEWICZ, J. Experimental study of evaporation and breakdown of thin liquid films driven by shear stress, *Trans. ASME*, Nov. 1979, **101**, 712–17.
45. FUJITA, T. and UEDA, T. Heat transfer to falling liquid films and film breakdown-I, Subcooled liquid films, *Int. J. Heat Mass Transfer*, 1978, **21**, 97–108.
46. FUJITA, T. and UEDA, T. Heat transfer to falling liquid films and film breakdown-II, Saturated films with nucleate boiling, *Int. J. Heat Mass Transfer*, 1978, **21**, 109–18.
47. HARTLEY, D. E. and MURGATROYD, W. Criteria for the break-up of thin liquid layers flowing isothermally over solid surfaces, *Int. J. Heat Mass Transfer*, 1964, **7**, 1003–15.
48. PONTER, A. B., DAVIES, G. A., ROSS, T. K. and THORNLEY, P. G. The influence of mass transfer on liquid film breakdown, *Int. J. Heat Mass Transfer*, 1967, **10**, 349–59.
49. GOGONIN, I. I., DOROKHOV, A. R. and BOCHAGOV, V. N. Stability of dry patches in thin falling liquid films, *Fluid Mechanics–Soviet Research*, May–June 1979, **8**(3), 103–9.
50. TAMIR, A., MERCHUK, J. C. and VIRKAR, P. D. The break-up of thin liquid films due to the intensity of mass transfer in absorption, *Chem. Engng. Sci.*, 1980, **35**, 1393–8.
51. SHARON, A. and ORELL, A. Dry patch formation in liquid films flowing in a heated horizontal channel, *Int. J. Heat Mass Transfer*, 1980, **23**, 547–57.
52. TOLUBINSKIY, V. I., ANTONEKO, V. A. and OSTROVSKIY, Yu. N. Breakup of non-flowing boiling liquid films, *Heat Transfer–Soviet Research*, June 1978, **10**(3), 1–4.
53. KOZIOL, K., ULATOWSKI, J. and FRANK, K. Velocity fields in falling films, *Int. Chem. Engng.* Oct. 1981, **21**(4), 580–4.
54. PONTER, A. B., YEKTA-FARD, M. and ALAMIR, A. A. Dry patch formation when a supported vertical water film undergoes heat transfer, *Termotecnica*, 1982, **36** (3), 56–65.
55. GANIC, E. N. and ROPPO, M. Breakdown of falling liquid film during heat transfer, *Heat Mass Transfer Metall. Syst.*, D. B. Spalding and N. H. Afgan (eds.) (Semin. Int. Cent. Heat Mass Transfer), 1981, Hemisphere, Washington D.C., 597–608.
56. GANIC, E. N. and ROPPO, M. N. Falling film heat transfer and film breakdown, multiphase transport: Fundam. React. Saf., Appl. (*Proc. Multi-Phase Flow Heat Transfer Symp.-Workshop*), T. N. Verziroglu (ed.), Vol. 2, 1980, Hemisphere, Washington D.C., 927–43.
57. GANIC, E. N. and MASTANAIAH, K. Hydrodynamics and heat transfer in falling film flow, *Low Reynolds Number Flow Heat Exchangers*, 1981, Hemisphere, New York, 487–528.

58. GANCHEV, V. G. and BOKOV, A. Ye. Stability of falling liquid water films at high heat fluxes, *Heat Transfer-Soviet Research*, May-June 1980, **12**, No. 3, May-June,   - .

59. COULON, H. Stability conditions in falling films, *Chemie-Ing.-Technik*, 1973, **45** (6), 363-8.

60. SPINDLER, B. Linear stability of liquid films with interfacial phase change, *Int. J. Heat Mass Transfer*, 1982, **25**(2) 161-73.

61. MARON, D. M., BRAUNER, N. and WEINBERG, J. Characteristics of wavy film flow in the presence of interfacial shear, *Chem. Eng. J. (Lausanne)*, 1984, **28**(3), 139-50.

62. ANDREUSSI, PAOLO, The onset of droplet entrainment in annular downward flows, *Can. J. Chem. Engng.*, 1980, **58**, 267.

63. BARBA, D. and GIONA, A. The pressure loss in a falling film evaporator, *Brit. Chem. Engng.* Nov. 1970, **15**(11),   - .

64. BERGELIN, O. P., KEGEL, P. K., CARPENTER, F. G. and GAZLEY, C., Jr. *Co-Current Gas-Liquid Flow II. Flow in Vertical Tubes*, 1964, Heat Transfer and Fluid Mechanics Institute, University of California, Berkeley.

65. KULUV, N. N., MAKSIMOV, V. V., MALJUSOV, V. A. and ZHAVORONKOV, N. M. Pressure drop, mean film thickness, and entrainment in downward two-phase flow, *Chem. Eng. J. (Netherlands)*, 1979, **18**, 183-8.

66. PORZHEZINSKIY, YU. G. and SAGAN, I. I. Experimental study of fricton losses in two-phase downflow of water and viscous fluid at low pressures, *Heat Transfer-Soviet Research*, Nov.-Dec. 1971, **3**(6),   - .

67. HIKATA, H. and ISHIMI, K. Frictional pressure drop for laminar gas streams in wetted-wall columns with cocurrent and countercurrent gas-liquid flow, *Japan. Chem. Engng.* 1976, **9**(5),   - .

68. SCHNABEL, G. Determination of local heat transfer during falling film evaporation and condensation on fluted surfaces for the purpose of designing high-efficiency evaporators, ORNL-TR-4934, 147 p., 1982.

69. SCHNABEL, G. Determination of local heat transfer during falling film evaporation and condensation on corrugated surfaces for the design of high-efficiency evaporators, Thesis, Karlsruhe, University, 179 p., 11 July 1980.

70. MAILEN, G. S. Experimental studies of OTEC heat transfer evaporation of ammonia on vertical smooth and fluted tubes, Oak Ridge National Laboratory, Tennessee, Dept. of Energy, 24 p., *Proc. Ocean Energy Conf.*, Washington D.C., 2 June 1980.

71. TOYAMA, S., ARAGAKI, T., NAKAYAMA, S. and SUZUKI, M. Effect of the wound thread around a vertical tube on flowing down of the liquid film and wave properties of the free surface, *Proc. Pac. Chem. Engng. Conf., 3rd*, C. Kim and S. K. Ihm (eds.), Vol. 1, pp. 24-28, 1983.

72. GOGONIN, I. I. and DOROKOV, A. R. Correlation of experimental data on critical heat fluxes, in falling liquid films, *Heat Transfer-Soviet Research*, March-April 1983, **15**(2), 91-5.

73. MOTTAGHIAN, R. and Nejat, Z. Analysis of critical heat flux for countercurrent two-phase flow of liquid and its vapor in vertical heated tubes, *Proc. Asian Congr. Fluid Mech. 1st*, Vol A, Paper no. A55, 6 pp., 1980.

74. BENNETT, D. L. and CHEN, J. C. Forced convective boiling in vertical tubes for

saturated pure components and binary mixtures, *AIChE J.*, 1980, **26**(3), 454–61.
75. CHEN, J. C. and PALEN, J. W. Two-phase flow and heat transfer in process equipment, *AIChE Today Series*, 1985, American Institute of Chemical Engineering, New York.
76. BOYADJIEV, C. Non-linear mass transfer in falling films, *Int. J. Heat Mass Transfer*, April 1982, **25**(4), 535–40.
77. Process Eng. (UK), (Journal Announcement), Saving Energy with MVR Falling Film Evaporators, pp. 82–83, Jan. 1980.
78. KIM, H. K., FAKEENA, A. and MESLER, R. Nucleate boiling in flowing and horizontal liquid films, HTD (Publ. ASME Heat Transfer Div.), *Interfacial Transp. Phenom.*, 1983, **23**, 61–5.
79. HOLMES, R. C. Limiting velocities in vertical tubes, du Pont Report ED 1750, Oct. 1946. (Also published in *Chemical Engineers Handbook*, J. H. Perry (Ed.), 1950, 3rd Edn., p. 686.)
80. GIMBUTIS, G. Heat transfer of a turbulent vertically falling film, *Proceedings of the 5th International Heat Transfer Conference*, Tokyo, Vol. II, 1974, 85–9.
81. DUKLER, A. E. Fluid mechanics and heat transfer in falling film systems, *Chem. Engng. Symp. Series*, 1960, **56**(30), 1–10.
82. LORENZ, J. J. and YUNG, D. A note on combined boiling and evaporation of liquid films on horizontal tubes, *J. Heat Transfer*, 1979, **101**, 178–80.
83. WALLIS, G. *One Dimensional Two Phase Flow*, 1969, McGraw-Hill, New York.
84. CHEN, J. C. Correlation of boiling heat transfer to saturated fluids in convective flow, *I&EC Process Design and Development*, July 1966, **5**(3), 322–9.
85. FORSTER, H. K. and ZUBER, N. Dynamics of vapor bubbles and boiling heat transfer, *AIChE J.*, 1955, **1**, 531.
86. STEPHAN, K. and ABDELSALAM, M. Heat transfer correlations for natural convection boiling *Int. J. Heat Mass Transfer*, 1980, **23**(9), 692–8.
87. MOSTINSKI, I. L. Application of the rule of corresponding states for the calculation of heat transfer and critical heat flux, *Teploenergetika*, 1963, **4**(66), Engl., Abstr., *Brit. Chem. Eng.*, 1963, **8**(8) 580.
88. STERNLING, C. V. and TICHACEK, L. J. Heat transfer coefficients for boiling mixtures, *Chem. Engng. Sci.*, 1961, **16**, 297.
89. PALEN, J. W. and SMALL, W. M. A new way to design kettle and internal reboilers, *Hydrocarbon Processing*, 1964, **43**(11), 199.
90. GROPP, U. and SCHLUENDER, E. U. The influence of liquid-side mass transfer on heat transfer and selectivity during surface and nucleate boiling of mixtures in a falling film, *Chem. Engng. Proc.* (in English), to be published, March 1986.
91. CHEN, J. C. and PALEN, J. W. Two-phase flow and heat transfer in process equipment, *AIChE Today Series*, 1984, American Institute of Chemical Engineers, New York.
92. PALEN, J. W., YANG, C. C. and TABOREK, J. Application of the resistance proration method to boiling in the presence of inert gas, *AIChE Symp. Series*, Vol. 76, No. 199, Orlando, 1980.
93. WAYNER, P. C., Jr. and PARKS, C. J. Effect of liquid composition on enhanced flow due to surface shear in the contact line region: constant vapor pressure boundary condition, *Multiphase Flow and Heat Transfer, 23rd Nat'l Heat*

Trans. Conf., Denver 1985, ASME Publication HTD-Vol. 47, 57–63, ASME, New York.
94. CICHELLI, M. T. and BONILLA, C. F. Heat transfer to boiling liquids under pressure, *Trans. AIChE*, 1945, **41**, 755.
95. CHISHOLM, D. *Two-Phase Flow in Pipelines and Heat Exchangers*, George Godwin, Harlow, UK.

Chapter 8

NON-NEWTONIAN FLOW AND HEAT TRANSFER IN TUBES

D. CHISHOLM

Heat Transfer Research Inc., Alhambra, California, USA

SUMMARY

Methods for predicting flow and heat transfer with non-Newtonian fluids in tubes are discussed. For both laminar and turbulent flow conditions, equations in terms of the generalised Reynolds number are recommended. For laminar heat transfer, equations developed by Bergles and co-workers are recommended; these equations are in the form of the 'general expression' of Churchill and Usagi. Predictive methods for turbulent heat transfer and combined forced and convective heat transfer are also presented.

NOTATION

A	Coefficient (eqn. (112))
A_0	Coefficient (eqn. (123))
A'	Term (eqn. (90))
a	Term (eqn. (62))
a_1	Coefficient (eqn. (31)) $(\text{kg}/(\text{m s}^{2-n}))$
a_2	Coefficient (eqn. (35)) $(\text{kg}/(\text{m s}^{2-n}))$
B	Coefficient (eqn. (112))
B'	Term (eqn. (91))
B_j	Term (eqn. (108))
B_o	Coefficient (eqn. (123))
b_j	Term (eqn. (108))
b_1	Coefficient (eqn. (31)) (K)
b_2	Coefficient (eqn. (35)) (1/K)

219

C	Exponent (eqn. (112))
C'	Term (eqn. (88))
c_p	Specific heat c_p(J/(kg K))
D	Tube diameter (m)
E	Activation energy (eqn. (136)) (J/mol)
E'	Term (eqn. (120))
f	Friction factor (eqn. (49))
Gr	Grashoff number (eqn. (168))
Gr_s	Grashoff number, mixed correction (eqn. (173))
Gr_w	Grashoff number at wall conditions (eqn. (169))
Gz	Graetz number (eqn. (109))
He	Hedstrom number (eqn. (58))
h	Heat transfer coefficient (eqn. (103)) (W/(m² K))
I_1	Integral (eqn. (136))
I_2	Integral (eqn. (137))
K	Consistency index (eqn. (5)) (kg/(m s²⁻ⁿ))
K_b	Consistency index at bulk temperature (eqn. (138))
K_w	Consistency index at wall temperature (eqn. (139))
K'	Coefficient (eqn. (11)) (kg/(m s²⁻ⁿ))
k	Thermal conductivity (eqn. (98)) (W/(m K))
k_1	Thermal conductivity of fluid (eqn. (155))
k_p	Thermal conductivity of particles (eqn. (155))
k_s	Thermal conductivity of suspension (eqn. (155))
ke	Kinetic energy (eqn. (78)) (J/kg)
m	Term (eqn. (91))
Nu	Nusselt number, local
Nu_{am}	Nusselt number, mean based on arithmetic mean temperature difference (eqn. (111))
Nu_m	Nusselt number based on logarithmic mean temperature difference
n	Flow behaviour index (eqn. (5))
n'	Exponent (eqn. (11))
Pn	Physical property number (eqn. (26))
Pr	Prandtl number (eqn. (150))
$Pr_{n'}$	Prandtl number, generalised (eqn. (163))
q	Heat flux (eqn. (98)) (W/m²)
Re	Reynolds number (eqn. (49))
$Re_{n'}$	Reynolds number generalised (eqn. (70))
Re'	Reynolds number using plastic viscosity (eqn. (57))
r	Radius (m)
r_w	Radius of tube (eqn. (30))
r_y	Plug radius (eqn. (68))

s	Exponent (eqn. (166))
s'	Coefficient (eqn. (79))
T	Temperature, absolute (K)
T_b	Temperature of bulk fluid (eqn. (102))
T_i	Temperature of fluid at inlet (eqn. (29))
T_o	Temperature of bulk fluid at outlet (eqn. (110))
T_w	Temperature of wall (eqn. (29))
u	Velocity (eqn. (1)) (m/s)
u_m	Velocity, average
u_{max}	Velocity, maximum
w	Function defined by eqn. (89)
x	Volume fraction
x_v	Volume fraction of particles in suspension (eqn. (155))
x_{vb}	Volume fraction of particles in suspension after settling (eqn. (156))
Y	Yield number (eqn. (59))
y	Distance from wall, $r - r_w$ (eqn. (10)) (m)
z	Displacement in flow direction (m)
z_0	Total length (eqn. (104))

Greek

α	Shear stress ratio (eqn. (24))
α_c	Shear stress ratio, critical (eqn. (84))
α'	Coefficient (eqn. (94))
β	Coefficient of volumetric expansion (eqn. (168))
β'	Exponent (eqn. (94))
γ	Group (eqn. (76)) ($kg/(m\,s^{2-n'})$)
$\Delta T_{process}$	Process temperature range (eqn. (29)) (K)
ΔT_{rheo}	Rheological temperature range (eqn. (27))
δ	Non-Newtonian correction factor (eqn. (14))
η	Plastic viscosity (eqn. (2)) ($kg/(m\,s)$)
μ	Absolute viscosity (eqn. (1)) ($kg/(m\,s)$)
μ_a	Absolute viscosity apparent (eqn. (6))
μ_b	Absolute viscosity at bulk conditions (eqn. (154))
μ_e	Absolute viscosity effective (eqn. (73))
μ_w	Absolute viscosity at wall conditions (eqn. (154))
ρ	Density (eqn. (48)) (kg/m^3)
ρ_w	Density at wall (eqn. (172))
τ	Shear stress (eqn. (1)) (n/m^2)
τ_w	Shear stress at wall (eqn. (10))
τ_y	Shear stress to yield (eqn. (2))

1. INTRODUCTION

The greater part of the literature on thermal design relates to fluids which, in laminar flow, satisfy the Newtonian relationship between shear stress and velocity gradient

$$\tau = \mu \frac{du}{dy} \tag{1}$$

where μ is the absolute or dynamic viscosity, and y is the distance from the wall. The velocity gradient can also be referred to as the rate of shear. This chapter surveys the literature for flow and heat transfer in tubes of viscous time-independent fluids which do not, in laminar flow, satisfy eqn. (1). These fluids are part of a range of fluids broadly classified as non-Newtonian fluids. For information on non-Newtonian flow and heat transfer with other geometries the reader is referred to references 1–5. Reference 6 concerns basic physics of non-Newtonian fluid behaviour. We will begin by classifying the various types of non-Newtonian fluids.

2. BASIC CLASSIFICATIONS

Table 1 indicates the manner in which non-Newtonian fluids are classified.[7]

TABLE 1
CLASSIFICATION OF FLUID BEHAVIOUR

	Fluids		
	Purely viscous		
Time-independent		*Time-dependent*	
No yield stress	*Yield stress*	Thixotropic	Viscoelastic
Newtonian	Bingham	Rheopectic	
Pseudoplastic	Yield-pseudoplastic		
Dilatant	Yield-dilatant		

2.1. Viscous and Viscoelastic Fluids
In the first instance non-Newtonian fluids are divided into fluids which exhibit purely viscous behaviour and those with viscoelastic characteristics.

A viscoelastic fluid has the property of partially recovering its original state after stress is removed; it has some of the characteristics of an elastic solid. Examples of viscoelastic fluids are polymer solutions and bitumens.

2.2. Time-independent and Time-dependent Fluids

Purely viscous fluids divide into two broad classes; fluids which are time-independent and fluids which are time-dependent. Newtonian fluids are time-independent, but a range of fluids have properties which under stress have properties which vary with time. The apparent viscosity of time-dependent fluids varies on the sudden imposition of shear, eventually reaching an equilibrium value. There are two classes of time-dependent fluids, thixotropic and rheopectic. A thixotropic fluid breaks down under shear, its viscosity decreasing until an asymptotic value is reached; it is a time-dependent pseudoplastic. The viscosity of a rheopectic fluid increases with time to an asymptotic value.

2.3. Time-independent Fluids; no Yield Stress

There are three classes of fluids which are time-independent and exhibit no yield stress, any application of load resulting in fluid motion. These are Newtonian, pseudoplastic, and dilatant fluids. The viscosity of a pseudoplastic fluid, or shear thinning fluid as it is sometimes called, decreases with stress, whereas the viscosity of a dilatant fluid increases.

Figure 1 illustrates the relationships between stress and shear rate for

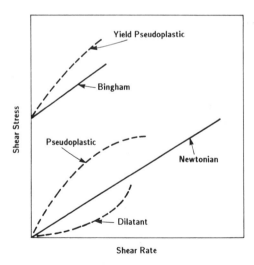

FIG. 1. Rheograms: linear plot.

these classes of fluids, and for fluids with a yield stress; these latter fluids are now discussed.

2.4. Time-independent Fluids; Yield Stress
A Bingham plastic obeys the law, where η is the 'plastic viscosity',

$$\tau \geqslant \tau_y \quad \tau = \tau_y + \eta \, du/dy \tag{2}$$

$$\tau < \tau_y \quad du/dy = 0 \tag{3}$$

Unlike a Newtonian fluid, a stress τ_y is required before motion begins. Similarly for yield-pseudoplastics and yield-dilatants, motion only commences when a certain shear stress is exceeded.

3. RHEOLOGICAL MODELS

Equations (1) and (2) have already introduced two of the relevant basic relationships between shear stress, shear rate, and fluid properties. These equations are referred to as either rheological models or as constitutive equations.

For non-Newtonian fluids an 'apparent viscosity' can be defined

$$\mu_a = \frac{\tau}{du/dy} \tag{4}$$

This viscosity, for a non-Newtonian fluid, is a function of the shear stress.

3.1. Non-shear Stress Fluids
The power law, or Ostwald-de Waele equation, is

$$\tau = K \left(\frac{du}{dy} \right)^n \tag{5}$$

where K is the consistency index and n is the flow behaviour index. Combining eqns. (4) and (5), the apparent viscosity is obtained as,

$$\mu_a = K \left(\frac{du}{dy} \right)^{n-1} \tag{6}$$

It is apparent, from the definitions in Section 2.3, that for a pseudoplastic fluid $n < 1{\cdot}0$, and for a dilatant fluid $n > 1{\cdot}0$. For a wide range of data the power law equation can be used to obtain good correlation, except at low and high values of velocity gradient.

As both gradient and stress can change sign over a flow field, more generally eqn. (5) should be expressed as

$$\tau = K \left| \frac{du}{dy} \right|^{n-1} \frac{du}{dy} \tag{7}$$

A large number of alternative forms of equations relating shear stress and shear rate have been proposed; these include the models of Prandtl–Eyring[8] and Sisko.[9] These forms generally overcome the inadequacies of the power law equation at low and high gradients.

An alternative form of rheological model relates the shear stress to the dimensional group $8u_m/D$ where u_m is the average fluid velocity over the flow cross-section and D is the tube diameter. Among those models are those of SyMonds et al.[10] and Spencer and Dillon.[11] This model is discussed further in Section 3.3.

3.2. Yield Stress Fluids

For Bingham fluids the relationship between stress and shear rate is given by eqn. (2), and from eqns. (2) and (4) the apparent viscosity is

$$\mu_a = \eta + \frac{\tau_y}{du/dy} \tag{8}$$

where η is the plastic viscosity. The apparent viscosity decreases with shear rate.

Yield-pseudoplastic and yield-dilatant fluids can be modelled using the equation

$$\tau = \tau_y + K \left(\frac{du}{dy} \right)^n \tag{9}$$

As for the non-yield fluids, $n < 1 \cdot 0$ corresponds to a pseudoplastic fluid, and $n > 1 \cdot 0$ to a dilatant fluid.

Other rheological models for flow with a yield stress include the models of Herschel and Buckley[12] and Crowley and Kitzes.[13]

3.3. The Flow Curve

Rabinowitsch[14] and Mooney[15] developed the following equation for the wall velocity gradient for any time-independent fluid

$$\left(\frac{du}{dy} \right)_w = \frac{3}{4} \left(\frac{8u_m}{D} \right) + \frac{1}{4} \left(\frac{8u_m}{D} \right) \frac{d \ln(8u_m/D)}{d \ln(\tau_w)} \tag{10}$$

It should be noted that the pipe diameter $D = 2r_w$, and $r = r_w - y$.

By analogy with eqn. (6) assume[16]

$$\tau_w = K'(8u_m/D)^{n'} \tag{11}$$

On differentiating and rearranging, the exponent is obtained as

$$n' = \frac{d \ln \tau_w}{d(8u_m/D)} \tag{12}$$

Combining eqns. (10) and (12) gives the relationship

$$\left(\frac{du}{dy}\right)_w = \frac{3n'+1}{4n'}\frac{8u_m}{D} = \delta\frac{8u_m}{D} \tag{13}$$

where

$$\delta = \frac{3n'+1}{4n'} \tag{14}$$

As δ is unity for a Newtonian fluid it follows that for the same value of $8u_m/D$

$$\delta = \frac{(du/dr)_{w \text{ non-Newtonian fluid}}}{(du/dr)_{w \text{ Newtonian fluid}}} \tag{15}$$

It should be noted that in a circular pipe the shear stress is related to the pressure gradient in the equation

$$\tau_w = \frac{D}{4}\frac{dp}{dz} \tag{16}$$

The index and exponent are obtained by plotting τ_w to a base of $8u_m/D$ on logarithmic paper. The exponent is the gradient of the tangent at any point, and the index the value of the tangent when $8u_m/D$ is unity. Figure 2 shows a plot for a power law fluid and for the general case of a non-Newtonian fluid; in the latter case K' and n' are functions of $8u_m/D$. The procedure can be shown to be applicable to any time-independent fluids including Bingham Plastic fluids.

Having obtained K' and n', eqn. (13) is used to obtain the wall shear rate and corresponding shear stress from eqn. (15). A plot of τ_w against du/dy, the flow curve, is obtained as shown in Fig. 3. To illustrate with reference to Fig. 2, where $8u_m/D = 400/s$, $\tau_w = 1900 \text{ N/m}^2$, and from the equation of the tangent $K' = 92 \text{ N s}^{n'}/\text{m}^2$, and $n' = 0.505$.

Using eqn. (14)

$$\delta = \frac{30.505 + 1}{40.506} = 1.245$$

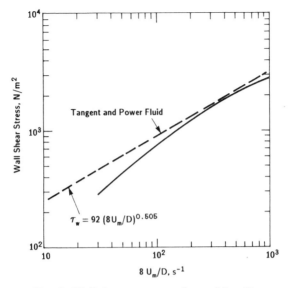

FIG. 2. Wall shear stress to a base of $8u_m/D$.

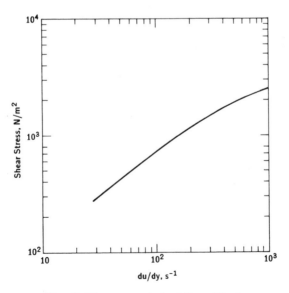

FIG. 3. Flow curve derived from Fig. 2.

Hence using eqn. (13)

$$(du/dy)_w = 498\ s^{-1}$$

This procedure is repeated for other tangents and the flow curve in Fig. 3 constructed. The flow curve is used in eqn. (44).

In certain non-Newtonian fluids, such as suspensions, a thin film of liquid may occur adjacent to the wall. This creates the appearance of slip at the wall, which must be allowed for in constructing the flow curve. If slip exists a plot of $Q/(\pi r_w^3 \tau_w)$ to a base of τ_w for a series of diameters will give a family of curves rather than a single curve. Skelland[2] discusses the method of allowing for this effect.

3.4. The Consistency Index and the Flow Behaviour Exponent

Integrating eqn. (5) leads to

$$\tau_w = K\left(\frac{3n+1}{4n}\right)^n \left(\frac{8u_m}{D}\right)^n \tag{17}$$

Combining eqns. (11) and (17)

$$K' = K\left(\frac{3n+1}{4n}\right)^n \left(\frac{8u_m}{D}\right)^{n-n'} \tag{18}$$

It is shown by Wilkinson[1] that

$$n = \frac{n'}{1 - \dfrac{1}{3n'+1}\left(\dfrac{dn'}{d\ln\tau_w}\right)} \tag{19}$$

If a logarithmic plot of τ and $8u_m/D$ is a straight line then

$$\frac{dn'}{d(\ln\tau_w)} = 0 \tag{20}$$

and hence, from eqn. (19)

$$n = n' \tag{21}$$

In that case eqn. (18) reduces to

$$K = K'\Big/\left(\frac{3n+1}{4n}\right)^n \tag{22}$$

This also follows from eqns. (5) and (13).

For Bingham plastic fluids Metzner[17] showed that

$$n' = \frac{3 - 4\alpha + \alpha^4}{3(1 - \alpha^4)} \tag{23}$$

where

$$\alpha = \tau_y / \tau_w \tag{24}$$

Equation (22) can be rearranged to give for a Bingham plastic fluid

$$\frac{3n' + 1}{4n'} = \delta = \frac{3(1 - \alpha)}{3 - 4\alpha + \alpha^4} \tag{25}$$

3.5. Physical Property Variation with Temperature

In most engineering situations all physical properties with the exception of the viscosity can be assumed independent of temperature. The criteria used to assess whether it is necessary to account for variation in viscosity we will refer to as the Physical Property number, Pn; there is no generally accepted name for this number.[18,19] This number is the ratio of the temperature range over the process to the rheological temperature range, that is

$$Pn = \frac{\Delta T_{\text{process}}}{\Delta T_{\text{rheo}}} \tag{26}$$

For a Newtonian fluid

$$\Delta T_{\text{rheo}} = -\mu \frac{dT}{d\mu} \tag{27}$$

and for a non-Newtonian fluid

$$\Delta T_{\text{rheo}} = -K \frac{dT}{dK} \tag{28}$$

The process fluid temperature range for a constant wall temperature has been defined

$$\Delta T_{\text{process}} = T_i - T_w \tag{29}$$

where T_i and T_w are respectively the fluid temperature at inlet and the constant wall temperature.

For a constant heat flux case (Joshi and Bergles[20])

$$\Delta T_{\text{process}} = \frac{qr_w}{k} \tag{30}$$

There are a variety of equations in the literature relating viscosity and temperature, the most commonly used being the Arrhenius equation

$$K = a_1 e^{b_1/T} \qquad (31)$$

where the coefficients a and b are independent of temperature. From eqns. (28) and (31)

$$\Delta T_{\text{rheo}} = \frac{T^2}{b_1} \qquad (32)$$

and taking the mean temperature (18) as $(T_i T_w)^{1/2}$ gives

$$\Delta T_{\text{rheo}} = \frac{T_i T_w}{b_1} \qquad (33)$$

From eqns. (26), (29) and (33)

$$Pn = b_1 \left(\frac{1}{T_w} - \frac{1}{T_i} \right) \qquad (34)$$

Bergles et al.[19-21] and Scirocco et al.[22] used the following form of viscosity equation

$$K = a_2 e^{-b_2 T} \qquad (35)$$

leading to, for the constant temperature case,

$$Pn = b_2 (T_i - T_w) \qquad (36)$$

Except at extremely low temperatures these approaches are essentially only marginally different. They are identical where

$$b_2 = b_1 / T^2 \qquad (37)$$

It should be noted the temperatures are absolute.

For constant heat flux the Physical Property number is, following Bergles,[21] from eqns. (30), (32) and (37)

$$Pn = b_2 \frac{q r_w}{k} \qquad (38)$$

4. LAMINAR FLOW IN TUBES

The laminar flow of non-Newtonian fluids is now discussed, first with reference to the relationships for friction factors, then in relation to velocity distribution.

The volume flow rate through a tube is

$$Q = \int_0^{r_w} u2\pi r\,dr \tag{39}$$

On integrating by parts

$$Q = \pi\left(ur^2 - \int r^2\,du\right)_0^{r_w} = \pi\int_0^{u_{max}} r^2\,du \tag{40}$$

This equation is, of course, applicable to both Newtonian and non-Newtonian fluids. When it is necessary to use the flow curve (stress against shear) this equation must be transformed as follows.

Shear and radius in a tube are related

$$r = r_w\frac{\tau}{\tau_w} \tag{41}$$

and on differentiating this

$$dr = \frac{r_w}{\tau_w}d\tau \tag{42}$$

From the flow curve, Fig. 3,

$$\frac{du}{dy} = f(\tau) \tag{43}$$

Substituting eqns. (41)–(43) in eqn. (40) gives

$$Q = \pi\left(\frac{r_w}{\tau_w}\right)^3\int_0^{\tau_0}\tau^2 f(\tau)\,d\tau \tag{44}$$

4.1. Newtonian Fluids: Friction

Consider first, for reference, the case of a Newtonian flow. The velocity differential is

$$du = \frac{\tau}{\mu}dy = \frac{\tau_w}{\mu}\frac{r}{r_w}dy \tag{45}$$

Hence from eqns. (40) and (45) the volume flow rate is

$$Q = \frac{\pi}{\mu}\frac{\tau_w}{r_w}\int_0^{r_w} r^3\,dr = \frac{\pi\tau_w}{4\mu}r_w^3 \tag{46}$$

and the average velocity is

$$u_m = \frac{r_w \tau_w}{4\mu} = \frac{D\tau_w}{8\mu} \tag{47}$$

A friction factor f is defined by the equation

$$\tau_w = f\frac{u_m^2 \rho}{2} \tag{48}$$

Combining eqns. (47) and (48) gives

$$f = \frac{16\mu}{\rho u_m D} = \frac{16}{Re} \tag{49}$$

where the Reynolds number is defined as

$$Re = \frac{\rho u_m D}{\mu} \tag{50}$$

4.2. Power-law Fluids: Friction

For a power-law fluid, using eqn. (5)

$$du = \left(\frac{\tau}{K}\right)^{1/n} dy = \left(\frac{\tau_w}{K r_w}\right)^{1/n} r^{1/n} dy \tag{51}$$

Hence the volume flow rate is obtained as

$$Q = \frac{\pi n}{3n+1} \left(\frac{\tau_w}{K}\right)^{1/n} r_w^3 \tag{52}$$

and the friction factor as[23]

$$f = \frac{16}{\dfrac{d^n u_m^{2-n} \rho}{K} 8\left(\dfrac{n}{6n+2}\right)^n} \tag{53}$$

This can also be expressed, using eqn. (18)

$$f = \frac{16}{\dfrac{d^{n'} u_m^{2-n'} \rho_{1-n}}{K'} 8} \tag{54}$$

This equation is discussed further in the section entitled 'Generalised Reynolds number' (Section 4.6).

4.3. Bingham Fluids

For a Bingham fluid, using eqn. (2)

$$du = \frac{(\tau - \tau_y)}{\eta} dy \tag{55}$$

Hence the volume flow rate is obtained using eqn. (39) as

$$Q = \frac{\pi \tau_0}{4\eta} \left(1 - \frac{4}{3} \left(\frac{\tau_y}{\tau_w} \right) + \frac{1}{3} \left(\frac{\tau_y}{\tau_w} \right)^4 \right) r_0^3 \tag{56}$$

and the friction factor as[24]

$$f = \frac{16}{Re'} + \frac{1}{6} \frac{He}{Re'^2} - \frac{1}{3} \frac{1}{f^3} \left(\frac{He}{Re'} \right)^4 \tag{57}$$

where He is the Hedstrom number

$$He = \frac{\tau_y D^2 \rho}{\eta^2} = Y Re' \tag{58}$$

The Reynolds number Re' is evaluated using the plastic viscosity. The yield number is

$$Y = \frac{D\tau_y}{u_m \eta} \tag{59}$$

Figure 4 shows a f–Re plot obtained using these equations. The basis of the turbulent plot will be discussed in Section 6.

4.4. Yield Fluids: Friction

For the case of yield-pseudoplastic and yield-dilatant fluids, using eqns. (8) and (9)

$$du = (\mu - \eta) = \left(\frac{\tau - \tau_y}{K} \right)^{1/n} dy \tag{60}$$

Hence the volume flow rate is obtained, using eqn. (39) as[25]

$$Q = \pi n \left(\frac{\tau_y}{K} \right)^{1/n} \left(\frac{\tau_y}{\tau_w} \right)^3 \left(\frac{a^3}{3n+1} + \frac{2a^2}{2n+1} + \frac{a}{n+1} \right) \tag{61}$$

where

$$a = (\tau_w/\tau_y - 1) \tag{62}$$

The friction factor is obtained as the following form of function

$$f = \phi \left(\frac{D^n u_m^{2-n} \rho}{K} \frac{v_y^2 D^2 \rho}{K^2} n \right) \tag{63}$$

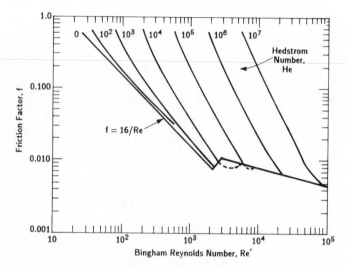

FIG. 4. Friction factor to a base of the Bingham Reynolds Number.[5]

The relationship is cumbersome. It is more convenient to obtain the pressure gradient using iteratively eqns. (16) and (61).

4.5. Velocity Distribution in Laminar Flow

For the case of a Newtonian fluid, integrating eqn. (45) gives the velocity distribution radially as

$$u = \frac{\tau_w r_w}{2\mu} \left(1 - \left(\frac{r}{r_w} \right)^2 \right) \tag{64}$$

The corresponding equations for non-Newtonian fluids are as follows:

Power-law fluid

$$u = \left(\frac{\tau_w}{K} \right)^{1/n} \frac{n r_w}{n+1} \left(1 - \left(\frac{r}{r_w} \right)^{(n+1)/n} \right) = u_m \frac{3n+1}{n+1} \left(1 - \left(\frac{r}{r_w} \right)^{(n+1)/n} \right) \tag{65}$$

Bingham fluid

$$0 < r < r_y \quad u = \frac{\tau_w r_w}{2\eta} \left(1 - \left(\frac{r}{r_w} \right) \right)^2 \tag{66}$$

$$r_y < r < r_w \quad u = \frac{\tau_y r_w}{2\eta} \left(1 - \left(\frac{r}{r_w} \right)^2 \right) - \frac{\tau_y r_w}{\mu} \left(1 - \frac{r}{r_w} \right) \tag{67}$$

where

$$\tau_y = \frac{\tau r_y}{r} \qquad (68)$$

Yield-power fluid

$$r_y < r < r_w \quad u = \frac{n}{n+1} \frac{r_w}{\tau_w} \frac{1}{K^{1/n}} \left((\tau_w - \tau_y) - \left(\tau_w \frac{r}{r_w} - \tau_y \right)^{(n+1)/n} \right) \qquad (69)$$

where $0 < r < r_y$, r_y is substituted for r in the above equation.

Figure 5 illustrates the velocity profiles for power law fluids for a range of n values. The case of a Bingham fluid is also shown; for $r < r_y$ the velocity is constant, while for $r > r_y$ the distribution is that for a Newtonian fluid $(n=1)$.

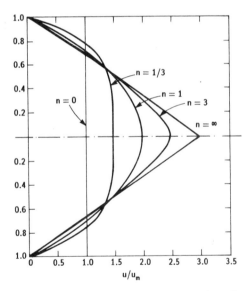

FIG. 5. Velocity distributions for power law fluids in laminar flow through tubes.

4.6. Generalised Reynolds Number

Define now a generalised Reynolds number[23]

$$Re_{n'} = \frac{D^{n'} u_m^{2-n'} \rho}{K'} 8^{1-n'} \qquad (70)$$

When $n = 1$ this reduces to the equation for Newtonian flow.
    Equation (54) can therefore be written

$$f = 16/Re_{n'}$$ (71)

4.7. Effective and Apparent Viscosities
An effective viscosity can be defined by the equation

$$Re_{n'} = \frac{Du_m \rho}{\mu_e}$$ (72)

This definition of viscosity is identical to the definition

$$\mu_e = \tau \left(\frac{D}{8u_m} \right)$$ (73)

which applies to all fluids as, for a Newtonian fluid (eqn. (13))

$$\left(\frac{du}{dy} \right) = \left(\frac{8u_m}{D} \right)$$ (74)

From eqns. (70) and (72)

$$\mu_e = K' 4^{n'+2} \left(\frac{u_m}{r_w} \right)^{n'-1}$$ (75)

Metzner and Reed[23] have shown that, for laminar flow, eqn. (75) agrees
closely with experimental data obtained with the fluids and pipe diameters
shown in Table 2. In this table

$$\gamma = K'/8^{1-n'}$$ (76)

The effective viscosity and the apparent viscosity are related, from eqns. (4),
(13) and (73)

$$\mu_e = \delta \mu_a$$ (77)

4.8. Kinetic Energy
The average kinetic energy per unit mass, the average specific kinetic
energy,

$$ke = \frac{1}{r_w^2 u_m} \int_0^{r_w} ru^2 \, dr$$ (78)

For the case of a power fluid this gives

$$ke = \frac{s' u_m^2}{2}$$ (79)

TABLE 2
RHEOLOGICAL CONSTANTS FOR FLUIDS SHOWN IN Fig. 6

Symbol used in figures	Nominal pipe size (in)	Composition of fluid	n'	γ
+	1	23·3% Illinois yellow clay in water	0·229	1·287
⊕	$\frac{7}{8}$ and $1\frac{1}{2}$	0·67% CMC in water	0·716	0·180
⊖	$\frac{7}{8}$ and $1\frac{1}{2}$	1·5% CMC in water	0·554	1·372
⊘	$\frac{7}{8}$ and $1\frac{1}{2}$	3·0% CMC in water	0·566	4·175
◊	$\frac{7}{8}$, $1\frac{1}{2}$ and 2	33% lime water	0·171	1·466
◁	$\frac{7}{8}$ and $1\frac{1}{2}$	10% napalm in kerosine	0·520	1·759
▼	8, 10 and 12	4% paper pulp in water	0·575	9·140
△	$\frac{3}{4}$ and $1\frac{1}{2}$	54·3% cement rock in water	0·153	0·494
▲	4	18·6% solids, Mississippi clay in water	0·022	0·157
○	$\frac{3}{4}$ and $1\frac{1}{4}$	14·3% clay in water	0·350	0·0513
▷	$\frac{3}{4}$ and $1\frac{1}{4}$	21·2% clay in water	0·335	0·127
×	$\frac{3}{4}$ and $1\frac{1}{4}$	25·0% clay in water	0·185	0·304
▽	$\frac{3}{4}$ and $1\frac{1}{4}$	31·9% clay in water	0·251	0·617
□	$\frac{3}{4}$ and $1\frac{1}{4}$	36·8% clay in water	0·176	1·595
■	$\frac{3}{4}$ and $1\frac{1}{4}$	40·4% clay in water	0·132	3·429
▲	$\frac{1}{8}$, $\frac{1}{4}$, $\frac{1}{2}$ and 2	23% lime in water	0·178	1·551

where

$$s' = \frac{3(3n+1)^2}{(2n+1)(5n+3)} \tag{80}$$

For a Newtonian fluid this reduces to

$$s' \neq 2 \tag{81}$$

For the case of a Bingham plastic a cumbersome exact solution can be obtained, which was fitted to an accuracy of 2·5% with the eqn. (24)

$$s' = 2 - \frac{\tau_y}{\tau_w} \tag{82}$$

5. TRANSITION TO TURBULENT FLOW

Figure 6 shows a plot of friction factor f to a base of the generalised Reynolds number $Re_{n'}$ for flow behaviour exponent n' varying from 0·2 to 2. The figure is applicable to all time-independent viscous Newtonian and non-Newtonian fluids.

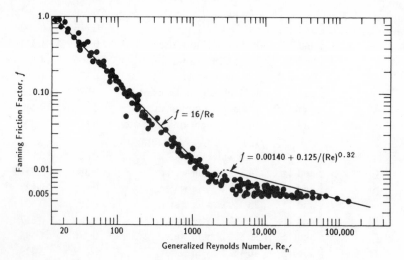

FIG. 6. Friction factor to a base of generalised Reynolds Number: prediction for turbulent conditions.[16]

For pipe flow with Newtonian fluids the transition from laminar flow to turbulent flow is assumed to occur at a Reynolds number of approximately 2000. For power-law fluids, from Fig. 6, it can be deduced that for $n < 1·0$ the critical generalised Reynolds number increases to a Reynolds number of approximately 5000 for $n' = 0·2$. For n' greater than unity it is believed that the transition occurs at approximately the same value of Reynolds number as for Newtonian fluids.

For Bingham plastics, as can be seen from Fig. 4 the transitional Reynolds number varies significantly with the Hedstrom number. Hanks[26] gives the following equation for the critical Reynolds number, defined using the plastic viscosity,

$$Re' = \frac{3 - 4\alpha_c + \alpha_c^4}{24\alpha_c} He = \frac{3(1 - \alpha_c)}{8\alpha_c \delta} He \tag{83}$$

where α_c is the corresponding value of α (eqn. (24)). Equation (25) is used in the transformation involving δ. The critical value is given in terms of the Hedstrom number (eqn. (58))

$$\frac{\alpha_c}{(1-\alpha_c)^3}=\frac{He}{16\,800} \tag{84}$$

The ratio α_c and n' are related in eqn. (23). By iteration related values are obtained as $n'=0.2$ and $\alpha=0.69$. Fom eqn. (14), $\delta=2$. With these values in eqns. (83) and (84), $Re'_c=10\,922$. This is generally consistent with Fig. 4. The effective and plastic viscosity are approximately related[2]

$$\frac{\mu_e}{\eta}=1+\frac{He}{6\,Re'}=1+\frac{8\alpha\delta}{3(1-\alpha)} \tag{85}$$

Combining eqns. (83)–(85) gives the transition in terms of the generalised Reynolds number $Re_{n'}$ (eqn. (70)) as

$$(Re_{n'})_c=\frac{2100}{\delta(1-\alpha)(1-\alpha+1.333\alpha\delta)} \tag{86}$$

For $n'=0.2$ this gives $(Re_{n'})_c=1579$. Binder and Busher[27] found that using the effective viscosity the transition with Bingham plastic fluids approximated to 2100.

Froishteter and Vinogradov[28] give the following equation for the critical Reynolds number with yield-power law fluids

$$(Re_{n'})_c=2100/C' \tag{87}$$

where

$$C'=\frac{1}{w^3}\left(\frac{\alpha^2}{2}+(1-\alpha^2)A'+\alpha(1-\alpha)B'\right) \tag{88}$$

$$w=\alpha^2+2\alpha(1-\alpha)\frac{m+1}{m+2}+(1-\alpha^2)\frac{m+1}{m+3} \tag{89}$$

$$A'=\frac{3(m+1)^3}{2(m+3)(m+2)(3m+5)} \tag{90}$$

$$B'=\frac{6(m+1)^3}{(m+2)(2m+3)(3m+4)} \tag{91}$$

$$m=1/n \tag{92}$$

$$\alpha=\tau_y/\tau_w \tag{24}$$

This procedure gives transitional values approximating Fig. 6.

6. TURBULENT FLOW

Dimensional analysis can be used to show that the friction factor is dependent only on the Reynolds number and, in the case of Bingham fluids, on the Hedstrom number.

Dodge and Metzner[29] obtained the following equation

$$\frac{1}{f^{0.5}} = \frac{4}{(n')^{0.75}} \log \left(Re_{n'} f^{(1-n)/2} \right) - \frac{0.4}{(n')^{1.2}} \qquad (93)$$

where $Re_{n'}$ is the generalised Reynolds number given by eqn. (70). Figure 7 shows the friction factors obtained on this basis. This they showed was applicable to both power law and Bingham fluids.

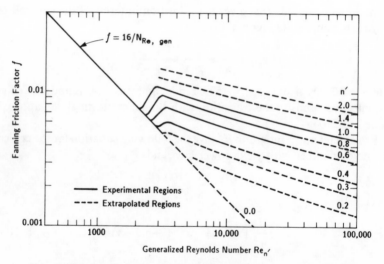

FIG. 7. Friction factor to base of generalised Reynolds Number.[29]

Equation (93) is not explicit in f. Dodge and Metzner[29] gave the following approximate explicit equation

$$f = \frac{\alpha'}{Re_{n'}^{\beta'}} \qquad (94)$$

where α and β were given graphically as functions of n. The graphs are given within 3% by the following equations

$$\alpha = 0.078 (n')^{0.1} \qquad (95)$$

and

$$\beta = 0.25/(n')^{0.2} \tag{96}$$

These equations reduce to the Blasius equation for $n' = 1.0$. Other correlations for turbulent friction factor are to be found in Skelland[2] and Govier and Aziz.[5]

Where these methods are applied to Bingham fluids, as n' and K' vary with wall shear stress an iterative solution is required. One problem with this approach is obtaining data for n' and K' at high enough shear stress under conditions of laminar flow.

Govier and Aziz[5] present correlations for rough tubes and viscoelastic fluids.

7. HEAT TRANSFER WITH LAMINAR FLOW

Considering the heat balance on an elemental ring of fluid in the pipe, neglecting axial heat conduction, gives

$$2\pi \frac{\partial(rq)}{\partial r} dr\, dz = 2\pi r\, dr\, u\rho c_p \frac{\partial T}{\partial z} dz \tag{97}$$

The radial heat flux, q, can be expressed for a laminar flow

$$q = k\frac{\partial T}{\partial r} \tag{98}$$

Combining eqns. (97) and (98) leads to

$$\frac{\partial T}{\partial x} = \frac{k}{\rho c_p u}\left(\frac{\partial^2 T}{\partial r^2} + \frac{1}{r}\frac{\partial T}{\partial r}\right) \tag{99}$$

which can be written

$$\frac{\partial T}{\partial x} = \frac{\alpha}{u}\left(\frac{\partial^2 T}{\partial r^2} + \frac{1}{r}\frac{\partial T}{\partial r}\right) \tag{100}$$

where the thermal diffusivity

$$\alpha = \frac{k}{\rho c_p} \tag{101}$$

With a given velocity distribution this requires to be solved to give the heat transfer coefficient. A computer program which does this for Newtonian and non-Newtonian fluids is listed by Joshi and Bergles.[30]

The heat flux is obtained from

$$q = \frac{r_w}{2} u_m \rho c_p \frac{dT_b}{dz} \tag{102}$$

and the local heat transfer coefficient from

$$h = \frac{q}{T_b - T_w} \tag{103}$$

One method of defining the average heat transfer coefficient is

$$h_m = \frac{1}{z_0} \int_0^{z_0} h \, dz \tag{104}$$

There are a number of other ways of defining or evaluating this coefficient. For example, the heat load is obtained from

$$Q = \pi r_w^2 u_m \rho c_p (T_o - T_i) \tag{105}$$

and the average heat transfer coefficient evaluated from

$$h_m = \frac{Q}{2\pi r_w z_0 \Delta T} \tag{106}$$

where the temperature difference is either the arithmetic mean or the logarithmic mean.

Three Nusselt numbers are used here. The local value, Nu, the mean value based on the arithmetic mean temperature difference, Nu_{am}, and the mean value based on the logarithmic mean temperature difference, Nu_m.

In this section the heat transfer coefficient in laminar flow where the conditions are such that physical property changes with temperature are negligible will be discussed. Conditions of constant physical properties correspond, as discussed in Section 3, to values of the Physical Property number (eqn. (26)) equal to zero.

7.1. Newtonian Fluids

Substituting in eqn. (100) the velocity distribution from eqn. (64) gives

$$\frac{\partial T}{\partial x} = \frac{\alpha}{2u\left(1 - \left(\frac{r}{r_w}\right)^2\right)} - \left(\frac{\partial^2 T}{\partial r^2} + \frac{1}{r}\frac{\partial T}{\partial r}\right) \tag{107}$$

Graetz[31,32] obtained the following solution to this equation

$$\frac{T_w - T}{T_w - T_i} = \sum_{j=1}^{\infty} B_j \phi_j \left(\Gamma \frac{r}{r_w}\right) \exp\left(-b_j^2 \frac{\pi}{2Gz}\right) \tag{108}$$

where

$$Gz = \frac{Wc_p}{kz} \qquad (109)$$

Sellers et al.[33] discuss the evaluation of the terms in eqn. (108). As mentioned earlier software code for solving the basic equations for both Newtonian and non-Newtonian flow is given by Joshi and Bergles.[30]

Figure 8 shows a plot of Nusselt numbers to a base of Graetz number

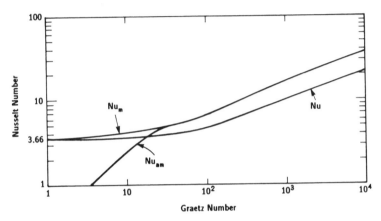

FIG. 8. Nusselt Number to base of Graetz Number for Newtonian flow.

obtained using these equations. The curves correspond to the case of uniform wall temperature and a fully developed velocity profile at inlet. Above a Prandtl number of about 10 the solution is essentially independent of the initial velocity profile. For a Prandtl number of 0·01 and a Graetz number of 1000 the Nusselt number with a uniform velocity profile at inlet is about twice that for parabolic profile; the difference becomes negligible for a Graetz number less than 5. Non-Newtonian fluids generally have Prandtl numbers in excess of 10.

For constant wall temperature, where the fluid outlet temperature is at the wall temperature, the heat balance for the tube is

$$h_m \pi Dz \frac{(T_o - T_i)}{2} = Wc_p(T_o - T_i) \qquad (110)$$

Rearranging gives

$$Nu_{am} = \frac{h_m D}{k} = \frac{2}{\pi} Gz \qquad (111)$$

TABLE 3
TERMS AND EXPONENTS IN eqns. (112) AND (141): $n = 1\cdot0$

	A	B	C	E	δ/Δ	Vp	Reference
					Equation		
T_w = Constant							
Nu	3·66	0·283	0·34	6	14/126	141	19
Nu_m	3·66	0·424	0·34	3	14/126		19
Q = Constant							
Nu	4·36	0·322	0·33	5	14/126	141	
Nu_m	4·36	0·347	0·33	6	14/126		20, 21

This is the equation in Fig. 8 at low values of Gz for an arithmetic mean temperature difference.

Joshi and Bergles[19-21] have correlated data for Newtonian and non-Newtonian heat transfer in tubes using a form of equation due to Churchill and Usagi[34]

$$Nu_{(m)} = A(1 + (BGz^C)^E)^{1/E} \qquad (112)$$

Values of the coefficients and exponents in this equation, for various Newtonian heat transfer processes, are tabulated in Table 3; the table also gives information, which is discussed later, related to non-Newtonian fluids. The coefficient A is the asymptotic value of the Nusselt number, corresponding to fully developed conditions. Table 4 compares these equations with the numerical solutions of McKillop.[35]

7.2. Leveque's Model
A well-known approximate solution for Newtonian flow for developing flow (higher Graetz numbers) is that of Leveque.[36,37] He assumed a linear velocity gradient at the wall

$$u = \frac{du}{dy}(r_w - r) \qquad (113)$$

This leads to the equation

$$Nu_{am} = 1\cdot75\ Gz^{1/3} \qquad (114)$$

This equation is applicable for $Gz > 100$.

Pigford[38] extended Leveque's treatment for Newtonian flows to non-

TABLE 4
COMPARISON OF METHODS

	T_w constant		Heat flux constant		T_w constant		Heat flux constant	
	Eqn. (112)	Reference 35	Eqn. (112)	Reference 35	Eqn. (123)	Reference 35	Eqn. (123)	Reference 35
Gz	$Nu: n = 1\cdot0$				$Nu: n = 0$			
314	7·34	7·44	9·40	9·37	13·34	13·04	20·93	20·49
157	5·85	5·98	7·55	7·53	9·88	9·89	15·29	15·35
78·5	4·75	4·91	6·16	6·17	7·75	7·75	11·69	11·89
52·4	4·31	4·43	5·56	5·56	6·98	6·89	10·33	10·45
31·4	3·95	4·00	5·02	4·98	6·39	6·18	9·22	9·17
15·7	3·74	3·71	4·61	4·52	6·01	5·82	8·48	8·24
10·6	3·70	3·66	4·50	4·41	5·90	5·78	8·26	8·01

Newtonian flows. Using eqns. (15) and (114) he obtained the equation

$$Nu_{am} = 1.75 \delta^{1/3} Gz^{1/3} \tag{115}$$

This equation has been found to be in good agreement with experiments for all non-Newtonian fluids for $n' > 0.1$.

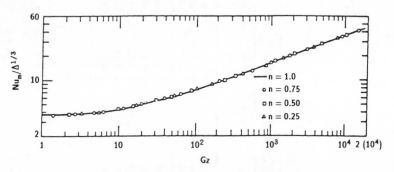

FIG. 9. Ratio $Nu_m/\Delta^{1/3}$ to a base of Graetz Number.[19]

More generally, as shown in Fig. 9, Joshi and Bergles[19-21] have correlated non-Newtonian data for both developing and fully-developed conditions using the equation

$$Nu_{am} = A(1 + (BGz^C)^E)^{1/E} \Delta^{1/3} \tag{116}$$

where Δ is a more general statement of δ as discussed in Section 7.4.

7.3. Plug Flow

For the case of plug flow ($n' = 0$) the differential equation is

$$\frac{\partial T}{\partial x} = \frac{\alpha}{u}\left(\frac{\partial^2 T}{\pi r^2} + \frac{1}{r}\frac{\partial T}{\partial r}\right) \tag{117}$$

which for the case of constant wall temperature leads to

$$\frac{T_w - T}{T_w - T_i} = \sum_{j=1}^{\infty} \frac{2}{a_j j_1(a_j)} J_0\left(a_j \frac{r}{r_w}\right)\exp\left(-a_j^2 \frac{\pi}{Gz}\right) \tag{118}$$

where J_0 and J_1 are Bessel functions of the first kind of order 0 and 1 respectively, and the eigenvalue a_j, is the jth root of the equation

$$J_0(a_j) = 0 \tag{119}$$

The average heat transfer coefficient is obtained[2] as

$$Nu_m = \frac{2}{\pi} Gz \left(\frac{1 - 4E'}{1 + 4E'} \right) \tag{120}$$

where

$$E' = \sum_{j=1}^{\infty} \frac{1}{\lambda_j^2} \exp(\pi \lambda_j^2 / Gz) \tag{121}$$

where λ_j are the roots of $J_0(\lambda)$.

A more convenient equation to use at high $Gz(Gz > 100)$ is[39]

$$Nu_m = \frac{4}{\pi}(2 + Gz^{1/2}) \tag{122}$$

For plug flow the Churchill–Usagi form of equation can be expressed

$$Nu_{n'=0} = A_o (1 + (B_o Gz^{C_o})^{E_o})^{1/E_o} \tag{123}$$

The coefficients and exponents are given in Table 5, and predictions compared with McKillop's[35] numerical solutions of eqn. (118) in Table 4.

TABLE 5
TERMS AND EXPONENTS IN eqn. (123): $n = 0$

	A_o	B_o	C_o	E_o
T_w constant				
Nu	5·77	0·127	1/2	3
Nu_m	5·77	0·220	1/2	7/4
Constant heat flux				
Nu	8·0	0·145	1/2	3
Nu_m	8·0	0·200	1/2	3/2

7.4. The Non-Newtonian Correction Factor

The case $n' < 0.1$ has been examined by Metzner et al.[39] who replaced δ by Δ which was obtained from a graph by linearly extrapolating to the solution for plug flow ($n' = 0$). The procedure for calculating Δ can be approximated as follows. Evaluate first

$$\Delta_0^{1/3} = \frac{Nu_{n'=0}}{Nu_{n'=1}} \tag{124}$$

where the ratio is that of the Nusselt number for pseudoplastic flow with $n' = 0$ to that for Newtonian flow. Evaluate now

$$n'_o = \frac{1}{1 \cdot 7 \Delta_o - 3} \tag{125}$$

The correction for pseudoplasticity is then obtained from

$$\Delta^{1/3} = 0 \cdot 75 \Delta_o^{1/3} + 0 \cdot 25 \Delta_o^{1/3} \left(1 - \frac{n'}{n'_o}\right) \tag{126}$$

If $\Delta < 3/1 \cdot 7$ use the smaller values of δ and Δ_o.

For the case studied by Metzner et al.[39], that of constant temperature and an arithmetic mean temperature difference, approximately

$$\Delta_o^{1/3} = 0 \cdot 64 \ Gz^{(0 \cdot 18 + 0 \cdot 49/Gz^{1/2})} \tag{127}$$

For non-Newtonian fluids therefore use eqn. (116) where for $n' > n'_o$

$$\Delta^{1/3} = \delta^{1/3} \tag{128}$$

and for $n' < n'_o$, $\Delta^{1/3}$ is obtained from eqn. (126).

It is relevant to note that for the case of infinite dilatancy $\Delta^{1/3}$ is 0·91.

7.5. Power Law Fluids

From eqns. (65) and (100)

$$u \left(\frac{3n+1}{n+1}\right) \left(1 - \left(\frac{r}{r_w}\right)^{(n+1)/n}\right) \frac{\partial T}{\partial x} = \alpha \left(\frac{\partial^2 T}{\partial r^2} + \frac{1}{r} \frac{\partial T}{\partial r}\right) \tag{129}$$

Christiansen and Craig[40] have obtained solutions of this equation. Solutions on this basis are shown in Fig. 10. These are closely approximated using eqn. (116).

7.6. Fully Developed Conditions

Some distance from inlet $(Gz < 5)$ an asymptotic value of the local heat transfer coefficient is approached. For a uniform wall temperature Beck and Eggink[41] correlated the exact analytic solutions, obtained using eqn. (100) with the appropriate velocity distribution, with the equation

$$Nu = \frac{n+1}{3n+1} \frac{16\pi}{9} \frac{\left(\dfrac{3n+1}{2n+2}\right)!}{\left(\dfrac{n}{n+1}\right)!} \tag{130}$$

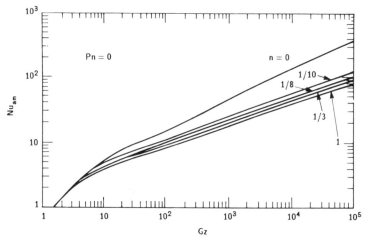

FIG. 10. Average Nusselt Number Nu_{am} to base of Graetz Number.[40]

For flow of a Newtonian fluid ($n = 1.0$) this reduces to 3.66, while for plug flow ($n = 0$) this reduces to 5.72.

For uniform heat flux Grigull[42] correlated the exact analytic solution using

$$Nu = \frac{2(N+1)^2}{5+N - \dfrac{2}{N+3} - \dfrac{4+(N+3)^2}{N+5} - \dfrac{(N+3)^2}{4}} \tag{131}$$

where $N = 1/n$. For Newtonian flow this reduces to 4.36 and for plug flow to 8.0.

7.7. Bingham Plastics

Solving eqns. (66) or (67) and (100) leads, for the case of constant wall temperature, to the equation

$$\frac{T_w - T}{T_w - T_i} = \sum_{j=1}^{\infty} C_j \exp(-\beta_j^2 \xi) R_j \left(\frac{r}{r_w}\right) \tag{132}$$

where the coefficient C_j and eigenvalues β_j and R_j are tabulated by Wissler and Schechter.[43] The symbol ξ is a reduced axial distance.

8. HEAT TRANSFER WITH LAMINAR FLOW: VARIABLE PHYSICAL PROPERTIES

8.1. Newtonian Fluids

Sieder and Tate's[44] is one of the earliest methods of allowing for the effects of the temperature change on the physical properties, with respect to the fluid viscosity, with Newtonian flow. Their equation was

$$Nu_m = 2 \cdot 0 \, Gz^{1/3}(\mu_b/\mu_w)^{0 \cdot 14} \qquad (133)$$

where the subscript b indicates properties at the bulk temperature. Satisfactory agreement was shown with experiment except at low Gz and high wall to bulk temperature difference where natural convection occurs.

8.2. Bingham Plastics

Hirai[45] has obtained good agreement with experiment with the development of the following equation

$$Nu_m = 1 \cdot 86 \, \delta^{1/3} Gz^{1/3}(\mu_b/\mu_w)^{0 \cdot 14} \qquad (134)$$

In this equation δ is given by eqn. (25). Thomas[46] has shown an extensive comparison of this equation with data.

8.3. Power Law Fluids: Constant Wall Temperature

The temperature distribution equation in this case is

$$\frac{\partial T}{\partial(1/Gz)} = 2\pi \frac{I_2}{I_1} \left(\frac{\partial^2 T}{\partial(r/r_w)^2} + \frac{r_w}{r} \frac{\partial T}{\partial(r/r_w)} \right) \qquad (135)$$

where

$$I_1 = \int_{r/r_w}^{1} (r/r_w)^{1/n} \exp(-E/R_G T) \, d(r/r_w) \qquad (136)$$

and

$$I_2 = \int_{0}^{1} I_1(r/r_w) \, d(r/r_w) \qquad (137)$$

where T is the absolute temperature, R_G is the gas constant, and E the activation energy per mole.

Christiansen and Craig[40] solved these equations for the case of a constant wall temperature for a series of Physical Property numbers Pn. This number has been discussed in Section 3.5; it is a measure of the variation in physical properties in the process.

Charm and Merrill[47] developed the Sieder–Tate approach as follows. They obtained the average viscosity radially as

$$\mu_b = \left(\frac{1}{2}\frac{dp}{dz}\right)^{(n-1)/n} K_b^{1/n} \frac{3n+1}{3(n-1)} r_w^{(n-1)/n} \tag{138}$$

and the wall viscosity is

$$\mu_w = \left(\frac{1}{2}\frac{dp}{dz}\right)^{(n-1)/n} K_w^{1/n} r_w^{(n-1)/n} \tag{139}$$

Hence using eqn. (133) they obtained

$$Nu_m = 2Gz^{1/2}\left(\frac{K_b}{K_w}\frac{3n+1}{2(3n+1)}\right)^{0.14} \tag{140}$$

Define now a variable property correction factor, Vp, to allow for physical property variation by the equation

$$Nu = A(1+(B\,Gz^C)^E)^{1/E}\Delta^{1/3}Vp \tag{141}$$

Joshi and Bergles[19] developed for the case of uniform wall temperature conditions

$$Vp = \left(\frac{K}{K_w}\right)^{0.11}(1.0+(C_1(K/K_w)^{xm})^{15})^{1/15} \tag{142}$$

This equation covers the entire range of conditions from inlet to fully developed conditions. The coefficient C_1 is given by

$$C_1 = d_1 \exp(-d_2 Pn) \tag{143}$$

The exponent xm is given by

$$xm = f_1 \exp(-f_2 \Delta T) \tag{144}$$

and

$$d_1 = 0.4230 + 0.6428n$$
$$d_2 = 0.6900 - 0.1n$$
$$f_1 = 2.8308 - 4.1030n + 1.9327n^2$$
$$f_2 = 0.215 - 0.22n$$

8.4. Power Law Fluids: Constant Heat Flux and Variable Properties

Only a few investigators have studied the constant flux case, despite its frequency in industrial practice. Mizushima et al.[48] correlated data obtained with methocel solutions using the following equations

$$Gz > 15 \cdot 7 \quad Nu_m = 1 \cdot 41 (2\delta Gz)^{1/3} \left(\frac{K_b}{K_w} \right)^{0 \cdot 1/n^{0 \cdot 7}} \tag{145}$$

$$Gz < 15 \cdot 7 \quad Nu_m = 4 \cdot 36 \Delta^{1/3} \left(\frac{K_b}{K_w} \right)^{0 \cdot 14/n^{0 \cdot 7}} \tag{146}$$

Deviations as large as 50% were obtained.

For the constant heat flux case Joshi and Bergles[20] recommend for developing conditions

$$(Vp)_e = \left(\frac{K}{K_w} \right)^{0 \cdot 11} \tag{147}$$

and for fully developed flow

$$(Vp)_\infty = 1 + (0 \cdot 1240 + 0 \cdot 0542 \, n') Pn - (0 \cdot 010 \, 13 + 0 \cdot 0068 \, n') Pn^2 \tag{148}$$

An equation covering the entire range is

$$Vp = \frac{(Vp)_\infty}{\left(1 - \left(\frac{(Vp)_\infty}{(Vp)_e} \right)^{30} \right)^{1/30}} \tag{149}$$

8.5. Heat Transfer with Laminar Flow: Summary

The recommended equation is

$$Nu = A(1 + (BG_z^C)^E)^{1/E} \Delta^{1/3} Vp \tag{141}$$

where Vp is obtained from eqns. (142) or (149), Δ is obtained as discussed in Section 7.4, and the coefficients and exponents are obtained from Table 3.

In practice neither the constant wall temperature solution nor the constant heat flux solution will normally be precisely applicable in practice. In heat exchangers the constant wall temperature solution will normally be the closest approximation.

9. HEAT TRANSFER WITH TURBULENT FLOW

The high consistency of most non-Newtonian fluids is such that in most industrial cases turbulent flow does not occur. For this reason only a small proportion of the literature on non-Newtonian heat transfer relates to turbulent conditions.

9.1. Newtonian Fluids

For the flow of Newtonian fluids in round pipes the following equations originally associated with Dittus and Boelter[49] are commonly used

$$\text{Heating} \qquad Nu = 0.023\, Re^{0.8} Pr^{0.4} \qquad (150)$$

$$\text{Cooling} \qquad Nu = 0.023\, Re^{0.8} Pr^{0.3} \qquad (151)$$

where the physical properties are evaluated at the bulk temperature.

Equation (150), for example, can also be expressed in terms of the Stanton number

$$St = 0.023/(Re^{0.2} Pr^{0.6}) \qquad (152)$$

as

$$St = h/(c_p u_m \rho) \qquad (153)$$

Sieder and Tate[44] correct for radial variation of viscosity as follows

$$Nu = 0.023\, Re^{0.8}\, Pr^{1/3} \left(\frac{\mu_b}{\mu_w}\right)^{0.14} \qquad (154)$$

where the viscosity ratio is that of the viscosity evaluated at the bulk temperature to that at the wall temperature.

Orr and Dalla Valle[50] found that, with appropriate evaluation of the mixture properties a slightly modified version of this equation could be used to correlate data for solid–liquid suspensions of up to 45% by mass of solid. Their equation corresponds to eqn. (150) but with the coefficient of 0.023 replaced by 0.027. Mass averaged values of μ and c_p were used. The thermal conductivity of the suspension k_s was obtained from

$$k_s = k_1 \left(\frac{2k_1 + k_p - 2x_v(k_1 - k_p)}{2k_1 + k_p + x_v(k_1 - k_p)}\right) \qquad (155)$$

where k_1 and k_p are the thermal conductivities of the fluid and particles respectively. The volume fraction of the particles in suspension is given by x_v. The viscosity is evaluated using

$$\mu_s = \frac{\mu_1}{(1 + (x_v/x_{vb}))^{1.8}} \qquad (156)$$

where x_{vb} is the value of x_v after prolonged standing of the slurry.

9.2. Heat Transfer Analogies

The analogy between heat and momentum transfer has been used by Prandtl,[51] Von Karman[52] and then Martinelli[53] to predict heat transfer in turbulent forced convection of Newtonian fluids in tubes. If the laminar layer is not included in the model the following relationship between Stanton number and the friction factor is obtained.

$$St = f/2 \tag{157}$$

Including the presence of the laminar layer (the Taylor–Prandtl analogy) gives

$$St = (f/2)(1 + (u_l/u_m)(Pr - 1)) \tag{158}$$

where u_l/u_m is the ratio of the velocity at the edge of the laminar layer to the average velocity. Wilkinson[1] quotes the equation

$$u_l/u_m = 1 \cdot 5/(Re^{1/8} Pr^{1/6}) \tag{159}$$

Substituting eqn. (159) in (158)

$$St = (f/2)/(1 + 1 \cdot 5/(Re^{1/8} Pr^{1/6})) \tag{160}$$

Metzner and Friend[54] have extended this concept to heat transfer with non-Newtonian fluids. For constant heat flux and Prandtl numbers equal or greater than unity they obtained the relationship

$$St = (f/2)/(1 \cdot 2 + c_1(f/2)^{1/2}) \tag{161}$$

where the friction factor is that from eqns. (94)–(96).

From experiment it was found that c_1 is the following function of Prandtl number

$$c_1 = 11 \cdot 8(Pr - 1)/Pr^{1/3} \tag{162}$$

for $0 \cdot 46 < Pr < 590$. The Prandtl number is evaluated using the apparent viscosity at the wall shearing stress. It was shown[55] that this equation applies where

$$\frac{Pr_{n'} \cdot Re_{n'}}{(n')^{1/4}} (f/2)^{1/2} > 5000 \tag{163}$$

The generalised Prandtl number $Pr_{n'}$ uses the effective viscosity

$$\mu_e = K' \left(\frac{8u_m}{D} \right)^{n' - 1} \tag{164}$$

The Prandtl numbers Pr and Pr_{gen} are related by

$$Pr_{n'}/Pr = \left(\frac{16}{Re_{n'}f}\right)^{(n'-1)/n'} \left(\frac{3n'+1}{4n'}\right) \tag{165}$$

9.3. Power Law Fluids: Turbulent Flow
Clapp[56] developed the following formula

$$Nu = 0.023 \, (9350)^{0.8-s} Re^s Pr^{0.4} \tag{166}$$

where

$$s = 0.8/n^n \tag{167}$$

This reduces to the Dittus–Boelter equation for Newtonian fluids $(n=1)$. The experiments used to derive the above equation covered the range

$$0.698 < n < 0.786$$

$$5480 < Re < 29\,200$$

9.4. Bingham Plastic Fluids: Turbulent Flow
Thomas[46,57] tested aqueous thorium oxide solutions which were found to behave as Bingham fluids. The data were correlated using eqns. (150), (155) and (156).

10. NATURAL CONVECTION HEAT TRANSFER

The greater part of the work on the effects of natural convection has concerned natural convection from flat plates or between parallel plates. A recent survey of that work is given by Shenoy.[58] As elsewhere this chapter confines itself to convection effects in tubes.

10.1. Laminar Flow with Natural Convection
De Young and Scheele[59] and Marner and Rehfus[60] have examined numerically the case of upward flow in tubes with constant heat flux. They ascertained that the controlling parameter in this case was Gr/Re where Gr is the Grashoff number, defined for Newtonian conditions as

$$Gr = \frac{g\rho^2 z^3 \beta \Delta T}{\mu^2} \tag{168}$$

The variation of Nusselt number, as estimated by Marner and Rehfus, with this parameter and the pseudoplasticity index n is shown in Fig. 11.

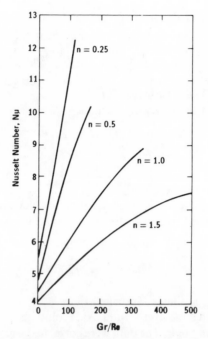

FIG. 11. Nusselt Number to base of Gr/Re: mixed convection flow in vertical tube
with constant heat flux.[58]

De Young and Scheele[59] also study the case of downward flow with
a constant heat flux, while Marner and McMillan [61] report on the case of
upward flow with constant wall temperature.

For horizontal flow Metzner and Gluck[62] obtained the equation

$$Nu_m = 1 \cdot 75 \delta^{1/3} \left(\frac{K_b}{K_w} \right)^{1/3} (Gz + 12 \cdot 6 (Gr_w Pr_w D/z)^{0 \cdot 4})^{1/3} \qquad (169)$$

Oliver and Jensen[63] developed the equation

$$Nu_m = 1 \cdot 75 \left(\frac{K_b}{K_w} \right)^{0 \cdot 14} (Gz + 0 \cdot 0083 (GrPr)_w^{0 \cdot 75})^{1/3} \qquad (170)$$

and Mahalingam et al.[64] obtained the equation

$$Nu_m = 1 \cdot 45 \delta^{1/3} \left(\frac{K_b}{K_w} \right)^{0 \cdot 14} (Gz + 0 \cdot 0083 (GrPr)_w^{0 \cdot 75})^{1/3} \qquad (171)$$

10.2. Turbulent Mixed Convection

Only one article on turbulent mixed convection with non-Newtonian fluids is to be found in the literature, that by Shenoy.[65] This was for the case of flow in vertical tubes with power-law fluids. The Nusselt number for mixed flow Nu_M is related to that without convection effects, Nu, in the equation

$$\frac{Nu_M}{Nu} = \left(1 - \left((2/\alpha)^{(2+n)/2} \exp^{(3\cdot05n+3\cdot8)/2\cdot22}\right)^{1/n} \times \right.$$

$$\left. \frac{Gr_s}{Pr^{1/2}Re^{(4n+2-\beta(2-n))/2n}} \left(\frac{K_w}{K_b}\right)^{1/n} \left(\frac{\rho_b}{\rho_w}\right)^{1/2}\right)^B \qquad (172)$$

where

$$Gr_s = \left(\frac{\rho_b(\rho_b - \rho_w)gD/2}{K_b^2}\right)^{2n+1} u^{2-2n} \qquad (173)$$

$$Re = Re_{n'}/8^{1-n'} \qquad (174)$$

$$Pr = \frac{r_b c_p}{k} \left(\frac{K_b}{\rho_b}\right)^{2/(n+1)} D^{(1-n)/(m+1)} u^{3(m-1)/(n+1)} \qquad (175)$$

Shenoy's values of the exponent B in eqn. (172) can be approximated to within 4% by the equation

$$B = 1\cdot70 - 1\cdot24n \qquad (176)$$

11. CONCLUSIONS

This chapter has reviewed methods for predicting flow and heat transfer with non-Newtonian fluids in tubes.

The use of the Flow Curve (Section 3.3) to obtain the consistency index K' and the flow behaviour exponent n' is the first step in the recommended prediction method.

For laminar flow pressure gradients can be predicted using the familiar relationship for Newtonian flow for friction factor, with a generalised Reynolds number defined by eqn. (70), or an effective viscosity defined by eqn. (75). An equation for turbulent flow in terms of the generalised Reynolds number has been developed (eqn. (93)).

For laminar flow heat transfer, equations of the form developed by Bergles and co-workers (eqns. (116) and (141)) are convenient for use in practice, though at present they are only readily applied to the cases of constant wall temperature and constant heat flux.

The chapter concluded by reviewing the relatively limited information on turbulent heat transfer and on natural convection effects.

REFERENCES

1. WILKINSON, W. L. Non-Newtonian Fluids, 1960, Pergamon Press, Oxford.
2. SKELLAND, A. H. P. Non-Newtonian Flow and Heat Transfer, 1967, John Wiley, New York.
3. BIRD, R. C., ARMSTRONG, R. C. and HASSAGER, O. Dynamics of Polymeric Fluids, Vol. 1, Fluids Mechanics, 1977, John Wiley, New York.
4. BIRD, R. C., HASSAGER, O., ARMSTRONG, R. C. and CRURTIS, C. F. Dynamics of Polymeric Liquids, Vol. 2, Kinetic Theory, 1977, John Wiley, New York.
5. GOVIER, G. A. and AZIZ, K. A. The Flow of Complex Mixtures in Pipes, 1977, Kreiger, New York.
6. SCHOWALTER, W. T. Mechanics of Non-Newtonian Fluids, 1978, Pergamon Press, Oxford.
7. PATEL, R. D. Non-newtonian flows. In: Handbook of Fluids in Motion N. P. Cheremisinoff and R. Gupta (eds.), Chapter 6, 1983, Ann Arbor Science, Michigan, 135–77.
8. EYRING, H. J. J. Chem. Phys., 1936, 4, 283.
9. SISKO, A. W. The flow of lubricating greases, Ind. Engng. Chem., 1958, 50, 1789–92.
10. SYMONDS, F. L., ROSENTHAL, A. J. et al. Sizing pipe for the flow of cellulose acetate solutions, Ind. Engng. Chem., 1955, 47, 2463–6.
11. SPENCER, R. S. and DILLON, R. E. J. Coll. Sci., 1948, 3, 168–9.
12. HERSCHELL, W. H. and BUCKLEY, R. Measurement of consistency as applied to rubber–benzene solutions, Proc. ASTM, 1926, XXVI, 621.
13. CROWLEY, P. R. and KITZES, A. S. Rheological behaviour of thorium oxide slurries in laminar flow, Ind. Engng. Chem., 1957 49(5), 888–92.
14. RABINOWITSCH, B. Z. Physik. Chem., 1929, A145, 1.
15. MOONEY, M. J. Rheol., 1931, 2, 210.
16. METZNER, A. B. and REED, J. C. Flow of non-Newtonian fluids, AIChE J., 1955, 1(4), 434–40.
17. METZNER, A. B. Non-Newtonian fluid flow: relationship between recent pressure drop correlations, Ind. Engng. Chem., 195, 49, 1429–38.
18. ARMSTRONG, R. C. and WINTER, H. H. Heat transfer for non-Newtonian fluids, Heat Exchanger Design Handbook, Section 2.5.12–16, 1983, Hemisphere, New York.
19. JOSHI, S. D. and BERGLES, A. E. Analytical study of laminar heat transfer to pseudoplastic fluids in tubes with uniform wall temperature, AIChE Symp. Series, Milwaukee 1981, 77(208), 114–22.
20. JOSHI, S. D. and BERGLES, A. E. Analytical study of heat transfer to laminar in-tube flow of non-Newtonian fluids, J. Heat Transfer, 1980, 102, 397–401.

21. BERGLES, A. E. Effects of temperature-dependent properties on non-Newtonian flows. In: *Heat Exchanger Sourcebook.* J. W. Palen (ed.), 1986, Hemisphere, Washington, D.C.

22. SCIROCCO, V., DEVIENNE, R. and LEBOUCHE, M. Ecoulement laminaire et transfert de chaleur pour un fluide pseudo-plastique dans la zone d'entree d'un tube, *Int. J. Heat Mass Transfer,* 1985, **22**(1), 91–9.

23. METZNER, A. B. and REED, J. C. Flow of non-Newtonian fluids—correlation of the laminar, transition, and turbulent flow regimes, *AIChE J.,* 1955, **1**, 434–40.

24. METZNER, A. B. In: *Advances in Chemical Engineering, Vol. 1*, 1956, Academic Press, New York, 92.

25. BUCKINGHAM, E. *Proc. ASTM,* 1921, **21**, 1154–61.

26. HANKS, R. W. The laminar-turbulent transitions for fluids with a yield stress, *AIChE J.,* 1963, **9**, 306–9.

27. BINDER, R. C. and BUSHER, J. E. Study of the flow of plastics through pipes, *J. Appl. Mech.,* 1946, **13**(2), A101–A105.

28. FROISHTETER, G. B. and VINOGRADOV, G. V. *Rheol Acta,* 1977, **16**, 620.

29. DODGE, D. W. and METZNER, A. B. Turbulent flow of non-Newtonian systems, *AIChE J.,* 1959, **5**, 189–204.

30. JOSHI, S. D. and BERGLES, A. E. Heat transfer to laminar in-tube flow of non-Newtonian fluids: Part 1, analytical study. Report HTL-17, ISU-ERI-AMES-79088. Heat Transfer Laboratory, Department of Mechanical Engineering, Engineering Research Institute, Iowa State University, 1978.

31. GRAETZ, L. *Ann. Physik.,* 1983, **18**, 79.

32. GRAETZ, L. Uber die warmeleitungsfahigkeit von flussigkeiten, *Ann. Physik.,* 1985, **25**, 337.

33. SELLERS, J. R., TRIBUS, M. and KLEIN, J. S. Heat transfer to laminar flow in a round tube or flat conduit—the Graetz problem extended, *Trans. ASME,* 1956, **78**, 441–8.

34. CHURCHILL, S. W. and USAGI, R. A general expression for the correlation of rates of transfer and other phenomenon, *AIChE J.,* 1972, **18**, 1121–8.

35. MCKILLOP, A. A. Heat transfer laminar flow in entrance region of a tube, *Int. J. Heat Mass Transfer,* 1964, **7**, 853–62.

36. LEVEQUE, A. Les lois de la transmission de chaleur par convection, *Annales des Mines Paris-Mem.,* 1928, Series 12, **13**, 283–90.

37. RICHARDSON, S. M. Extended Leveque solutions for flows of power fluids in pipes and channels, *Int. J. Heat Mass Transfer,* 1979, **22**, 1417–23.

38. PIGFORD, R. L. Non-isothermal flow and heat transfer inside vertical tubes, *Chem. Engng. Prog. Symposium Series,* 1955, **51** (17), 79–92.

39. METZNER, A. B., VAUGHN, R. D. and HOUGHTON, G. L. Heat transfer to non-Newtonian fluids, *AIChE J.,* 1957, **3**(1), 92–100.

40. CHRISTIANSEN, E. B. and CRAIG, S. E. Jr, Heat transfer to pseudoplastic fluids in laminar flow, *AIChE J.,* 1962, **8**(1402), 154–60.

41. BECK, W. J. and EGGINK, R. Warmteoverdracht naar een laminaire stroming van een neit-Newtonse vloeistof in enn ronde buise, *De Ingenuir, Chemische Techniek,* 1962, **7**, 81–9.

42. GRIGULL, U. V. Warmeubergang an nicht-Newtonsche flussigkeiten bei laminar rohrstromung, *Chemie-Ingenieur-Technik,* 1956, **8/9**, 553–6.

43. WISSLER, E. H. and SCHECHTER, R. S. *Chem. Engng. Prog. Symposium Series,* 1959, **55**(29), 203–8.
44. SIEDER, E. N. and TATE, G. E. Heat transfer and pressure drop of liquid in tubes, *Ind. Engng. Chem.,* 1936, **24**, 1429.
45. HIRAI, E. Theoretical explanation of heat transfer in the laminar region of Bingham fluids, *AIChE J.,* 1959, **5**, 130–3-9M.
46. THOMAS, D. G. Heat and momentum transfer characteristics of non-Newtonian aqueous thorium oxide suspensions, *AIChE J.,* 1960, **6**, 631–9.
47. CHARM, S. E. and MERRILL, E. W. *Food Research,* 1959, **24**, 319–31.
48. MIZUSHIMA, T., ITO, R., KURIWAKE, Y. and YAHIKAZAWA, K. Boundary layer heat transfer in a circular tube to Newtonian and non-Newtonian fluids, *Kakagu Kogaku,* 1967, **31**, 250–5.
49. DITTUS, R. G. and BOELTER, L. M. K. *Univ. Calif., Pubs Eng.,* 1930, **2**, 443.
50. ORR, C. and DALLA VALLE, J. M. *Chem. Engng. Prog. Symposium Series,* No. 9, 1954, **50**, 29–45.
51. PRANDTL, L. Bemerkung uber den warmeubergang in rohr, *Physikalische Zeitschrift,* 1928, **29**, 487.
52. VON KARMAN, T. The analogy between fluid friction and heat transfer, *ASME Trans.,* 1939, **61**, 705–10.
53. MARTINELLI, R. C. Heat transfer to molten metals, *ASME Trans.,* 1947, **69**, 947–59.
54. METZNER, A. B. and FRIEND, W. L. Theoretical analogies between heat, mass and momentum transfer and modification for fluids of high Prandtl and Schmidt numbers, *Can. J. Chem. Engng.,* 1958, **36**, 235–40.
55. METZNER, A. B. and FRIEND, W. L. Heat transfer to turbulent non-Newtonian fluids, *Ind. Engng. Chem.,* 1959, **51**, 879–82.
56. CLAPP, M. *Int. Developments in Heat Transfer,* Part III, 652–61, D-159, D-211-215, 1961, ASME, New York.
57. THOMAS, D. G. Non-Newtonian suspensions, *Ind. Engng. Chem.,* 1963, **11**, 27–35.
58. SHENOY, A. V. Natural convection heat transfer to power-law fluids. In: *Handbook of Heat and Mass Transfer, Vol. 1*; 1986 *Heat Mass Trasfer Operations,* N. P. Cheremesinoff (ed.), Chapter 5, 183–210.
59. DE YOUNG, S. H. and SCHEELE, G. F. Natural convection distorted non-Newtonian flow in a pipe, *AIChE J.,* 1970, **16**(5), 712–7.
60. MARNER, W. J. and REHFUS, R. A. Buoyancy effects of fully developed laminar non-Newtonian flow in a vertical pipe, *Chem. Engng. J.,* 1972, **3**, 294–300.
61. MARNER, W. J. and McMILLAN, H. K. Combined free and forced laminar non-Newtonian flow in a vertical pipe, *Chem. Engng. Sci.,* 1972, **27**, 473–88.
62. METZNER, A. B. and GLUCK, D. F. Heat transfer to non-Newtonian fluids under laminar flow conditions. *Chem. Engng. Sci.,* 1960, **12**, 185–90.
63. OLIVER, D. R. and JENSEN, V. G. Heat transfer to pseudoplastic fluids in laminar flow in tubes, *Chem. Engng. Sci.,* 1964, **19**, 115–29.
64. MAHALINGAM, R., CHEN, S. F. and COULSON, J. M. Laminar pseudoplastic flow heat transfer with prescribed wall heat flux, *Chem. Engng. J.,* 1975, **9**, 161–6.
65. SHENOY, A. V. Natural convection effects on heat transfer to power-law fluids flowing under turbulent conditions in vertical pipes, *Int. Comm. Heat Mass Transfer,* 1984, **11**, 467–76.

Chapter 9

RUN-AROUND COIL SYSTEMS

W. H. EMERSON*

National Engineering Laboratory, East Kilbride, Glasgow, UK

SUMMARY

This chapter defines and describes run-around coil systems and discusses the circumstances in which they are most likely to offer advantages over more conventional heat-exchange systems. It concludes by examining the problems of design and operation which are peculiar to these systems, and presents some solutions.

NOTATION

A	Surface area for heat transfer
C	Specific heat capacity of primary fluid
c	Specific heat capacity of secondary fluid
K	Fixed part of cost of heat exchanger
L	Total cost of heat exchanger(s)
$\dot{M}$	Mass flow rate of primary fluid
$\dot{m}$	Mass circulation rate of secondary fluid
p	Cost per unit of surface area
Q	Rate of heat transfer
q	Cost per unit UA
R	$UA/\dot{M}C$
r	$\dot{m}/\dot{m}_o$
T	Temperature
ΔT	Logarithmic mean temperature difference
U	Overall heat-transfer coefficient

*Present address: Bureau International de Métrologie Légale, Paris, France.

Subscripts

1   At hotter end of heat exchanger
2   At cooler end of heat exchanger
c   Cooler primary fluid or heat exchanger
h   Hotter primary fluid or heat exchanger
o   Optimum
s   Secondary fluid

1. DEFINITION

The term 'run-around coil' was first used in the air-conditioning industry for a particular application of a system which already had a long history of use in other fields. The name has since been adopted to mean any system in which heat is transferred from one medium to another by means of two heat exchangers having a secondary fluid circulating between them. The term is frequently associated with 'heat recovery', which often has the connotation of an add-on system to recover energy that was formerly lost to the environment; but run-around coil systems have played an important and fundamental part in engineering systems since the invention of the cooling tower, the domestic hot-water system and the car radiator. The meaning of the term is now being extended to include systems in which there are more than two heat exchangers, which may be in series or parallel, so that the conventional cooling-water system on an industrial site becomes a 'run-around' system, as does the conventional central-heating system.

Figure 1 shows the essential elements of a run-around coil system. The

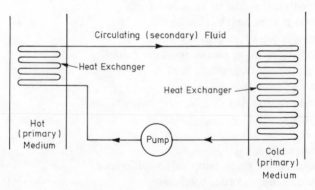

FIG. 1. A run-around coil system.

pump is normally an essential element, but it may be replaced by a gravity-driven thermosyphon, as in an old-fashioned, indirect, domestic water-heating system. The secondary fluid may be either a pressurised liquid, as in the cooling system of an internal-combustion engine; or it may be a pure fluid which boils in one heat exchanger and condenses in another or others, as when steam is supplied from a central boiler to processes scattered about a site, with return of condensate. A disadvantage of a pure, two-phase secondary fluid is that, with it, effectively counterflow heat exchange is not possible. If a pressurised liquid is used it is necessary to include a header tank or expansion tank which may either be open, sealed with a diaphragm, or sealed over a padding gas. The only application of which I am aware in which a gas is used as the secondary fluid is in gas-cooled nuclear reactors.

The design and operation of site cooling systems, steam services and central heating systems is outside the scope of this chapter.

2. APPLICATIONS

Run-around coil sytems may be used wherever it is impractical, un-economic or unsafe to bring the two primary media together in a single conventional heat exchanger. They may also be used as a means of controlling the rate of heat transfer between the primary fluids, and as an aid to metering it.

An example of impracticality in using a single heat-exchange surface is in the large condensing steam turbine. The heat sink, the primary medium of lower temperature, is the atmosphere, a fluid of low density. Steam at sub-atmospheric pressure is a fluid of even lower density. For a large turbine set an air-cooled condenser would have to be very large indeed, so the exhaust steam would have to be taken outside the turbine hall through ducting of very large section and with many opportunities for loss of pressure and for the development of air leaks. The conventional alternative is a water-cooled condenser adjacent to the turbine, with the cooling water circulating through an air-cooled or evaporatively-cooled heat exchanger outside the turbine hall. If evaporative cooling is an economic necessity (as it is in all but the dryest countries) a run-around system is essential.

It is also impractical to dispense with a run-around system if heat is to be rejected to the atmosphere from a surface at moderate temperature with a very high heat flux. An example is the cooling of a large thermionic valve, where cooling with treated water is the only practical means by which the heat can be removed from the valve at an acceptable temperature. The treated water must then be circulated through an air-cooled heat exchanger. Another example is the cooling of an arc-melting crucible for the production of titanium ingot. The cooling medium is liquid sodium, which is circulated through an air cooler. The cooling system of a fast-breeder nuclear reactor is a similar example.

Normally the only practical place at which to extract the heat of compression from a gas is immediately after the compressor—otherwise the gas duct must be insulated up to the point where the heat is extracted, at significant cost, if the heat is to be recovered for a useful purpose. If the heat sink cannot readily be brought to the compressor, a run-around system is a solution.

Run-around coil systems should be considered when the two primary media are separated by distance and when each of the primary media has one or more of the following characteristics:

(a) Low density. Fluids of low density are expensive to contain, especially in insulated ducts, and to pump over any distance.

(b) Corrosive. Pipes and ducts for corrosive materials are expensive: it is cheaper to cover the distance with a non-corrosive secondary fluid.

(c) Toxic. The precautions against leaks and the consequences of leaks may be expensive. It is cheaper to convey enthalpy across the site using a benign secondary fluid.

(d) Of high specific value. Long pipes or ducts containing an expensive fluid entail an expensive investment in process material held up in the system.

(e) Of high purity—especially at sub-atmospheric pressure. Long pipes or ducts increase the risk of contamination through inward leaks.
A run-around system should also be considered if:

(f) The capacity of the system to transfer heat is to be controlled, or

(g) The rate of heat transfer is to be metered.

2.1. Examples of Applications
Low-density fluids. The condenser cooling system for steam turbines has already been mentioned as an example of two low-density primary fluids. Another very common one is an air-to-air exchange of heat to be incorporated in an existing ventilation system, to preheat incoming air by exchange with the heated air being discharged, or to precool the incoming air in summer. In a large system of forced ventilation the points of entry of air to the system and of discharge may not be far apart: but the ducts are so

large that the structure of the building, or the presence of machinery or other plant, may make even minor re-routing of the ductwork out of the question. In such circumstances the installation of an air–water exchanger in each duct, with a circulation of water between them, is a practical solution and is the classical application of run-around coils in the air conditioning industry. Such systems are also commonly used where a hot process gas, or hot, contaminated air, is used to provide heat for space heating, often through a large number of heat exchangers. The system is equally applicable to industrial plant, such as furnaces and ovens, where it is desired to preheat the ingoing air by exchange with the hot gases being discharged, and where large and awkward ducting cannot be tolerated or is impractical.

Run-around systems are used in sulphuric-acid plant to cool hot acid and preheat boiler feed water. The system is designed to prevent the disaster which would accompany a leak of acid into the boiler feed, such as might occur if the two were separated only by the surfaces of an acid-to-feed heat exchanger. By continuously monitoring the pH of the circulating water, an alarm may be sounded if a leak of acid occurs, before any harm is done.

A run-around coil system can serve to protect a system against frost damage. Many solar water heaters use a glycol mixture as the medium which is heated by the sun and which circulates by gravity through a calorifier to heat domestic hot water. At night, when the atmospheric temperature drops the circulation ceases and the solar heater is prevented from freezing by the presence of the glycol.

3. CONTROLS

Run-around systems provide an easy method of controlling the rate of heat transfer between the primary media, especially if the latter are gases or are hostile to valves. Within certain limits, the rate of heat transfer can be increased or diminished by raising or lowering the rate of circulation of the secondary liquid, or by varying the amount of throttling of the vapour in a two-phase secondary fluid.

In many run-around coil systems the objective is simply to transfer as much heat as the system will allow, in all circumstances. Many operators believe, mistakenly, that the circulation rate of the secondary fluid should therefore always remain at its maximum possible. It will be shown later in the chapter that, unless both primary fluids are isothermally boiling or condensing substances, there is a unique circulation rate which is the optimum for maximum heat transfer, and which is a function of the rates of flow of the primary fluids. If automatic controls are used to vary the circulation rate of the secondary fluid in order to modulate the rate of heat transfer, the circulation rate must never be allowed to exceed the optimum for maximum heat transfer. A method of detecting when the optimum circulation rate occurs is described later in the chapter.

The usual method of varying the secondary rate of circulation is by incorporating a by-pass valve in the secondary circuit, controlled by a temperature sensor in one of the primary fluids. It is common in ventilating systems to provide protection against frosting of the coil in which warm, humid air is cooled, by progressively opening the by-pass and, finally, by switching off the pump motor, in response to signals from a temperature sensor in the discharged air. In mild weather, when the building's solar gain and internal gains are almost sufficient to maintain comfort, the effectiveness of the run-around system is reduced by operation of a by-pass valve controlled by a sensor in the pre-heated supply air; or the motor is switched off when the heat exchange is no longer desired. Examples of such controls are given in reference 1.

In large systems where an extended modulating range of heat transfer is desired, consideration should be given to the use of variable-speed motors in order to reduce the cost of pumping.

If there is a need to meter the heat which is transferred, it is a simple matter to install an integrating heat meter in a single-phase secondary loop, or to meter the condensate in a two-phase system.

4. THE OPTIMUM CIRCULATION RATE

The optimum circulating rate of the secondary fluid is defined here as the circulation rate which gives the highest rate of heat transfer under the prevailing conditions of flow of the primary fluids. It is also necessary to make some simplifying or limiting assumptions, and to distinguish between two types of system.

First we shall consider an idealised system comprising two heat exchangers. The two exchangers are identical in design and dimensions (which commonly occurs in air-to-air systems), there is no loss of heat from the pipework, the two primary fluids have the same flow rates and physical properties, and the relevant transport properties of all three fluids remain unchanged with change of temperature, within the operating range of the system. It will also be assumed that both heat exchangers operate in pure counterflow and, more dubiously, that the overall heat-transfer coefficient in each heat exchanger is insensitive to the rate of flow of the secondary fluid, which is least likely in liquid–liquid heat exchangers. Such a system may be called 'symmetrical'. It approximates to a system in which the emergent fluid from a plant pre-heats (or pre-cools) the feed of the same substance (Fig. 2).

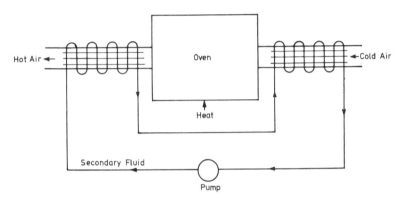

FIG. 2. A 'symmetrical' run-around coil system.

It is easy to show that in a symmetrical system the optimum rate of circulation of the secondary fluid is that which gives rise to a temperature change in that fluid equal to that of each of the primary fluids, or

$$\dot{m} = \dot{M}_h C_h / c = \dot{M}_c C_c / c \qquad (1)$$

Having established the optimum rate, it is important to know how sensitive the performance of the system is to departures of the circulating rate from the optimum (reference 2). Figure 3 shows the temperature profiles in a symmetrical system when the flow rate of the secondary fluid is non-optimum. Using the notation defined by that figure, the rate of heat transfer is

$$Q = U A \frac{(_1 T_h - _1 T_s) - (_2 T_h - _2 T_s)}{\ln((_1 T_h - _1 T_s)/(_2 T_h - _2 T_s))} \qquad (2)$$

Symmetry requires that

$$_1 T_h - _1 T_s = _2 T_s - _2 T_c$$

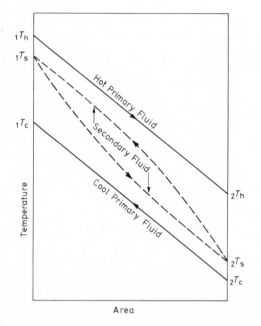

FIG. 3. Temperature profiles for a symmetrical system.

and the conservation of energy dictates that

$$_1T_s = {_2}T_s + Q/\dot{m}c;$$

so, combining these last two equations,

$$_1T_s = (_1T_h + {_2}T_c + Q/\dot{m}c),$$
$$_2T_s = (_1T_h + {_2}T_c - Q/\dot{m}c).$$

Substituting in eqn. (1),

$$Q = \frac{(_1T_h - {_2}T_c)(\exp(UA(1/\dot{M}C - 1/\dot{m}c)) - 1}{(2/\dot{M}C - 1/\dot{m}c)\exp(UA(1/\dot{M}C - 1/\dot{m}c)) - 1/\dot{m}c} \qquad (3)$$

The maximum possible value of Q is

$$Q_o = UA(_1T_h - {_1}T_{c\,max})/2$$

where $_1T_{c\,max} = {_2}T_c + Q_o/\dot{M}C$ and is the value of $_1T_c$ when $Q = Q_o$, whence

$$Q_o = \frac{UA(_1T_h - {_2}T_c)}{2 + UA/\dot{M}C}$$

$$= \frac{UA(_1 T_h - _2 T_c)}{2 + R} \qquad (4)$$

Dividing eqn. (3) by eqn. (4),

$$\frac{Q}{Q_o} = \frac{(2 + R)(\exp(R(1 - 1/r)) - 1)}{R(2 - 1/r)\exp(R(1 - 1/r)) - R/r} \qquad (5)$$

R is also the ratio of the temperature change to the temperature difference when the system is operating optimally.

Figure 4 is a dimensionless plot showing the effect on the rate of heat transfer when the circulation rate of the secondary fluid differs from the optimum, that is when r departs from unity. It shows that the system is most sensitive to the circulation rate when R, the ratio of the temperature change to the temperature difference, is great. In other words, if the system is being used for heat recovery, the more of the available energy that the system is designed to recover, the more sensitive is its relative performance to the circulation rate as a percentage of the optimum. To take a specific example, suppose that a run-around system, when operating with the optimum circulation rate, preheats the air entering an oven by 200 K by bringing its temperature to within 10 K of that of the air leaving the oven. If the circulation rate is increased by 40% the rate of heat transfer falls by 18%: if the circulation falls by 20% the rate of heat transfer is diminished by 16%.

If the rate of circulation is used to control the rate of heat transfer, obviously the control is stable only if the maximum rate of circulation is kept always below the 'optimum' rate. If the circulation rate ever goes over the optimum, the controller cannot bring it down again. As shown by eqn. (1), the optimum circulation rate varies with the flow rates of the primary fluids, so the design of the controller is rather complex if those flow rates vary and control is always to be stable.

Equation (5) and Fig. 4 apply strictly only to symmetrical systems satisfying all the assumptions made in the analysis, but they illustrate qualitatively features which are common to all systems, that is an optimum circulation rate and a sensitivity to departures from the optimum which increases with the duty required of the system to exchange heat between a given pair of primary fluids.

Many systems are not symmetrical, in that one or more of the simplifying assumptions made above are not satisfied. To size a pump for an otherwise existing system for a given pair of primary fluids (or to replace the pump for a change of duty) it is necessary to calculate the optimum flow rate for asymmetrical systems. In the analysis that follows (reference 2) all the

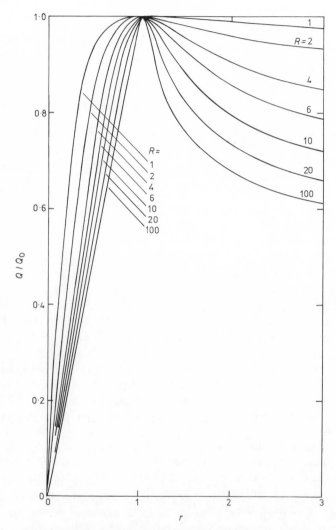

FIG. 4. Effect of departure from optimum circulation rate.

earlier assumptions are removed except the requirements that the fluids in each exchanger shall be in counterflow and that the heat losses from the pipework shall be negligible in relation to the amount of heat transferred.

Figure 5 shows the temperature profiles of the fluids in an asymmetrical system in which the circulation rate of the secondary fluid is non-optimum.

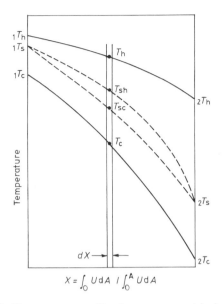

FIG. 5. Temperature profiles for an asymmetrical system.

They have been plotted as functions of $\int U \, dA$, that is the integral of $U \, dA$ between the hot end of the relevant exchanger and the points in each exchanger where the temperatures are as given by the ordinate, normalised by dividing by the integral for the whole exchanger.

At any particular value of the abscissa X the rate of heat transfer associated with an increment δX is equivalent to that given by a pair of small run-around coil systems in series, as illustrated in Fig. 6. It is assumed that the increment is small enough that the changes of temperature of the fluids in the increment are very small in relation to the differences of temperature between the fluids. Using the notation of Fig. 6,

$$\delta Q = \delta(UA)_{\mathrm{h}}(T_{\mathrm{h}} - T_{\mathrm{sh}})$$
$$= \delta(UA)_{\mathrm{s}}(T_{\mathrm{sh}} - T_{\mathrm{sc}})$$
$$= \delta(UA)_{\mathrm{c}}(T_{\mathrm{sc}} - T_{\mathrm{c}})$$

Eliminating T_{sh} and T_{sc},

$$\delta Q = \frac{T_{\mathrm{h}} - T_{\mathrm{c}}}{1/\delta(UA)_{\mathrm{h}} + 1/\delta(UA)_{\mathrm{s}} + 1/\delta(UA)_{\mathrm{c}}}$$

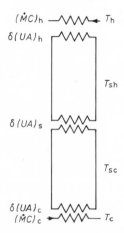

FIG. 6. An element of the run-around coil system.

The resistance to heat transfer, $1/\delta(UA)_s$, represents the effect on heat transfer of operation at a non-optimum circulation rate. When the system is operating with the optimum circulation rate, the resistance to heat transfer $1/\delta(UA)_s$ in each of the equivalent elemental systems must be zero and $T_{sh} = T_{sc} = T_s$. Under that condition,

$$\frac{T_h - T_s}{T_s - T_c} = \frac{\delta(UA)_c}{\delta(UA)_h}$$

By definition of X, the abscissa in Fig. 5, the right-hand expression in the last equation is constant and equal to $(\int U \, dA)_c / (\int U \, dA)_h$ for the whole exchanger, whence

$$\frac{_1T_h - _1T_s}{_1T_s - _1T_c} = \frac{_2T_h - _2T_s}{_2T_s - _2T_c} = \frac{(\int U \, dA)_c}{(\int U \, dA)_h} \tag{6,7}$$

From energy balances,

$$_2T_h = _1T_h - Q/(\dot{M}C)_h$$
$$_1T_c = _2T_c + Q/(\dot{m}c)$$

and

$$_1T_s = _2T_s + Q/(\dot{M}C)_s$$

where $\dot{M}C$ or $\dot{m}c$ is the mean heat capacity of the fluid between the temperatures of each equation.

By elimination of $_1T_c$ and $_1T_s$ from eqn. (6), and of $_2T_h$ from eqn. (7), the optimum circulation rate is

$$\dot{m} = \frac{1}{c} \frac{(\int U \, dA)_c + (\int U \, dA)_h}{(\int U \, dA)_c/(\dot{M}C)_c + (\int U \, dA)_h/(\dot{M}C)_h}$$

or, if the heat-transfer coefficients U in each exchanger are uniform,

$$\dot{m} = \frac{1}{c} \frac{(UA)_c + (UA)_h}{(UA)_c/(\dot{M}C)_c + (UA)_h/(\dot{M}C)_h}$$

It is apparent from the last equation that the optimum circulation rate is dependent on the flow rates of the primary fluids and on the heat-transfer coefficients. If any of those quantities change it is beneficial to change the circulation rate to restore it to its optimum value, if the maximum possible rate of heat transfer is desired.

Equation (6) suggests a method by which a departure from the optimum circulation rate may be detected, without a knowledge of the primary flow rates or of the heat-transfer coefficients. Four pairs of thermocouples placed in the terminals of the heat exchangers may be used to determine whether the equation is satisfied and, if it is not, the direction in which the circulation rate must be changed to restore the rate to the optimum. Changes in $_1T_h$ or $_2T_c$ do not alone change the magnitude of the optimum circulation rate.

When a heat-recovery system which employs a run-around coil system is commissioned, it should be a matter of routine to check that the circulation rate is at or near the optimum.

5. DESIGN

The design of a 'symmetrical' run-around coil system is a straight-forward matter, once the circulation rate is established from eqn. (1). The sizing of the heat exchangers for an asymmetrical system (reference 3) is less simple, especially if one of them must be made of costly materials. There is, of course, an infinite number of pairs of heat exchangers, each of a given type, which would be capable of delivering the required duty; but the designer must seek the pair whose total cost is a minimum. In the analysis that follows it is again assumed that the fluids are in counterflow, and it is also assumed that the overall heat-transfer coefficient in each exchanger is uniform. The circulation rate is the optimum rate so that eqn. (6) is satisfied.

The costs of the exchangers, which are assumed to vary linearly with surface area, are respectively $L_h = K_h + A_h p_h$ and $L_c = K_c + A_c p_c$. The total cost of the two exchangers is

$$L = K_h + K_c + Q\left(\frac{p_h}{U_h \Delta T_h} + \frac{p_c}{U_c \Delta T_c}\right)$$

It follows from eqn. (6) that the logarithmic mean of the temperature difference between the primary fluids, which is given and constant, is the sum of that in each of the two exchangers, that is,

$$\Delta T = \Delta T_h + \Delta T_c,$$

$$\frac{dL}{d\Delta T_h} = Q\left(-\frac{p_h}{U_h(\Delta T_h)^2} + \frac{p_c}{U_c(\Delta T - \Delta T_h)^2}\right)$$

and L is a minimum when $dL/d\Delta T_h = 0$, or when

$$\frac{\Delta T_h}{\Delta T_h + \Delta T_c} = \frac{1}{1 + \sqrt{\left(\dfrac{p_c U_h}{p_h U_c}\right)}} \tag{8}$$

The last equation shows how the optimum division, between the two exchangers, of the available temperature difference is related to their respective heat-transfer coefficients and material costs. p_c and p_h are the marginal costs of units of area in the respective heat exchangers.

If the heat exchangers are to be chosen from catalogues which do not reveal the heat transfer coefficients or areas of the heat exchangers listed (some catalogues give only the product of the two, or information which allows it to be calculated), eqn. (8) needs to be expressed in the form in which the expression $p_c U_h / p_h U_c$ is replaced by q_c / q_h, where q_c and q_h are defined by the equations

$$L_c = K_c + q_c (UA)_c$$
$$L_h = K_h + q_h (UA)_h$$

If vendors' quotations do not give sufficient information to allow either p or q to be determined for one or both exchangers one is reduced to making the crude assumption that the cost of a particular kind of exchanger in a particular material is proportional to the area it offers for heat transfer. With that assumption, K_c and K_h become zero and eqn. (8) can be shown (reference 3) to reduce to

$$\frac{\Delta T_h}{\Delta T} = \frac{L_h}{L_h + L_c}$$

According to the last equation, in the optimum design the temperature differences in the two exchangers should be in inverse ratio to their costs.

6. CONCLUSION

The normal method of transferring heat between one medium and another is, if the media are immiscible, by direct contact, or, if they are not, through the surfaces of a heat exchanger. It will probably always be so. Where, however, the media are separated by distance or other obstacles to bringing them together, there are some readily defined circumstances when it may be profitable or essential to employ a run-around coil system. The use of such a system may also be desirable, in some applications, for reasons of safety or of the security of the process. In designing systems where the unit costs of the materials in the two exchangers differ, or where they have different heat-transfer coefficients, the problem to be solved is the choice of the most economic division, between the two exchangers, of the available temperature difference. There is also a rate of circulation of the secondary fluid at which the rate of heat transfer is a maximum, and which is a function of the flow rates of the primary fluids, and of the heat-transfer coefficients. This fact has implications for the design of automatic controls, and for the operation and maintenance of run-around coil systems.

REFERENCES

1. REAY, D. D. *Heat Recovery Systems*, 1979, Spon, London.
2. EMERSON, W. H. Making the most of run-around coil systems, *Heat Recovery Systems*, 1984, **4**(4), 265–70.
3. EMERSON, W. H. Designing run-around coil systems, *Heat Recovery Systems*, 1983, **3**(4), 305–9.

INDEX